THE MATHEMATICAL THEORY
OF VISCOUS INCOMPRESSIBLE FLOW

Mathematics and its Applications

A Series of Monographs and Texts
Jacob T. Schwartz, Courant Institute of Mathematical Sciences
New York University, General Editor

Volume 1

Jacob T. Schwartz, LECTURES ON THE MATHEMATICAL METHOD IN ANALYTICAL ECONOMICS

Volume 2

O. A. Ladyzhenskaya, THE MATHEMATICAL THEORY OF VISCOUS INCOMPRESSIBLE FLOW

Volume 3

R. L. Stratonovich, TOPICS IN THE THEORY OF RANDOM NOISE *(in two volumes)*

Additional volumes in preparation

O A Ladyzhenskaia

The Mathematical Theory of Viscous Incompressible Flow

By O. A. LADYZHENSKAYA

Revised English Edition

Translated from the Russian by
Richard A. Silverman

G|B

GORDON AND BREACH
SCIENCE PUBLISHERS · NEW YORK — LONDON

Library of Congress Catalog Card Number 63-16283

Gordon and Breach, Science Publishers, Inc.
150 Fifth Avenue, New York 11, New York

For Great Britain and Europe:

Gordon and Breach, Science Publishers, Ltd.
171 Strand, London W.C. 2, England

Printed in the United States of America

First published August 1963
Second printing May 1964

This book is dedicated to three very different persons whom I hold in deep regard: my father Alexander Ivanovich Ladyzhenski, Vladimir Ivanovich Smirnov, and Jean Leray.

Translator's Preface

This book is a translation of O. A. Ladyzhenskaya's *Matematicheskiye Voprosy Dinamiki Vyazkoi Neszhimayemoi Zhidkosti* (literally, *Mathematical Problems of the Dynamics of a Viscous Incompressible Liquid*), which appeared in 1961 in the series *Contemporary Problems of Mathematics*, published under the auspices of the editorial board of the journal *Uspekhi Matematicheskikh Nauk*. The present edition has benefited greatly from the author's continued (and indefatigable) interest. Thus, it incorporates numerous corrections, additional references, further comments, and even an extra section. This "feedback process" has been facilitated by Prof. Ladyzhenskaya's examination of the translation in the galley proof stage.

The subject index is a somewhat modified version of one proposed by the author. Of the various systems for transliterating the Cyrillic alphabet into the Latin alphabet, I prefer and have used that due to Prof. E. J. Simmons.

I would like to take this opportunity to thank the author for her help, with the hope that I have acted as her faithful amanuensis, insofar as permitted by the divergence of stylistic and grammatical norms in our two languages. I would also like to thank Prof. L. Nirenberg of New York University for patiently assisting me in my quest for suitable terminological compromises.

R. A. S.

Author's Preface to the Russian Edition

The aim of this book is to acquaint mathematicians and hydrodynamicists with the success which has been achieved so far in investigating the existence, uniqueness and solvability of boundary-value problems for both the linearized and the general nonlinear Navier-Stokes equations. Many of the fundamental results obtained are of such a simple and definitive form that it has been possible to present them in this small monograph. The reader is not required to know more than the elements of classical and functional analysis.

The author is grateful to her young colleagues V. A. Solonnikov and K. K. Golovkin, and especially to A. P. Oskolkov and A. V. Ivanov, for their assistance in preparing the manuscript of this book.

O. A. L.

Author's Preface to the Revised English Edition

In the three years since the Russian edition of this book was written, quite a few papers devoted to a mathematically rigorous analysis of nonstationary solutions of the Navier-Stokes equations have been published. These papers either pursue the investigation of differential properties of the solutions whose existence and uniqueness is proved in the present book, or else they give other methods for obtaining such solutions. However, the basic problem of the unique solvability "in the large" of the boundary-value problem for the general three-dimensional nonstationary Navier-Stokes equations (with no assumptions other than a certain smoothness of the initial field and of the external forces) remains as open as ever.

The most delicate results on differential properties of generalized solutions are those due to K. K. Golovkin and V. A. Solonnikov, formulated in Chapter 6, Section 1. As for stationary problems, we call attention to the interesting papers by R. Finn, in which the behavior of solutions of the problem of stationary flow past objects is studied as $|x| \to \infty$.

In the analysis of stationary problems given here, we have directed our attention to problems involving flow past objects, or more exactly, problems in which the total flow through the boundary of an arbitrary object in the flow is equal to zero. Of no less importance are problems involving sources, where this condition is not satisfied. The possibility is not precluded that such problems, unlike problems involving flow past objects, are not always solvable for large Reynolds numbers. In fact, in the case of an unbounded planar domain, the problem of flow with sources can have infinitely many solutions (so that extra conditions must be imposed to single out a unique solution). For example, the functions

$$u_r = \frac{c}{r}; \; u_\varphi = c_1\left(\frac{1}{r} - r^{(c/\nu)+1}\right),$$

$$p = -\frac{c^2 + c_1^2}{2\,r^2} - \frac{2\,c_1^2\,\nu\,r^{/\nu}}{c} + \frac{c_1^2}{(2\,c/\nu) + 2}\,r^{(2c/\nu)+2},$$

where c and c_1 are arbitrary constants, satisfy the equations of continuity and the Navier-Stokes equations, written in polar coordinates r and φ. For fixed $c < -2\nu$, these functions give infinitely many solutions in the domain $r \geqslant 1$, which fall off sufficiently rapidly as $r \to \infty$ and satisfy the same boundary conditions

$$u_r|_{r=1} = c, \quad u_\varphi|_{r=1} = 0$$

at $r = 1$.

In the present edition of the book, all detected misprints have been eliminated. Moreover, an extra section on effective estimates of solutions of the nonlinear stationary problem (Chapter 5, Section 4) has been added.

O. A. L.

Leningrad, January 7, 1963

Contents

Introduction

Theoretical hydrodynamics has long attracted the attention of scientists working in a variety of specialized fields; the clear-cut nature of its experiments, the relative simplicity of its basic equations, and the clear-cut statement of its problems led to the hope of finding a complete quantitative description of the dynamical phenomena which take place in a viscous medium. In reality, however, the seeming simplicity of these problems turned out to be deceptive, and so far, the effort expended in trying to answer the following two fundamental questions has not yet been rewarded with complete success:

1. Do the equations of hydrodynamics, together with suitable boundary and initial conditions, have a unique solution?

2. How satisfactory is the description of real flows given by the solutions of these equations?

Apparently, as abundant as it is, accumulated hydrodynamical information, both theoretical and experimental, is still not adequate for a rigorous mathematical analysis of the phenomena occurring in fluids. Indeed, the numerous paradoxes of hydrodynamics* serve as landmarks indicating the long and thorny path traversed since the beginnings of the subject.

The first stage in the development of hydrodynamics, and one which extended over a long period of time, involved the study of so-called *potential flows* of an ideal incompressible fluid. It was found that there is quite a large class of such flows, and that the means for investigating them (by using the theory of functions of a complex variable) are almost perfect. However, the famous Euler-D'Alembert paradox, according to which the total force acting on an object located in a potential flow is equal to zero, indicated that the theory of ideal fluids was incomplete. All attempts to eliminate this and a series of other paradoxes, within the framework of the theory of ideal fluids, turned out

* A detailed analysis of these paradoxes is given in Birkhoff's book [1].

to be futile. This led to the creation of the mathematical model of a viscous fluid governed by the basic Navier-Stokes equations. This model had to serve as a scapegoat, answering for all the accumulated absurdities of the theory of ideal fluids, as well as accounting for the lifting force, the drag, the turbulent wake, and many other things. For a while, this scapegoat was silent and meek in face of the demands made on it; most of the time, it could neither answer yes or no with complete assurance, since in the case of the Navier-Stokes equations, it turned out to be impossible to solve the problem of flow past an object, for even the simplest objects of finite size. Unlike the case of the ideal fluid, there are no potential flows satisfying the boundary conditions at the surface of the object. Moreover, very few exact solutions of the Navier-Stokes equations were found, and almost all of these do not involve the specifically nonlinear aspects of the problem, since the corresponding nonlinear terms in the Navier-Stokes equations vanish.

However, in conjunction with a large number of experiments and approximate calculations, even this meager information on the Navier-Stokes equations made it possible to reveal various discrepancies between the mathematical model of a viscous fluid and actual phenomena occuring in such a fluid. Thus, paradoxes involving a viscous fluid came to light, of which only two will be discussed here.

The first paradox is the following: It is well-known that for any Reynolds number R, the only possible solutions of the Navier-Stokes equations in an infinitely long pipe which are symmetric with respect to its axis (directed along the x-axis, say) are given by

$$v_x = a(c^2 - r^2), \quad v_r = v_\theta = 0,$$

where c is the radius of the pipe, and a is a free numerical parameter. However, flows corresponding to these formulas (Poiseuille flows) are only observed for values of R which do not exceed a certain critical value, and the flows become turbulent when this critical value is exeeded.

The second paradox was first observed in Couette flow, i.e., stationary flows between rotating coaxial cylinders which are symmetric with respect to their common axis and any plane perpendicular to this axis. Solutions possessing this same symmetry exist for all R, but in fact are observed only for small values of R; for large values of R, the flows are replaced by flows which are still laminar but no longer symmetric. This paradox leads to a contradiction with the deeply rooted belief that symmetric causes must produce symmetric effects.

In both cases, it is not known whether the Navier-Stokes equations have solutions for large R which correspond to the observed flows; this would lead *ipso facto* to violation of the uniqueness theorem for stationary solutions of the Navier-Stokes equations.

In connection with this second paradox, the following result proved by M. A. Goldshtik* is of interest: In the problem of the interaction between an infinite vortex filament and a plane, there is a unique solution with the same symmetry as that of the problem itself, provided that R does not exceed a certain number R_1, but if R exceeds a certain number $R_2 > R_1$, there are no such solutions.

Nevertheless, it might seem that this paradox and others involving viscous fluids can be quite satisfactorily explained within the framework of the mathematical model of a viscous fluid due to Stokes. Indeed, the Navier-Stokes equations are nonlinear, and it is well known that for nonlinear equations, a well-behaved solution of a nonstationary problem may not exist on the entire interval $t \geqslant 0$; outside of a finite time interval, the solution may either "go to infinity" or else "split up," by losing its regularity, ceasing to satisfy the equations, and beginning to form branches. Moreover, even if a solution exists for all $t \geqslant 0$, it may not approach the solution of the stationary problem as the boundary conditions and the external forces are stabilized. In fact, depending on the values of the relevant parameters, a stationary boundary-value problem can have a unique solution, several solutions, or even no solutions at all (cf. the boundary-value problems for nonlinear elliptic equations, and the related problems of geometry and mechanics).

Such comparisons of boundary-value problems for the Navier-Stokes equation with previously studied boundary-value problems quite naturally suggested the following conclusions: Because of the nonlinearity of the Navier-Stokes equations, the stationary problem has a unique solution for values of R less than a certain R_1, several solutions for $R_2 > R > R_1$, and no solution at all for $R > R_2$**. The above-mentioned result of Goldshtik might appear to confirm this point of view. (However, actually this result only shows that there ceases to exist a solution with the symmetry prescribed by the author, starting from

* M. A. Goldshtik, *On a paradoxical solution of the Navier-Stokes equations*, Appl. Math. Mech. (English translation of Prik. Mat. Mekh.) **24**, 913—929 (1960).

** The inadequacy of this explanation of the paradoxes cited above may be seen by noting that the size of the critical value of R depends on the conditions of the experiment, and can be considerably increased by performing the experiment very carefully.

the corresponding symmetry of the data of the problem. It is not known whether the problem has an asymmetric solution, but I suspect that it does.) On the other hand, even when the initial regime and the external forces are smooth, the solutions of the nonstationary problem may become progressively less regular as time increases, going over to "irregular", "turbulent" regimes and forming branches, where the particular branch which is actually "realized" depends on extraneous factors which are not taken into account by the Navier-Stokes equations.

However, the only way to verify what the Navier-Stokes equations really have to say about the motion of actual fluids is first of all to carry out a rigorous mathematical analysis of the solution of boundary-value problems for the Navier-Stokes equations, corresponding to actual hydrodynamical situations. It turns out that incompressible fluids are the most suitable for such an analysis; in fact, for incompressible fluids, a whole series of results have been obtained which shed a great deal of light on the potentialities of the Stokes theory. The present book is devoted to a presentation of these results, and in it we have tried to touch upon everything of importance which has been discovered so far in this field. Without going into a detailed description of the contents of the book, we shall now state in general terms the main results proved here.

It is proved that in the general nonlinear case, a stationary boundary-value problem has solutions for any Reynolds number whatsoever, where both the boundaries of the object past which the flow occurs and the external forces can be quite irregular. However, these solutions are stable only for small values of the number R.

A nonstationary boundary-value problem for the Navier-Stokes equations has a unique solution for all instants of time if the data of the problem are independent of one of the space coordinates; the same is true for a problem with axial symmetry. In the general three-dimensional case, it is proved that the problem has a unique solution if the external forces can be derived from a potential and if the number R is small at the initial instant of time. In the general case, where these conditions are not satisfied, for all instants of time there exists at least one "weak solution" $\mathbf{v}(x, t)$ which has derivatives appearing in the Navier-Stokes equations (i.e., $\mathbf{v}_t$ and $\mathbf{v}_{x_i x_j}$) which are summable with respect to (x, t), with exponent $5/4$. It is still not known whether this solution is unique on the whole time axis $t \geqslant 0$. If the initial conditions are not too bad (from the standpoint of their smoothness), this solution is unique, at least during a certain time interval, whose size is determined by the data of the problem.

As regards the stability of solutions of nonstationary problems for finite and infinite time intervals, the following results are proved: If in the course of time, the external forces die out, and if the boundary conditions correspond to a state of rest (i.e., $\mathbf{v}|_S = 0$), then the motion also dies out, regardless of what the motion was at the initial instant of time. If as $t \to +\infty$, the values $\mathbf{f}(x, t)$ of the external forces approach stationary values $\mathbf{f}_0(x)$, for which the corresponding boundary-value problem has a solution $\mathbf{v}_0(x)$ when the Reynolds number R_0 is small, then the solutions $\mathbf{v}(x, t)$ of the nonstationary problem corresponding to arbitrary initial regimes $\mathbf{v}(x, 0)$ approach $\mathbf{v}_0(x)$ (and rather rapidly, at that) as $t \to +\infty$. However, if the number R_0 is large, then in general the solutions $\mathbf{v}(x, t)$ do not approach any definite limits as $t \to +\infty$.

On a finite time interval, the solutions $\mathbf{v}(x, t)$ depend continuously on the initial values $\mathbf{v}(x, 0)$ and on the external forces $\mathbf{f}(x, t)$. (This interval is arbitrary for plane-parallel flows, and fixed for arbitrary three-dimensional flows.) All these results are presented in the last two chapters.

Before studying the nonlinear Navier-Stokes equations, we investigate various linearized versions of the equation. These studies show that the boundary-value problems for the linearized equations always have unique solutions, and that properties of the operators corresponding to stationary problems are very much like those of the Laplace operator, while the properties of the operators corresponding to nonstationary problems resemble those of the heat-conduction operator.

We call the reader's attention to the following four problems:

1. In the general three-dimensional case, is there a uniqueness theorem valid at all instants of time for the "weak solution" mentioned above?

2. Can the nonlinear stationary problem have more than one regular solution for large R?

3. If $\mathbf{v}(x, t)$ is the solution of the problem of flow past an object, where the velocity is held constant at infinity and there are no volume forces, will $\mathbf{v}(x, t)$ be bounded (and hence stationary, in a certain sense) on the whole interval $t \geqslant 0$?

4. Does the solution of the boundary-value problem for the nonstationary Navier-Stokes equations approach the solution of the boundary-value problem for an ideal fluid as $\nu \to 0$?*

The results given in this book support the belief that it is reasonable to use the Navier-Stokes equations to describe the motions of a viscous fluid in the case of Reynolds numbers which do not exceed certain limits, and indicate that the Navier-Stokes equations are not adequate for large R. They partially refute the statements described above concerning the properties of solutions of the Navier-Stokes equations, and they force us to find other explanations for observed phenomena in real fluids, in particular, for the familiar paradoxes involving viscous fluids. Apparently, in seeking these explanations, one must not ignore the fact that if a large force $\mathbf{f}$ acts on the fluid for an extended interval of time, then the quantities $D_x^m v_k$ (where $\mathbf{v} = (v_1, v_2, v_3)$ is the solution) can become so large that the assumption that they are comparatively small, made in deriving the Navier-Stokes equations from the statistical Maxwell-Boltzmann equations, will no longer be satisfied, just as other assumptions of the Stokes theory, i.e., the assumption that the kinematic viscosity and the thermal regime are constant, will be far from valid. Because of this, it is hardly possible to explain the transition from laminar to turbulent flows within the framework of the classical Navier-Stokes theory.

The reader will find that the present book reflects the influence of Odqvist's work on linear stationary problems, Leray's results on nonlinear stationary problems, Hopf's investigations on the nonstationary problem, and finally investigations by the author and her colleagues A. A. Kiselev, V. A. Solonnikov and K. K. Golovkin.

We have not dealt with the theory of nonstationary hydrodynamical potentials, developed by Leray for two space variables, and by K. K. Golovkin and V. A. Solonnikov for three variables, partly because of its complexity and partly because the results enumerated above concerning the solution of the general nonlinear nonstationary problem were obtained by a different and simpler method. In the text and in the Comments (starting on p. 165), we give a more detailed description of what is done in various papers on the problems discussed in this book.

Finally, we warn the reader who is accustomed to the classical methods of mathematical physics that the interpretations given here

* This is true for the solution of the Cauchy problem in the planar case.

of what is understood by the solution of a problem and what it means to solve a problem differ from those with which he is familiar. To a large extent, a precise analysis of these matters is responsible for the success of the investigations reported here.

CHAPTER 1

Preliminaries

In this chapter, we present most of the auxiliary results from functional analysis which are used in this book. Since many of these results are well known, we only give proofs in cases where our proofs seem to be simpler than those available elsewhere.

1. Some Function Spaces and Inequalities

1.1. Throughout the entire book, we shall consider various functions of a point $x = (x_1, x_2, x_3)$ of three-dimensional Euclidean space E_3; these functions may also depend on the time t, as well. The symbol Ω will denote a domain of the space E_3 (i.e., a connected open set), $\bar{\Omega}$ will denote the closure of Ω and S its boundary, so that $\bar{\Omega} = \Omega + S$. All our functions will be assumed to be real and locally summable in the sense of Lebesgue, while all derivatives will be interpreted in the generalized sense [6, 16]. A variety of Hilbert spaces will be used. For example, in the case of scalar functions, we shall consider the spaces

$$W_2^l(\Omega) \qquad (l = 0, 1, 2, \ldots),$$

introduced and studied in detail by S. L. Sobolev [6, 16].*

The Hilbert space $W_2^l(\Omega)$ consists of all functions $u(x)$ which are measurable on Ω, have derivatives $D^k u$ with respect to x of all orders $k \leqslant l$, and are such that both the function $u(x)$ and all these derivatives are square-integrable over Ω. The scalar product in $W_2^l(\Omega)$ is defined by the relation

$$(u, v)_l = \int_\Omega \sum_{0 \leqslant k \leqslant l} D^k u \, D^k v \, dx,$$

and the norm is defined by

$$\| u \|_l = \| u \|_{W_2^l(\Omega)} = (u, u)_l^{1/2}.$$

* Numbers in brackets refer to items in the References, which begin on p. 177.

The space $W_2^l(\Omega)$ is complete. For $l = 0$, the space $W_2^l(\Omega)$ is usually denoted by $L_2(\Omega)$, and then the scalar product and norm are denoted simply by $(\ ,\ )$ and $\|\quad\|$, respectively.

The Hilbert space $\overset{\circ}{W}{}_2^1(\Omega)$ is the subspace of the space $W_2^1(\Omega)$ which has as a dense subset the set of all infinitely differentiable functions which are of compact support in Ω. A function is said to be *of compact support in* Ω if it is nonzero only on a bounded subdomain Ω' of the domain Ω, where Ω' lies at a positive distance from S, the boundary of Ω.

A whole series of integral inequalities and properties have been established for functions in $W_2^l(\Omega)$; it is customary to refer to these results briefly as *imbedding theorems* [6, 16]. We now prove several other inequalities which imply as simple consequences most of the imbedding theorems used in this book. The proofs given here are quite simple.

In most cases, we shall be concerned with functions in $\overset{\circ}{W}{}_2^1(\Omega)$. Every such function can be regarded as a function of compact support defined on the whole space, if we extend the function by setting it equal to zero outside Ω. Because of this fact, the inequalities given below will be proved only for functions of compact support, although they can all be generalized to the case of functions defined on a domain Ω which are not of compact support, provided only that the boundary of Ω is subject to certain regularity conditions [6, 16]. Moreover, since the smooth functions are dense in $\overset{\circ}{W}{}_2^1(\Omega)$, all the inequalities given below are automatically valid for any function in $\overset{\circ}{W}{}_2^1(\Omega)$, although they are proved only for smooth functions.

We begin by proving the following lemma:

LEMMA 1. *For any smooth function $u(x_1, x_2)$ of compact support in E_2, the inequality*

$$\iint\limits_{-\infty}^{\infty} u^4\, dx_1\, dx_2 \leqslant 2 \iint\limits_{-\infty}^{\infty} u^2\, dx_1\, dx_2 \iint\limits_{-\infty}^{\infty} \operatorname{grad}^2 u\, dx_1\, dx_2 \tag{1}$$

holds.

Proof: Because of the equality

$$u^2(x_1, x_2) = 2 \int\limits_{-\infty}^{x_k} u u_{x_k}\, dx_k \qquad (k = 1, 2),$$

we have

$$\max_{x_k} u^2(x_1, x_2) \leqslant 2 \int\limits_{-\infty}^{\infty} |u u_{x_k}|\, dx_k \qquad (k = 1, 2). \tag{2}$$

Then, using Schwarz' inequality, we obtain

$$\iint_{-\infty}^{\infty} u^4\,dx_1\,dx_2 \leqslant \int_{-\infty}^{\infty} \max_{x_2} u^2\,dx_1 \int_{-\infty}^{\infty} \max_{x_1} u^2\,dx_2$$

$$\leqslant 4 \iint_{-\infty}^{\infty} |uu_{x_2}|\,dx_1\,dx_2 \iint_{-\infty}^{\infty} |uu_{x_1}|\,dx_1\,dx_2$$

$$\leqslant 2 \iint_{-\infty}^{\infty} u^2\,dx_1\,dx_2 \iint_{-\infty}^{\infty} \operatorname{grad}^2 u\,dx_1\,dx_2,$$

which proves the lemma.

For the case of three space variables, we have the following generalization of Lemma 1:

LEMMA 2. *For any smooth function $u(x_1, x_2, x_3)$ of compact support in E_3, the inequality*

$$\iiint_{-\infty}^{\infty} u^4\,dx_1\,dx_2\,dx_3 \leqslant 4\left(\iiint_{-\infty}^{\infty} u^2\,dx_1\,dx_2\,dx_3\right)^{1/2}\left(\iiint_{-\infty}^{\infty} \operatorname{grad}^2 u\,dx_1\,dx_2\,dx_3\right)^{3/2} \tag{3}$$

holds.

Proof: To estimate the integral in the left-hand side, we use (1) and (2). This gives

$$\iiint_{-\infty}^{\infty} u^4\,dx_1\,dx_2\,dx_3$$

$$\leqslant 2 \int_{-\infty}^{\infty} dx_3\left[\iint_{-\infty}^{\infty} u^2\,dx_1\,dx_2 \iint_{-\infty}^{\infty} (u_{x_1}^2 + u_{x_2}^2)\,dx_1\,dx_2\right]$$

$$\leqslant 2 \max_{x_3} \iint_{-\infty}^{\infty} u^2\,dx_1\,dx_2 \iiint_{-\infty}^{\infty} \operatorname{grad}^2 u\,dx_1\,dx_2\,dx_3$$

$$\leqslant 4 \iiint_{-\infty}^{\infty} |uu_{x_3}|\,dx_1\,dx_2\,dx_3 \iiint_{-\infty}^{\infty} \operatorname{grad}^2 u\,dx_1\,dx_2\,dx_3$$

$$\leqslant 4\left(\iiint_{-\infty}^{\infty} u^2\,dx_1\,dx_2\,dx_3\right)^{1/2}\left(\iiint_{-\infty}^{\infty} \operatorname{grad}^2 u\,dx_1\,dx_2\,dx_3\right)^{3/2},$$

which proves the inequality (3).

We can derive certain consequences from the inequalities (1) and (3) by using Young's inequality

$$ab \leqslant \frac{a^p}{p} + \frac{b^{p'}}{p'} \qquad \left(\frac{1}{p} + \frac{1}{p'} = 1\right).$$

In fact, (1) implies the inequality

$$\iint_{-\infty}^{\infty} u^4\,dx_1\,dx_2 \leqslant \varepsilon\left(\iint_{-\infty}^{\infty} \operatorname{grad}^2 u\,dx_1\,dx_2\right)^2 + \frac{1}{\varepsilon}\left(\iint_{-\infty}^{\infty} u^2\,dx_1\,dx_2\right)^2, \tag{4}$$

which is valid for any $\varepsilon > 0$, and (3) implies

$$\iiint_{-\infty}^{\infty} u^4\,dx_1\,dx_2\,dx_3 \leqslant \frac{1}{\varepsilon^3}\left(\iiint_{-\infty}^{\infty} u_2\,dx_1\,dx_2\,dx_3\right)^2 + 3\varepsilon\left(\iiint_{-\infty}^{\infty} \operatorname{grad}^2 u\,dx_1\,dx_2\,dx_3\right)^2 \tag{5}$$

for any $\varepsilon > 0$.

By using a method of proof similar to those given above, we can convince ourselves of the validity of the following lemma:

LEMMA 3. *For any smooth function* $u(x_1, x_2, x_3)$ *of compact support, the inequality*

$$\iiint_{-\infty}^{\infty} u^6\,dx_1\,dx_2\,dx_3 \leqslant 48\left(\iiint_{-\infty}^{\infty} \operatorname{grad}^2 u\,dx_1\,dx_2\,dx_3\right)^3 \tag{6}$$

holds.

Proof: It is easy to see that we can assume $u \geqslant 0$ without loss of generality. Then, setting $dx = dx_1\,dx_2\,dx_3$, we have

$$J \equiv \iiint_{-\infty}^{\infty} u^6\,dx = \int_{-\infty}^{\infty} dx_1 \iint_{-\infty}^{\infty} u^3 u^3\,dx_2\,dx_3$$

$$\leqslant \int_{-\infty}^{\infty} dx_1 \left[\max_{x_2} \int_{-\infty}^{\infty} u^3\,dx_3 \int_{-\infty}^{\infty} \max u^3\,dx_2\right]$$

$$\leqslant 9 \int_{-\infty}^{\infty} dx_1 \left[\iint_{-\infty}^{\infty} |u^2 u_{x_2}|\,dx_2\,dx_3 \iint_{-\infty}^{\infty} u^2\,u_{x_3}|\,dx_2\,dx_3\right]$$

$$\leqslant 9 \int_{-\infty}^{\infty} dx_1 \left[\iint_{-\infty}^{\infty} u^4\,dx_2\,dx_3 \left(\iint_{-\infty}^{\infty} u_{x_2}^2\,dx_2\,dx_3\right)^{1/2} \left(\iint_{-\infty}^{\infty} u_{x_3}^2\,dx_2\,dx_3\right)^{1/2}\right].$$

Next, we bring the first factor in the brackets outside the integral $\int_{-\infty}^{\infty} dx_1 \ldots$, replace it by its maximum, and use Schwarz' inequality to estimate the product of the last two factors. The result is

$$J \leqslant 9 \max_{x_1} \iint_{-\infty}^{\infty} u^4\, dx_2\, dx_3 \left(\iiint_{-\infty}^{\infty} u_{x_2}^2\, dx \right)^{1/2} \left(\iiint_{-\infty}^{\infty} u_{x_3}^2\, dx \right)^{1/2}$$

$$\leqslant 36 \iiint_{-\infty}^{\infty} |u^3 u_{x_1}|\, dx \left(\iiint_{-\infty}^{\infty} u_{x_2}^2\, dx \right)^{1/2} \left(\iiint_{-\infty}^{\infty} u_{x_3}^2\, dx \right)^{1/2}$$

$$\leqslant 36 \sqrt{J} \left(\iiint_{-\infty}^{\infty} u_{x_1}^2\, dx \right)^{1/2} \left(\iiint_{-\infty}^{\infty} u_{x_2}^2\, dx \right)^{1/2} \left(\iiint_{-\infty}^{\infty} u_{x_3}^2\, dx \right)^{1/2}.$$

Dividing both sides of the inequality by $\sqrt{J}$ and replacing the geometric mean by the arithmetic mean in the right-hand side, we obtain

$$\sqrt{J} \leqslant 36 \cdot 3^{-3/2} \left(\iiint_{-\infty}^{\infty} \operatorname{grad}^2 u\, dx \right)^{3/2},$$

which implies (6).

A remarkable feature of all the inequalities derived above is that the constants appearing in them do not depend on the size of the domain in which the function u is of compact support. However, in general, most of the inequalities appearing in the imbedding theorems do not have this property.

Next, we exhibit a series of well-known inequalities which will be needed later. For any function $u(x) \in \overset{\circ}{W}{}_2^1(\Omega)$, we have

$$\int_{\Omega} u^2\, dx \leqslant \frac{1}{\mu_1} \int_{\Omega} \operatorname{grad}^2 u\, dx. \tag{7}$$

Here, the number μ_1 is the smallest eigenvalue of the operator $-\Delta$ in the domain Ω with zero boundary conditions, i.e., the smallest number μ such that there exists a solution (which does not vanish identically) of the problem

$$-\Delta v = \mu v, \quad v|_S = 0.$$

It is not hard to give an upper bound for $1/\mu_1$. Thus, for example, $1/\mu_1 \leqslant d^2$, where d is the width of an n-dimensional strip containing the domain Ω. As the domain Ω is made larger, the constant $1/\mu_1$ increases without limit, so that for unbounded domains, the inequality (7) is in general not valid (it may turn out that $\mu_1 = 0$). The inequality (7) with the constant d^2 replacing $1/\mu_1$ can easily be derived from the representation

$$u(x_1, \ldots, x_n) = u(a_1, \ldots, x_n) + \int_{a_1}^{x_1} u_{x_1}\, dx_1, \tag{8}$$

by using Schwarz' inequality. It follows from this same formula that if $u(x) \in \mathring{W}_2^1(\Omega)$, then

$$\int_{S_1} u^2 \, dS \leqslant C(S_1) \, \| u \|^2_{W_2^1(\Omega)}, \tag{9}$$

for any smooth $(n-1)$-dimensional surface S_1 of finite size lying in $\bar{\Omega}$. It is also well-known that the functions $u(x)$ in $W_2^2(\Omega)$ are continuous functions of x if the dimension of the space of points x is no greater than 3; moreover, the functions $u(x)$ obey the inequality

$$|u(x)| \leqslant C(\Omega) \, \| u \|_{W_2^2(\Omega)}. \tag{10}$$

If we restrict ourselves to functions $u(x_1, x_2, x_3)$ of compact support, then it is easy to derive (10) by starting from the representation

$$u(x) = -\frac{1}{4\pi} \int_{E_3} \frac{\Delta u(y)}{|x-y|} \, dy,$$

which is familiar from the theory of the Newtonian potential. This implies the continuity of $u(x)$ in the whole space, as well as the inequality

$$|u(x)| \leqslant \frac{1}{4\pi} \left(\int_{\Omega} \frac{dy}{|x-y|^2} \right)^{1/2} \left(\int_{\Omega} |\Delta u|^2 \, dy \right)^{1/2} \leqslant C(\Omega) \, \| u \|_{W_2^2(\Omega)},$$

where Ω denotes the domain in which u is of compact support, and the constant C obviously depends on the size of the domain Ω.

1.2. We now give some compactness criteria for families of functions in $W_2^l(\Omega)$. In the first place, any bounded set in $W_2^l(\Omega)$ is weakly compact, since $W_2^l(\Omega)$ is a Hilbert space (see e.g. [16]). Moreover, if Ω is a bounded domain, then any bounded set $\{u_n(x)\}$ in $\mathring{W}_2^1(\Omega)$ is compact in $L_2(\Omega)$. This is Rellich's theorem (see [3]) and is most easily proved as follows: Extend each $u_n(x)$ onto the whole space by setting it equal to zero outside Ω, and then use formula (8) and Schwarz' inequality to see that the family of functions is equicontinuous in the norm of $L_2(\Omega)$. However, as is well-known, a uniformly bounded, equicontinuous family in $L_2(\Omega)$ is compact in $L_2(\Omega)$. Moreover, this theorem and the inequality (3) imply the following lemma:

LEMMA 4. *A uniformly bounded family of functions in $\mathring{W}_2^1(\Omega)$ is compact in the space $L_4(\Omega)$.*

In fact, if a subsequence in $\mathring{W}_2^1(\Omega)$ converges in $L_2(\Omega)$, then, according to (3), it also converges in $L_4(\Omega)$. The compactness criteria given here are special cases of the above-mentioned imbedding theorems, and we only give those which will be used later.

In Sec. 4 of Chap. 5, devoted to the investigation of the differential properties of generalized solutions of nonlinear stationary problems, we shall use the following properties of integrals

$$v(x) = \int_{\Omega} \frac{f(y)}{|x-y|^{\lambda}}\, dy.$$

"of potential type" [6, 16]:

LEMMA 5. *If $f(y)$ is a function of a point in an n-dimensional space and if $f \in L_p(\Omega)$, where Ω is a bounded domain, then*

1. *For $\lambda < n\left(1 - \frac{1}{p}\right)$, the function $v(x)$ is continuous and*

$$\begin{gathered} |v(x)| \leqslant C\, \|f\|_{L_p(\Omega)}, \\ |v(x) - v(x')| \leqslant C\, \|f\|_{L_p(\Omega)} |x - x'|^{\alpha}, \\ \alpha = n - \frac{n}{p} - \lambda. \end{gathered} \tag{11}$$

2. *For $\lambda > n\left(1 - \frac{1}{p}\right)$, the function $v(x)$ is summable with exponent*

$$q \leqslant \frac{1}{\dfrac{\lambda}{n} - \left(1 - \dfrac{1}{p}\right)}$$

over any bounded domain Ω_1, and

$$\|v\|_{L_q(\Omega_1)} \leqslant C(\Omega_1)\, \|f\|_{L_p(\Omega)}. \tag{12}$$

3. *For $\lambda = n\left(1 - \frac{1}{p}\right)$, the function $v(x)$ is summable over Ω_1 with any finite exponent, and* (12) *holds for any q, where the constant depends on q.*

1.3. In investigating the differential properties of generalized solutions, the averaging operation is used [6, 16]. Here, we define the averaging operation and list only its basic properties. As an averaging kernel we take a function which depends only on x. In fact, let $\omega(\xi)$ be a nonnegative, infinitely differentiable function which is not identically zero, but vanishes identically for $\xi \geqslant 1$. The function $\omega(|x|/\varrho)$ obviously vanishes for $|x| \geqslant \varrho$, and its integral over the whole space equals some constant $\varkappa$ multiplied by ϱ^n, i.e.,

$$\int \omega\left(\frac{|x|}{\varrho}\right) dx = \varkappa\varrho^n .$$

Then we choose the function

$$\omega_\varrho(x) = \frac{1}{\varkappa\varrho^n}\,\omega\left(\frac{|x|}{\varrho}\right)$$

as the averaging kernel. For an arbitrary summable function $f(x)$, the averaging operation takes the form

$$f_\varrho(x) = \int \omega_\varrho\,(|x-y|)\,f(y)\,dy,$$

where the integration is nominally over the whole space, but effectively over the ball $|x-y| \leqslant \varrho$. If $f(y)$ is specified only in the domain Ω, then $f_\varrho(y)$ is defined in the smaller domain $\Omega_\varrho \subset \Omega$ whose boundary lies at the distance ϱ from the boundary of Ω.

We now enumerate some properties of the averaging operator:

1. The averaging operator commutes with the differentiation operator, i.e.,

$$\frac{\partial}{\partial x_k} f_\varrho(x) = \left(\frac{\partial f}{\partial x_k}\right)_\varrho$$

wherever $\partial f/\partial x_k$ and $f_\varrho(x)$ exist.

2. Suppose that $f(y) \in L_p(\Omega)$, $p \geqslant 1$, and let $f(y) \equiv 0$ outside Ω. Then $f_\varrho(y)$ is defined on the whole domain Ω, is infinitely differentiable in Ω, and converges as $\varrho \to 0$ to $f(y)$ in the $L_p(\Omega)$ norm.

3. Suppose that f and $g \in L_p(\Omega)$, $p \geqslant 1$, and let f and g vanish outside Ω. Then, we have

$$\int_\Omega f_\varrho\, g\, dx = \int_\Omega f\, g_\varrho\, dx .$$

1.4. We now derive some other inequalities which will be used in studying stationary problems in unbounded domains. First we show that the inequality

$$\int \frac{u^2(x)}{|x-y|^2}\,dx \leqslant 4 \int \sum_{k=1}^{3} u_{x_k}^2\, dx \tag{13}$$

holds for any smooth function $u(x)$ of compact support, where the integral is carried out over the whole space E_3, and y is an arbitrary point of E_3. To prove this, consider the equality

$$2\int\sum_{k=1}^{3} u_{x_k}(x)\,u(x)\,\frac{x_k-y_k}{|x-y|^2}\,dx$$

$$=\int\sum_{k=1}^{3}\frac{\partial u^2}{\partial x_k}\,\frac{x_k-y_k}{|x-y|^2}\,dx=-\int\frac{u^2}{|x-y|^2}\,dx,$$

obtained by making a single integration by parts. Using the Schwarz inequality to estimate the left-hand side, we obtain

$$\int\frac{u^2(x)}{|x-y|^2}\,dx$$

$$\leqslant 2\sqrt{\int\frac{u^2}{|x-y|^2}\sum_{k=1}^{3}\frac{(x_k-y_k)^2}{|x-y|^2}\,dx}\sqrt{\int\sum_{k=1}^{3}u_{x_k}^2\,dx},$$

which implies (13), since

$$\sum_{k=1}^{3}\frac{(x_k-y_k)^2}{|x-y|^2}=1.$$

It is easy to see that inequalities of the type (13) are valid for functions of compact support, in any number of variables greater than 2, except that the factor 4 in (13) is replaced by $\left(\frac{2}{n-2}\right)^2$. For $n = 2$, instead of (13), certain other relations hold, from which we choose the following result: Let $u(x)$ be an arbitrary smooth function of the variable $x = (x_1, x_2)$, of compact support in $\Omega = \{1 \leqslant |x| < \infty\}$. Then, $u(x)$ satisfies the inequality

$$\int\limits_{|x|\geqslant 1}\frac{u^2(x)}{|x|^2\ln^2|x|}\,dx\leqslant 4\int\limits_{|x|\geqslant 1}\sum_{k=1}^{2}u_{x_k}^2\,dx. \tag{14}$$

In fact, integration by parts gives

$$2\int\limits_{|x|\geqslant 1}\sum_{k=1}^{2}u_{x_k}\,u\,\frac{x_k}{|x|^2\ln|x|}\,dx$$

$$=\int\limits_{|x|\geqslant 1}\sum_{k=1}^{2}\frac{\partial u^2}{\partial x_k}\,\frac{x_k}{|x|^2\ln|x|}\,dx=\int\limits_{|x|\geqslant 1}\frac{u^2(x)}{|x|^2\ln^2|x|}\,dx,$$

and from this we obtain (14), just as before. A noteworthy and useful feature of the inequalities (13) and (14) is that they involve constants which do not depend on the size of the domain in which $u(x)$ is of compact support. There exist more complicated inequalities where the constants have the same property, but they will not be discussed here.

Using (13) and (14), we now construct Hilbert spaces $\overset{\circ}{D}(\Omega)$ for the case of two and three space variables. In fact, let Ω be any domain (bounded or unbounded) in one of these Euclidean spaces, and let $\dot{D}(\Omega)$ be the set of all smooth functions of compact support in Ω. We introduce the scalar product*

$$[u, v] = \int_\Omega u_{x_k} v_{x_k} \, dx \tag{15}$$

in $\dot{D}(\Omega)$. It is clear from the symmetry of (15) with respect to u and v, and from the inequalities (13) and (14), that (15) actually defines a scalar product in $\dot{D}(\Omega)$. The completion of $\dot{D}(\Omega)$ in the norm corresponding to this scalar product gives just the Hilbert space which we denote by $\overset{\circ}{D}(\Omega)$. It is not hard to prove that $\overset{\circ}{D}(\Omega)$ contains all locally square-summable functions $u(x)$ which vanish on S, have square-summable first derivatives over all Ω, and obey the inequality (13) or (14), as the case may be. For $n = 3$, the functions $u(x)$ also obey the inequality (6).

When Ω is unbounded, there is an important difference between $\overset{\circ}{D}(\Omega)$ for the cases of two and three space variables: When $n = 2$, $\overset{\circ}{D}(\Omega)$ contains functions which do not go to as zero $|x| \to \infty$. It can be shown that if Ω is the exterior of any bounded domain, then the smooth function which equals a constant for large $|x|$ belongs to $\overset{\circ}{D}(\Omega)$. However, this is impossible if $n = 3$, as is at once apparent from (13). Roughly speaking, the inequality (13) implies that the functions in $\overset{\circ}{D}(\Omega)$ "go to zero" as $|x| \to \infty$.

1.5. Finally, we give some further inequalities, which are special cases of inequalities we have derived for elliptic operators [2, 17].

If the domain Ω is bounded and if its boundary S has bounded first and second derivatives, then the inequality

$$\| u \|_{W_2^2(\Omega)} \leqslant C \, \| \Delta u \|_{L_2(\Omega)} \tag{16}$$

---

* Here and below, unless the contrary is explicitly stated, pairs of identical indices imply summation from 1 to 3.

holds for any function $u(x) \in W_2^2(\Omega) \cap \mathring{W}_2^1(\Omega)$. We now give a short derivation of (16). As before, all the arguments can be carried out for sufficiently smooth functions. Let $u(x)$ be a function which is continuously differentiable three times and vanishes on S. Integration by parts gives

$$\begin{aligned}\int_\Omega (\Delta u)^2\,dx &= -\int_\Omega \frac{\partial \Delta u}{\partial x_i}\frac{\partial u}{\partial x_i}\,dx + \int_S \Delta u \frac{\partial u}{\partial n}\,ds \\ &= \int_\Omega \frac{\partial^2 u}{\partial x_i\,\partial x_j}\frac{\partial^2 u}{\partial x_i\,\partial x_j}\,dx + \int_S \left(\Delta u \frac{\partial u}{\partial n} - \frac{\partial^2 u}{\partial x_i\,\partial n}\frac{\partial u}{\partial x_i}\right) ds.\end{aligned} \tag{17}$$

Take any point $\xi \in S$, and introduce local Cartesian coordinates $y = (y_1, y_2, y_3)$ at ξ, i.e., let the y_1 and y_2 axes lie in the tangent plane to S at ξ, and let y_3 be directed along the exterior normal to S at ξ. The expression

$$I_S = \Delta u \frac{\partial u}{\partial n} - \frac{\partial^2 u}{\partial x_i\,\partial n}\frac{\partial u}{\partial x_i}$$

is invariant with respect to rotations of the coordinate system, and hence

$$\begin{aligned}I_S &= \sum_{i=1}^{3}\left(\frac{\partial^2 u}{\partial y_i^2}\frac{\partial u}{\partial y_3} - \frac{\partial^2 u}{\partial y_i\,\partial y_3}\frac{\partial u}{\partial y_i}\right) \\ &= \sum_{i=1}^{2}\left(\frac{\partial^2 u}{\partial y_i^2}\frac{\partial u}{\partial y_3} - \frac{\partial^2 u}{\partial y_i\,\partial y_3}\frac{\partial u}{\partial y_i}\right).\end{aligned} \tag{18}$$

The derivates $\partial u/\partial y_i$ $(i = 1,2)$ vanish, since $u|_S = 0$. Moreover, the derivatives $\partial^2 u/\partial y_i^2$ $(i = 1, 2)$ can be expressed in terms of the derivative $\partial u/\partial n$. In fact, let $y_3 = \omega(y_1, y_2)$ be the equation of the piece of the surface S in the neighborhood of the point $\xi = (0, 0, 0)$. Differentiating the identity

$$u(y_1, y_2, \omega(y_1, y_2)) = 0$$

twice with respect to y_1 and y_2, we obtain

$$\frac{\partial u}{\partial y_i} + \frac{\partial u}{\partial y_3}\frac{\partial \omega}{\partial y_i} = 0,$$

$$\frac{\partial^2 u}{\partial y_i^2} + 2\frac{\partial^2 u}{\partial y_i\,\partial y_3}\frac{\partial \omega}{\partial y_i} + \frac{\partial^2 u}{\partial y_3^2}\left(\frac{\partial \omega}{\partial y_i}\right)^2 + \frac{\partial u}{\partial y_3}\frac{\partial^2 \omega}{\partial y_i^2} = 0 \quad (i = 1, 2).$$

At the point ξ, the last equality gives

$$\frac{\partial^2 u}{\partial y_i^2} = - \frac{\partial u}{\partial y_3} \frac{\partial^2 \omega}{\partial y_i^2},$$

since at ξ

$$\frac{\partial \omega}{\partial y_i} = 0 \qquad (i = 1, 2).$$

It follows that

$$I_S = - \left(\frac{\partial u}{\partial n}\right)^2 \sum_{i=1}^{2} \frac{\partial^2 \omega}{\partial y_i^2}$$

and (17) can be written in the form

$$\int_\Omega (\Delta u)^2 \, dx = \int_\Omega \sum_{i,j=1}^{3} \left(\frac{\partial^2 u}{\partial x_i \, \partial x_j}\right)^2 dx - \int_S \left(\frac{\partial u}{\partial n}\right)^2 K \, ds, \tag{19}$$

where

$$K(S) = \sum_{i=1}^{2} \frac{\partial^2 \omega}{\partial y_i^2}.$$

If the surface S is convex, it is not hard to see that $K(S) \leqslant 0$, and hence

$$\int_\Omega \sum_{i,j=1}^{3} \left(\frac{\partial^2 u}{\partial x_i \, \partial x_j}\right)^2 dx \leqslant \int_\Omega (\Delta u)^2 \, dx \tag{20}$$

for such S. Moreover, in the case of an arbitrary surface S with bounded first and second derivatives, we have the following estimate of the surface integral, where ε is an arbitrary positive number:

$$\left| \int_S \left(\frac{\partial u}{\partial n}\right)^2 K \, ds \right| \leqslant C \int_S \left(\frac{\partial u}{\partial n}\right)^2 ds$$

$$\leqslant C_1 \left[\varepsilon \int_\Omega \sum_{i,j=1}^{3} \left(\frac{\partial^2 u}{\partial x_i \, \partial x_j}\right)^2 dx + \frac{1}{\varepsilon} \int_\Omega \sum_{i=1}^{3} \left(\frac{\partial u}{\partial x_i}\right)^2 dx \right]. \tag{21}$$

To see this, it is sufficient to reduce the surface integral to a volume integral by using Gauss' formula (after first extending $\cos(n, x_k)$ from S to all Ω) and then use the inequality

$$2ab \leqslant \varepsilon a^2 + \frac{1}{\varepsilon} b^2.$$

We now substitute (21) with $\varepsilon = 1/2C_1$ into (19). After simply collecting similar terms, we obtain

$$\int_{\Omega} \sum_{i,j=1}^{3} \left(\frac{\partial^2 u}{\partial x_i \, \partial x_j} \right)^2 dx \leqslant C \int_{\Omega} [(\Delta u)^2 + \operatorname{grad}^2 u] \, dx. \tag{22}$$

The term in $\operatorname{grad}^2 u$ can be eliminated from the right-hand side, since in view of the inequality (7) we have

$$\int_{\Omega} \operatorname{grad}^2 u \, dx = - \int_{\Omega} \Delta u \, u \, dx \leqslant \frac{\varepsilon}{2} \int_{\Omega} u^2 \, dx$$

$$+ \frac{1}{2\varepsilon} \int_{\Omega} (\Delta u)^2 \, dx \leqslant \frac{\varepsilon}{2\mu_1} \int_{\Omega} \operatorname{grad}^2 u \, dx + \frac{1}{2\varepsilon} \int_{\Omega} (\Delta u)^2 \, dx$$

for any $\varepsilon > 0$. Setting $\varepsilon = \mu_1$, we see that

$$\int_{\Omega} \operatorname{grad}^2 u \, dx \leqslant \frac{1}{\mu_1} \int_{\Omega} (\Delta u)^2 \, dx. \tag{23}$$

Together with (7) and (22), this inequality gives (16), as required. It also follows from this derivation of the inequality (16) that the estimate

$$\| u \|^2_{W_2^2(E_n)} \leqslant \frac{3}{2} (\| u \|^2_{L_2(E_n)} + \| \Delta u \|^2_{L_2(E_n)}) \tag{24}$$

holds for any twice continuously differentiable function $u(x)$ of compact support in E_n, and since the set of such functions is dense in $W_2^2(E_n)$, (24) also holds for any $u(x) \in W_2^2(E_n)$.

The inequality (24) is also valid for any unbounded domain Ω whose boundary has bounded first and second derivatives, i.e., for any $u(x) \in W_2^2(\Omega) \cap \mathring{W}_2^1(\Omega)$, we have

$$\| u \|^2_{W_2^2(\Omega)} \leqslant C (\| u \|^2_{L_2(\Omega)} + \| \Delta u \|^2_{L_2(\Omega)}). \tag{25}$$

Moreover, the inequality

$$\int_{\Omega} \sum_{i,j=1}^{n} u^2_{x_i x_j} \, dx \leqslant C \left[\int_{\Omega} \sum_{k=1}^{n} u^2_{x_k} \, dx + \| \Delta u \|^2_{L_2(\Omega)} \right] \tag{26}$$

also holds. Particularly simple estimates of the type (16) and (24) can be established for the Newtonian potential

$$u(x) = - \frac{1}{4\pi} \int \frac{f(y)}{|x - y|} \, dy.$$

In fact, first let $f(y)$ be a twice continuously differentiable function of compact support. Then, $u(x)$ will be a function of x which is continuously differentiable three times and satisfies Poisson's equation $\Delta u = f$. As $|x| \to \infty$, the functions u, u_{x_i} and $u_{x_i x_j}$ fall off like $|x|^{-1}$, $|x|^{-2}$ and $|x|^{-3}$, respectively. Consider the equality

$$\int_{E_3} f^2\, dx = \int_{E_3} \Delta u\, \Delta u\, dx .$$

Integration by parts transforms the right-hand side into

$$\int_{E_3} (\Delta u)^2\, dx = \int_{E_3} \sum_{i,j=1}^{3} u^2_{x_i x_j}\, dx ,$$

where all the surface integrals vanish because of the above-mentioned behavior of u_{x_i} and $u_{x_i x_j}$ for large $|x|$. The last equality gives the desired estimate of the second derivatives and shows that if f is of compact support and belongs to $L_2(E_3)$, then u has generalized second-order derivatives which are square-summable over E_3. Moreover, the estimates of u and u_{x_i} follow from Lemma 5 on integrals "of potential type." Thus, if f vanishes outside a finite domain, the corresponding Newtonian potential

$$u(x) = -\frac{1}{4\pi} \int_{\Omega_1} \frac{f(y)}{|x-y|}\, dy$$

satisfies the inequality

$$\| u \|_{W_2^2(\Omega)} \leqslant C(\Omega, \Omega_1) \| f \|_{L_2(\Omega_1)}, \tag{27}$$

with a constant C which is finite for any bounded Ω and Ω_1.

In addition to the Newtonian potential, we shall also encounter the volume potential

$$v(x) = -\frac{1}{8\pi} \int |x-y|\, f(y)\, dy, \quad x = (x_1, x_2, x_3),$$

which is a solution of the nonhomogeneous biharmonic equation

$$\Delta^2 v = f .$$

If f is a function of compact support which is square-summable over E_3, then Lemma 5 enables us to assert that v has derivatives up to order 3, inclusively, which are summable with exponents greater than 2 over any bounded domain. Moreover, estimates of the fourth derivatives are obtained as follows: Let f be of compact support and twice continuously differentiable. Then v has continuous derivatives up to order 5 and satisfies $\Delta^2 v = f$, while

$$\int_{E_3} f^2\,dx = \int_{E_3} \Delta^2 v\,\Delta^2 v\,dx = \int_{E_3} \sum_{i,j,k,l=1}^{3} v^2_{x_i x_j x_k x_l}\,dx. \tag{28}$$

The surface integrals vanish in this case too, since as $|x| \to \infty$, $D^3 v$ and $D^4 v$ fall off like $|x|^{-2}$ and $|x|^{-3}$, respectively. The equation (28), which remains valid for any $f \in L_2(E_3)$, gives the desired estimate of $D^4 v$. Because of (28) and Lemma 5, the inequality

$$\|v\|_{W_2^4(\Omega)} \leqslant C(\Omega, \Omega_1)\,\|f\|_{L_2(\Omega_1)} \tag{29}$$

holds for the biharmonic volume potential v, when f vanishes outside a bounded domain Ω_1; here the constant C is finite for any bounded Ω and Ω_1.

Here, we have given estimates for the potentials u and v and their derivatives in the L_2 norm. Estimates of these same quantities in the norms of the "Hölder spaces" $C_{l,h}(\Omega)$ are more familiar [12, 13], i.e.,

$$\|u\|_{2,h} \leqslant C\,\|f\|_{0,h} \tag{30}$$

and

$$\|v\|_{4,h} \leqslant C\,\|f_{0,h}\|, \tag{31}$$

where $\|f\|_{0,h}$ denotes

$$\max_{x,x' \in \Omega} \left\{ |f(x)|, \frac{|f(x) - f(x')|}{|x - x'|^h} \right\}$$

and $\|f\|_{l,h}$ denotes the analogous maximum for f and its derivatives up to order l, inclusively. If f is a function of compact support in E_3, which satisfies a Hölder condition with exponent h in E_3, then the norms $\|\ \|_{2,h}$ and $\|\ \|_{4,h}$ in (30) and (31) can be taken over any bounded domain. However, if the integrals u and v do not extend over all of E_3, but just over a bounded domain Ω, then the norms $\|\ \|_{2,h}$, $\|\ \|_{4,h}$ and $\|\ \|_{0,h}$ in (30) and (31) can be taken over the domain Ω, provided that its boundary is sufficiently smooth.

We shall say that the boundary S of the domain Ω belongs to $\Lambda_{1,h}$ if it is a Lyapunov surface of index h (see e.g. [18, 19]), i.e., if it can be decomposed into a finite number of overlapping pieces each of which has an equation of the form

$$x_{i_n} = \varphi(x_{i_1}, \ldots, x_{i_{n-1}}) \qquad (i_k \neq i_j),$$

where $\varphi \in C_{1,h}$. Moreover, if $\varphi \in C_{2,h}$, we shall write $S \in \Lambda_{2,h}$.

2. The Vector Space $\mathbf{L}_2(\Omega)$ and Its Decomposition into Orthogonal Subspaces

Let Ω be a domain of E_3 (or E_2), and let $\mathbf{L}_2(\Omega)$ be the Hilbert space of vector functions $\mathbf{u}(x) = (u_1(x), u_2(x), u_3(x))$, $x \in \Omega$ (or $\mathbf{u} = (u_1, u_2)$) with components u_k in $L_2(\Omega)$. The scalar product in $\mathbf{L}_2(\Omega)$ is defined by the relation

$$(\mathbf{u}, \mathbf{v}) = \int_\Omega \mathbf{u} \cdot \mathbf{v}\, dx = \int_\Omega u_k v_k\, dx,$$

and the length of the vector $\mathbf{u}$ is denoted by

$$|\mathbf{u}| = \sqrt{\sum_k u_k^2} = \sqrt{\mathbf{u} \cdot \mathbf{u}} = \sqrt{\mathbf{u}^2}.$$

The basic problem of this section is to decompose the space $\mathbf{L}_2(\Omega)$ into two orthogonal subspaces $G(\Omega)$ and $\mathring{J}(\Omega)$. The first of these subspaces contains the gradients of all functions which are single-valued in Ω (and only gradients of such functions). The second subspace contains the set of all smooth solenoidal vectors of compact support in Ω as a dense subset. To solve this problem (and for use in subsequent sections), we must first consider the following auxiliary problem:

2.1. PROBLEM.* *Construct a solenoidal vector field* $\mathbf{a}(x)$ *in* Ω *which takes specified values* $\mathbf{a}|_S = \boldsymbol{\alpha}$ *on the boundary* S.

Since $\mathbf{a}(x)$ is solenoidal, i.e., since $\operatorname{div} \mathbf{a} = 0$, the field $\boldsymbol{\alpha}$ must satisfy the condition

$$\int_S \boldsymbol{\alpha} \cdot \mathbf{n}\, dS = 0, \tag{32}$$

where $\mathbf{n}$ denotes the exterior (with respect to Ω) normal to S, because

$$\int_\Omega \operatorname{div} \mathbf{a}\, dx = \int_S \boldsymbol{\alpha} \cdot \mathbf{n}\, dS.$$

Thus, suppose (32) holds. This problem has an infinite set of solutions. Construct one of these solutions, which will be used in what follows. The smoothness requirements on S and $\boldsymbol{\alpha}$ will vary, depending on how smooth $\mathbf{a}$ must be for various purposes.

First, we consider the more complicated case where the domain Ω is three-dimensional. We decompose $\boldsymbol{\alpha}$ into normal and tangential

* In Chap. 3, we give another method for solving this problem, which uses the theory of hydrodynamic potentials.

components with respect to S, i.e.,

$$\boldsymbol{\alpha} = \alpha_n \mathbf{n} + \boldsymbol{\alpha}_\tau, \qquad \alpha_n = \boldsymbol{\alpha} \cdot \mathbf{n},$$

and we use α_n to construct a solenoidal vector field of the form $\mathbf{b} =$ grad φ with $b_n|_S = \alpha_n$. This reduces to the Neumann problem

$$\Delta\varphi = 0, \qquad \left.\frac{\partial\varphi}{\partial n}\right|_S = \alpha_n \tag{33}$$

in the domain Ω. It is well known that because of (32), this problem can be solved to within an additive constant, which we fix by requiring that $\varphi(x_0) = 0$, $x_0 \in S$. We now set

$$\mathbf{a}(x) = \mathbf{b}(x) + \mathbf{c}(x).$$

Then, we have to find $\mathbf{c}(x)$ from the conditions

$$\operatorname{div} \mathbf{c} = 0, \quad \mathbf{c}|_S = (\boldsymbol{\alpha} - \mathbf{b})|_S = \boldsymbol{\beta},$$

where $(\boldsymbol{\beta} \cdot \mathbf{n})|_S = 0$.

Next, we represent the function identically equal to 1 in Ω as a sum of sufficiently smooth functions of compact support in E_3, i.e.,

$$1 \equiv \sum_{k=1}^{N} \zeta_k(x).$$

Moreover, we choose the $\zeta_k(x)$ such that we can introduce smooth curvilinear coordinates (y_1^k, y_2^k, y_3^k) in terms of which the intersection S_k of the surface S with the domain where $\zeta_k(x) \not\equiv 0$ (this domain has a nonempty intersection with Ω) has the equation $y_3^k = 0$ and such that the curvilinear net (y_1^k, y_2^k, y_3^k) is orthogonal on the surface S_k. Writing $\boldsymbol{\beta}^k = \zeta_k \boldsymbol{\beta}$, we construct a vector $\mathbf{d}^k(x)$ in Ω such that curl $\mathbf{d}^k \equiv \mathbf{c}^k(x)$ is equal to $\boldsymbol{\beta}^k$ on S. Then $\sum_{k=1}^{N} \mathbf{c}^k(x)$ gives us the desired vector $\mathbf{c}(x)$. We now show how to choose $\mathbf{d}^k(x)$ on S so as to satisfy the condition

$$\operatorname{curl} \mathbf{d}^k(x)|_S = \boldsymbol{\beta}^k. \tag{34}$$

If the point $M \in S - S_k$, then $\boldsymbol{\beta}^k = 0$ at M, and we can take $\mathbf{d}^k$ and $\mathbf{d}^k_{x_l}$ to be zero at M. If $M \in S_k$, then in a neighborhood of M, we introduce local Cartesian coordinates (z_1, z_2, z_3) such that all the z_k vanish at M and such that the axes are directed along the coordinate lines (y_1^k, y_2^k, y_3^k). In the (z) coordinate system, equation (34) takes the

form
$$\frac{\partial d_3^k}{\partial z_2} - \frac{\partial d_2^k}{\partial z_3} = \beta_1^k,$$
$$\frac{\partial d_1^k}{\partial z_3} - \frac{\partial d_3^k}{\partial z_1} = \beta_2^k,$$
$$\frac{\partial d_2^k}{\partial z_1} - \frac{\partial d_1^k}{\partial z_2} = \beta_3^k.$$

We satisfy these equations at the point M by setting all the $\partial d_l^k / \partial z_m$ equal to zero except for
$$\frac{\partial d_2^k}{\partial z_3} = -\beta_1^k, \quad \frac{\partial d_1^k}{\partial z_3} = \beta_2^k.$$

We also set $d_m^k = 0$ $(m = 1, 2, 3)$ at the point M, and then return to the (x) coordinates. The values $\mathbf{d}^k(z) = 0$ and $\partial \mathbf{d}^k(z)/\partial z_m$ at the point M uniquely determine $\mathbf{d}^k(x)$ and $\partial \mathbf{d}^k(x)/\partial x_m$ at M; since $\mathbf{d}^k = 0$, the dependence of $\cos(x_k, z_m)$ on the point of the surface does matter, and only $\boldsymbol{\beta}_k$ and $\cos(x_k, z_m)$, but not their derivatives, appear in the expression for $\partial \mathbf{d}^k(x)/\partial x_m$.

It only remains to show that the values of $\mathbf{d}^k$ and $\partial \mathbf{d}^k/\partial x_m$ calculated in this way at every point $M \in S$ are compatible. The only condition relating these quantities is the fact that the derivatives of $\mathbf{d}^k(x)$ with respect to the tangent directions to S must vanish (since $\mathbf{d}^k = 0$). But it is easy to see that this condition is satisfied by our choice of $\partial \mathbf{d}^k(z)/\partial z_m (m = 1,2)$.

The smoothness of $\mathbf{d}^k(x)$ and of $\partial \mathbf{d}^k/\partial x_m$ on S is guaranteed by the smoothness of the system of (y) coordinates and of the fields $\boldsymbol{\beta}^k$, which amounts to the smoothness of S and of the field $\boldsymbol{\beta}$. The vector $\mathbf{d}^k$ vanishes everywhere on S, and $\partial \mathbf{d}^k(x)/\partial x_m$ vanishes everywhere on $S - S_k$. From the values of these quantities, we can construct the field $\mathbf{d}^k(x)$ in Ω. In so doing, we can assume that $\mathbf{d}^k(x)$ is very smooth inside Ω and vanishes for points x at a fixed distance from S. The sum $\sum_{k=1}^{N} \operatorname{curl} \mathbf{d}^k(x)$, as already noted, gives the desired vector $\mathbf{c}(x)$, which in turn determines $\mathbf{a}(x) = \mathbf{c}(x) + \operatorname{grad} \varphi$.

If S is a Lyapunov surface and $\boldsymbol{\alpha}$ is a continuous field on S, then the above method allows us to construct a field $\mathbf{a}(x)$ which is continuous on $\bar{\Omega}$ and is as smooth as we please inside Ω. If S is a surface with bounded first and second derivatives, and if $\boldsymbol{\alpha}/_S \in W_2^{1/2}(S)$ [20, 21, 22], i.e., if each component of $\boldsymbol{\alpha}$ can be continued inside S onto Ω in such a way that the continuation belongs to $W_2^1(\Omega)$, then the above construction gives a vector field $\mathbf{a}(x)$ in $W_2^1(\Omega)$. Moreover, this field can be represented in the form [17]

$$\mathbf{a}(x) = \operatorname{grad} \varphi + \operatorname{curl} \mathbf{d},$$

where

$$\Delta\varphi = 0, \quad \varphi \in W_2^2(\Omega) \quad \text{and} \quad \mathbf{d} \in W_2^2(\Omega).$$

If S and $\boldsymbol{\alpha}$ are smoother, we can take $\mathbf{a}(x)$ to be smoother in $\bar{\Omega}$.

Below, we shall be interested in the solution of the problem for a domain Ω with a surface S which has "edges," specifically, for a tubular domain Ω whose ends are right cylinders with bases S_1 and S_2. Thus, the whole surface S will consist of three pieces, two planes S_1 and S_2, and a third piece S_3, which is the lateral surface of the tube. On S_3, the vector $\boldsymbol{\alpha} = 0$, while on S_1 and S_2, the vector $\boldsymbol{\alpha}$ is smooth and vanishes on the intersections Σ_1, Σ_2 of the bases S_1, S_2 with S_3. Then, concerning the solution φ of the problem (33), we can say that it is continuous in $\bar{\Omega} - \Sigma_1 - \Sigma_2$, and its first derivatives are continuous in $\bar{\Omega} - \Sigma_1 - \Sigma_2$ and bounded in Ω. Moreover, the vector $\mathbf{c}(x)$ can be constructed to be continuous in $\bar{\Omega} - \Sigma_1 - \Sigma_2$, bounded in Ω, and infinitely differentiable inside Ω, by using the construction given above. Then the $\partial d_i^k/\partial x_j$ will be bounded on S and continuous everywhere on S except on $\Sigma_1 + \Sigma_2$.

In the case where the domain Ω is planar, the solution of the problem is very simple. In fact, if Ω is a simply connected domain, the field $\mathbf{a}$ can be found in the form

$$\mathbf{a} = \left(\frac{\partial \psi}{\partial x_2}, -\frac{\partial \psi}{\partial x_1}\right) \equiv \operatorname{curl} \psi.$$

The condition $\mathbf{a}|_S = \boldsymbol{\alpha}$ gives the values of $\partial\psi/\partial n$ and $\partial\psi/\partial\tau$ on S. From the values of $\partial\psi/\partial\tau$, we find ψ on S (to within an arbitrary constant), where ψ is a single-valued continuous function, since

$$\oint_S \frac{\partial \psi}{\partial \tau}\, d\tau = \int_S \mathbf{a} \cdot \mathbf{n}\, dS = 0.$$

Then, from the functions $\psi|_S$ and $\left.\frac{\partial \psi}{\partial n}\right|_S$, we construct a smooth function ψ. If the domain Ω is multiply connected, then we look for $\mathbf{a}(x)$ in the form $\mathbf{a} = \operatorname{grad} p + \operatorname{curl} \psi$, where p is a solution of the problem (33), and ψ is defined just as before.

2.2. We now turn to the decomposition of the space $\mathbf{L}_2(\Omega)$, discussed at the beginning of this section. Let $\dot{J}(\Omega)$ denote the set of infinitely differentiable solenoidal vectors of compact support in Ω, and let $\mathring{J}(\Omega)$ denote its closure in the $\mathbf{L}_2(\Omega)$ norm. The set of elements of $\mathbf{L}_2(\Omega)$ which are orthogonal to $\mathring{J}(\Omega)$ form a space which we denote by $G(\Omega)$, so that

$$\mathbf{L}_2(\Omega) = G(\Omega) \oplus \mathring{J}(\Omega). \tag{35}$$

We now prove the following theorem:

THEOREM 1. *$G(\Omega)$ consists of elements grad φ, where φ is a single-valued function on Ω, which is locally square-summable and has first derivatives in $\mathbf{L}_2(\Omega)$.*

Proof: Let $\mathbf{u} \in G(\Omega)$, i. e., let

$$\int_\Omega \mathbf{u} \cdot \mathbf{v}\, dx = 0 \tag{36}$$

for all $\mathbf{v} \in \mathring{J}(\Omega)$. Choose $\mathbf{v} = \text{curl}\, \mathbf{w}_\varrho$ as the vector $\mathbf{v}$, where $\mathbf{w}$ is a smooth vector of compact support in Ω, and $\mathbf{w}_\varrho$ is its average:

$$\mathbf{w}_\varrho(x) = \int_{|x-y|<\varrho} \omega_\varrho(|x-y|)\, \mathbf{w}(y)\, dy. \tag{37}$$

We chose the number ϱ to be smaller than the distance from the domain Ω' where $\mathbf{w} \not\equiv 0$ to the boundary S, so that $\mathbf{w}_\varrho(x)$ is defined over all Ω and is of compact support in Ω, if we set $\mathbf{w}$ equal to zero outside Ω. Substituting curl $\mathbf{w}_\varrho$ into (36) and bearing in mind that curl $\mathbf{w}_\varrho = (\text{curl}\, \mathbf{w})_\varrho$ and that the functions $\mathbf{w}$ and $\mathbf{w}_\varrho$ vanish outside Ω, we obtain

$$\begin{aligned} 0 &= \int_\Omega \mathbf{u}(x) \int_{|x-y|<\varrho} \omega_\varrho(|x-y|)\, \text{curl}\, \mathbf{w}(y)\, dy\, dx \\ &= \int_\Omega \mathbf{u}_\varrho(y) \cdot \text{curl}\, \mathbf{w}\, dy. \end{aligned} \tag{38}$$

Here, the function $\mathbf{u}_\varrho(y)$ is infinitely differentiable and is given by formula (37) in $\Omega' \subset \Omega$. Integrating (38) by parts, we obtain

$$\int_\Omega \text{curl}\, \mathbf{u}_\varrho \cdot \mathbf{w}\, dy = 0.$$

It follows from this identity that curl $\mathbf{u}_\varrho = 0$, since $\mathbf{w}$ is sufficiently arbitrary. The function $\mathbf{u}_\varrho$ is defined for all $x \in \Omega_\varrho$, where Ω_ϱ is the subdomain of Ω at the distance ϱ from S, and curl $\mathbf{u}_\varrho = 0$ in Ω_ϱ.

Next, we make suitable cuts in Ω, so that Ω becomes simply connected, and we construct the function

$$\varphi(x, \varrho) = \int_{x_0}^{x} \sum_{k=1}^{3} u_{k\varrho} dx_k$$

in Ω_ϱ, choosing a fixed point x_0. Since curl $\mathbf{u}_\varrho = 0$, the function $\varphi(x, \varrho)$ is defined by the given integral and $\mathbf{u}_\varrho = \text{grad } \varphi(x, \varrho)$. We now let $\varrho \to 0$. It is well-known (see [6] or [16]) that for any fixed interior subdomain Ω' of the domain Ω, $\mathbf{u}_\varrho$ will converge to $\mathbf{u}$ in $\mathbf{L}_2(\Omega')$, and then, as is easily verified, $\varphi(x, \varrho)$ will converge to a function $\varphi(x)$ in $W_2^1(\Omega')$ (if Ω' is bounded), and grad $\varphi = \mathbf{u}$. Since Ω' is an arbitrary subdomain of Ω, the function $\varphi(x)$ is defined on all Ω and grad $\varphi = \mathbf{u}$. If the domain Ω is bounded, then $\varphi \in L_2(\Omega)$. However, the domain Ω was just assumed to have cuts, and if we want to remove these cuts, we have to verify that φ is continuous in Ω without cuts, or, more precisely, that $\oint_l d\varphi = 0$ for almost all closed paths in Ω.

We now take a smooth tube $T \subset \Omega$ and draw a transverse planar cross-section S_1 in T. We choose the tube as in the preceding problem, except that in this case S_1 and S_2 coincide. On S_1 we specify an arbitrary smooth field of vectors $\boldsymbol{\alpha}$, which have directions orthogonal to S_1 and equal zero near the boundary S_1. In T, we construct a solenoidal field $\mathbf{a}(x)$ which is smooth inside T, vanishes on the lateral surface of T and equals $\boldsymbol{\alpha}$ on S_1, S_2. The field $\mathbf{a}(x)$ is bounded in T and continuous in the tube and on its boundary, with the possible exception of the curve Σ_1 in which S_1 intersects the surface T. It was shown in the auxiliary problem (Sec. 2.1) that such a construction is possible.

We now extend $\mathbf{a}(x)$ onto all E_3 by setting $\mathbf{a}(x) \equiv 0$ outside T, and we then average $\mathbf{a}(x)$ by using a kernel $\omega_\varrho(|x-y|)$, where ϱ is smaller than the distance from T to S. If we let

$$\mathbf{v} = \mathbf{a}_\varrho,$$

it is easy to see that $\mathbf{v} \in \dot{J}(\Omega)$. In fact, $\mathbf{v}$ is of compact support in Ω, $\mathbf{v}$ is infinitely differentiable, and

$$\begin{aligned}\text{div } \mathbf{v} &= \frac{\partial}{\partial x_k} \int_{|x-y| \leq \varrho} \omega_\varrho(|x-y|)\, a_k(y)\, dy \\ &= -\int_{|x-y| \leq \varrho} \frac{\partial}{\partial y_k} \omega_\varrho(|x-y|)\, a_k(y)\, dy \\ &= \int_{|x-y| \leq \varrho} \omega_\varrho(|x-y|) \text{ div } \mathbf{a}\, dy = 0.\end{aligned}$$

Here we have used

$$\frac{\partial}{\partial x_k}|x-y| = -\frac{\partial}{\partial y_k}|x-y|,$$

the fact that $\omega_\varrho(|x-y|)$ vanishes for $|x-y| \geqslant \varrho$, and the fact that integration by parts is permissible for our $\mathbf{a}(x)$. We substitute this $\mathbf{v}$ into (36) and integrate the resulting equality by parts, obtaining

$$\begin{aligned} 0 = \int_\Omega \operatorname{grad}\varphi \cdot \mathbf{v}\, dx = -\int_\Omega \varphi \operatorname{div} \mathbf{v}\, dx \\ + \int_{\tilde{S}_1} [\varphi]\, v_n\, dS = \int_{\tilde{S}_1} [\varphi]\, v_n\, dS, \end{aligned} \tag{39}$$

where $\tilde{S}_1$ is the planar cross-section of Ω containing S_1, and $[\varphi]$ is the jump of the function φ on this cross-section. We take the number ϱ to be so small that the domain $\tilde{T}$, outside which $\mathbf{v}$ vanishes, differs by very little from T, and the cross-section $\tilde{S}_1$ differs only slightly from S_1. As $\varrho \to 0$, the field $\mathbf{a}_\varrho$ remains uniformly bounded and approaches $\mathbf{a}$ uniformly in $\Omega - \Sigma_1$.

Therefore, we have

$$v_n|_{\tilde{S}_1} = (\mathbf{a}_\varrho)_n|_{\tilde{S}_1} \to \mathbf{a}|_{\tilde{S}_1} \qquad (\boldsymbol{\alpha} = 0 \text{ on } \tilde{S}_1 - S_1).$$

Taking the limit as $\varrho \to 0$ in (39), we obtain

$$\int_{S_1} [\varphi]\, \alpha_n\, ds = 0,$$

from which, since $\boldsymbol{\alpha} = \alpha_n \mathbf{n}$ is arbitrary on S_1, it follows that $[\varphi] = 0$, i. e., φ is continuous as we pass through the cross-section S_1. This proves the theorem. Theorem 1 is also valid for planar domains.

Remark. It is not hard to show that for wide classes of domains Ω, the inequality

$$\int_\Omega \varphi^2\, dx \leqslant C_1 \int_\Omega \mathbf{u}^2\, dx, \tag{40}$$

holds, where

$$\varphi(x) = \int_{x_0}^{x} \sum_k u_k\, dx_k, \qquad x_0, x \in \Omega,$$

if Ω is bounded, and the inequality

$$\int_\Omega \frac{\varphi^2(x)\, dx}{1+|x|^2} \leqslant C_2 \int_\Omega \mathbf{u}^2\, dx, \tag{41}$$

holds if Ω is unbounded. The constants C_1 and C_2 are determined by Ω and do not depend on **u**. The inequality (40) is certainly true if Ω is the sum of a finite number of star-shaped domains. The inequality (41) is true, for example, for a domain Ω which is the sum of a finite number of star-shaped domains and the exterior of a sphere. The proofs of the inequalities (40) and (41) will not be given here, but the inequalities themselves will be used later.

2.3. We now consider the set $\dot{J}(\Omega)$ of all sufficiently smooth solenoidal vectors of compact support in Ω, and in $J(\Omega)$ we introduce the scalar product

$$[\mathbf{u}, \mathbf{v}] = \int_\Omega \mathbf{u}_{x_k} \cdot \mathbf{v}_{x_k}\, dx$$

and the norm

$$\|\mathbf{u}\|_H = \sqrt{[\mathbf{u}, \mathbf{u}]}.$$

The completion of $\dot{J}(\Omega)$ in the metric corresponding to this scalar product leads us to a complete Hilbert space, which we denote by $H(\Omega)$. What was said about the elements of $\overset{\circ}{D}(\Omega)$ in Sec. 1.4. is certainly true for the elements of $H(\Omega)$.

Finally, we denote by $J_{0,1}(\Omega)$ the Hilbert space of vector functions, obtained by completing $\dot{J}(\Omega)$ in the norm corresponding to the scalar product

$$(\mathbf{u}, \mathbf{v})_1 = \int_\Omega (\mathbf{u} \cdot \mathbf{v} + \mathbf{u}_{x_k} \cdot \mathbf{v}_{x_k})\, dx.$$

In the case where the domain Ω is bounded, the spaces $H(\Omega)$ and $J_{0,1}(\Omega)$ coincide, and the corresponding norms are equivalent. However, if Ω is the exterior of a bounded domain (for example), then the norm in $J_{0,1}(\Omega)$ is stronger than the norm in $H(\Omega)$, and $H(\Omega)$ is a larger set than $J_{0,1}(\Omega)$.

3. Riesz' Theorem and the Leray-Schauder Principle

We now state two theorems which will be used later to prove existence theorems for stationary problems. The solution of linear problems will be based on Riesz' theorem (see e.g. [16]):

RIESZ' THEOREM. *A linear functional* $l(u)$ on a Hilbert space H can be expressed as a scalar product of a fixed element $a \in H$ with the element $u \in H$, i.e.,*

$$l(u) = (a, u).$$

The element a is uniquely determined by the functional l.

* In this book, all linear functionals are assumed to be bounded (and hence continuous).

As for the solution of nonlinear stationary problems, we shall use one of the "fixed-point theorems," i.e., the so-called *Leray-Schauder principle*. We shall not need this principle in its full generality, and therefore here we only state one of its implications. Suppose that we are given an equation

$$x = A\,x \tag{42}$$

in a separable Hilbert space, where A is a completely continuous and, in general, nonlinear operator. We recall that an operator A is said to be *completely continuous* in H if it maps any weakly convergent sequence $\{x_1, x_2, \ldots\}$ in H into a strongly convergent sequence $\{A\,x_1, A\,x_2, \ldots\}$ in H. The existence of solutions for equation (42) is guaranteed by the following result:

LERAY-SCHAUDER PRINCIPLE. *If all possible solutions of the equation*

$$x = \lambda\,A\,x$$

for $\lambda \in [0,1]$ *lie within some ball* $|x| \leqslant \varrho$, *then the equation* (42) *has at least one solution inside this ball.*

This principle is particularly remarkable in that it can even be used to investigate problems for whose solution there is no uniqueness theorem.

CHAPTER 2

The Linearized Stationary Problem

The basic problem investigated in this book is that of determining the motion of a viscous incompressible fluid, when we know the volume forces acting on the fluid, the boundary regime, and, in the case of nonstationary flows, the initial velocity field. In all cases considered here, the only important assumption is that a system of coordinates can be chosen in which the domain Ω filled by the fluid does not change. This assumption is satisfied in the following important practical problems, and in many others:

1. The problem of the motion of a rigid body in an infinite flow, or equivalently, the problem of an infinite flow past a rigid body immersed in the flow;

2. The problem of the motion of a fluid acted upon by volume forces in a vessel with rigid walls, whose spatial position is varied in a known way;

3. The problem of the motion of a fluid between two coaxial cylinders, or two concentric spheres, rotating with different velocities.

In an inertial Cartesian coordinate system, the characteristics of the motion of the fluid which can be determined, i. e., the velocity field $\mathbf{v}$ and the pressure p, satisfy the system consisting of the Navier-Stokes equations and the equation of continuity:

$$\left.\begin{aligned} \mathbf{v}_t - \nu \Delta \mathbf{v} + v_k \mathbf{v}_{x_k} &= - \operatorname{grad} p + \mathbf{f}(x, t) \\ \operatorname{div} \mathbf{v} &= 0 \end{aligned}\right\}. \tag{1}$$

Here, and henceforth, we set the density of the fluid equal to 1, and we assume that the kinematic viscosity ν is constant.

In any other Cartesian coordinate system which moves with respect to the given inertial system, the second equation (1) has the same form, but new linear terms in $\mathbf{v}$ and $\mathbf{v}_{x_k}$ can appear in the first equation. The methods presented here are such that if we include such terms with bounded coefficients in the Navier-Stokes equations, no basic technical difficulties are introduced. Because of this, we can confine ourselves to the case of Navier-Stokes equations in inertial systems, and to linearizations of the Navier-Stokes equations in which all nonlinear terms are discarded. We reiterate that the investigation of the problem in other, noninertial coordinate systems and the investigation of other linearizations of the system (1) can be carried out in an analogous fashion.

The system (1) has to be supplemented by boundary conditions. In the case of rigid walls, we obtain the "adhesion condition", according to which the velocity $\mathbf{v}$ of the fluid at points next to the wall coincides with the velocity of motion of the corresponding points of the wall. In the general case, this condition takes the form

$$\mathbf{v}|_S = \boldsymbol{\alpha}, \tag{2}$$

where $\boldsymbol{\alpha}$ is a specified velocity field on S.

It follows from the equation $\operatorname{div} \mathbf{v} = 0$ that

$$\int_S \boldsymbol{\alpha} \cdot \mathbf{n}\, dS = 0. \tag{3}$$

Except for the case of exterior two-dimensional problems, it can be assumed that $\boldsymbol{\alpha}$ always satisfies this condition.

In the present chapter, we establish our first basic result, i. e., we shall prove that when they are linearized, the above-mentioned stationary problems have unique solutions. This fact is most easily established in the Hilbert space $\mathbf{L}_2(\Omega)$ of vector functions, after we have made a certain well-defined extension of the concept of a solution, to be described below. The comparative simplicity of investigations in $\mathbf{L}_2(\Omega)$ is largely explained by the fact that in this space it is easy to separate the problem of finding $\mathbf{v}$ from that of finding p. In fact, we can obtain a closed system of equations for $\mathbf{v}$ from which $\mathbf{v}$ can be determined uniquely, and then p can be found either directly from the Navier-Stokes equations or from a corresponding integral identity. Because of this, in defining the "generalized solution of the problem", we shall discuss only the function $\mathbf{v}$, and not the pair $\mathbf{v}$, p.

The considerations given in this chapter allow us to assert not only that the problems in question have unique solutions but also that various approximation methods, e.g., Galerkin's method, can be used to find these solutions.

The reader who is familiar with approximate methods for solving the Dirichlet problem for the Laplace operator will see in reading Secs. 1 and 2 of this chapter that these methods carry over to hydrodynamical problems, except that here the basic functions must satisfy the solenoidality condition.

1. The Case of a Bounded Domain

In this section, we consider the so-called *Stokes problem*, i.e., the problem of determining $\mathbf{v}$ and p in a domain Ω from the conditions

$$\left.\begin{aligned} \nu\,\Delta \mathbf{v} &= \operatorname{grad} p - \mathbf{f}, \\ \operatorname{div} \mathbf{v} &= 0, \end{aligned}\right\} \tag{4}$$

$$\mathbf{v}|_S = \boldsymbol{\alpha}. \tag{4a}$$

Concerning $\boldsymbol{\alpha}$ and S, we require that $\boldsymbol{\alpha}$ can be extended inside Ω as a solenoidal field $\mathbf{a}(x)$ with $\mathbf{a}(x) \in W_2^1(\Omega)$; sufficient conditions for this are given in Chap. 1, Sec. 2. In this section, we assume that the domain Ω is bounded.

By a *generalized solution* of the problem (4), (4a), we mean a function $\mathbf{v}(x)$ which satisfies the identity

$$\nu \int_\Omega \mathbf{v}_{x_k} \cdot \boldsymbol{\Phi}_{x_k}\, dx = \int_\Omega \mathbf{f} \cdot \boldsymbol{\Phi}\, dx \tag{5}$$

for any $\boldsymbol{\Phi} \in H(\Omega)$, such that $\mathbf{v} - \mathbf{a} \in H(\Omega)$. It is easy to see that the classical solution of the problem is a generalized solution. In fact, if we multiply the first of the equations (4), (4a) by $\boldsymbol{\Phi} \in H(\Omega)$, integrate over Ω, and carry out an integration by parts in the first term, we obtain (5) as a result. The term containing p drops out, due to the orthogonality of grad $p \in G(\Omega)$ and $\boldsymbol{\Phi} \in \mathring{J}(\Omega)$. Conversely, if it is known that a generalized solution $\mathbf{v}$ belongs to $W_2^2(\Omega')$, where Ω' is any interior subdomain of Ω, and if $\mathbf{f} \in \mathbf{L}_2(\Omega)$, then (5) can be transformed into

$$\int_{\Omega'} (\nu\,\Delta \mathbf{v} + \mathbf{f}) \cdot \boldsymbol{\Phi}\, dx = 0 \tag{6}$$

for $\boldsymbol{\Phi} \in \dot{J}(\Omega')$. Since $\dot{J}(\Omega')$ is dense in $\mathring{J}(\Omega')$ (see Chap. 1, Sec. 2), since $\boldsymbol{\Phi}$ is an arbitrary element of $J(\Omega')$, and since $\nu\,\Delta\mathbf{v} + f \in \mathbf{L}_2(\Omega')$, it follows from (6) that $\nu\,\Delta \mathbf{v} + \mathbf{f}$ is the gradient of some function $p(x)$.

Since $\Omega \subset \Omega'$ is arbitrary, we find that

$$\nu \Delta \mathbf{v} + \mathbf{f} = \operatorname{grad} p$$

inside Ω, i.e., $\mathbf{v}(x)$ actually satisfies the Navier-Stokes system.

This extended notion of a solution is also justified from another point of view, i.e., the uniqueness theorem is preserved. Thus, if we find a generalized solution, it will also be the classical solution, if the latter exists. However, with the weak restrictions on the data of the problem for which a generalized solution can be found, there may not be a classical solution, whereas the existence of a generalized solution follows from very general and very simple considerations. All this shows how reasonable it is to go from classical solutions to generalized solutions. The generalized solution of the problem (4), (4a) and of the boundary-value problems to be considered below, can be found for a large class of function $\mathbf{f}$ describing the external forces. In fact, the only restriction on $\mathbf{f}$ in this chapter and in Chap. 5, unless the contrary is explicitly stated, is that the integral

$$\int_{\Omega} \mathbf{f} \cdot \mathbf{\Phi} \, dx$$

should define a linear functional for $\mathbf{\Phi}$ in the space $H(\Omega)$. This in turn will be the case if and only if the inequality

$$\left| \int_{\Omega} \mathbf{f} \cdot \mathbf{\Phi} \, dx \right| \leqslant C \|\mathbf{\Phi}\|_H$$

holds. The following are among a variety of conditions which imply the validity of this inequality:

1. If Ω is an arbitrary domain and if $\mathbf{f} \in \mathbf{L}_{6/5}(\Omega)$, then according to Hölder's inequality and the inequality (6) of Chap. 1, Sec. 1,

$$\left| \int_{\Omega} \mathbf{f} \cdot \mathbf{\Phi} \, dx \right| \leqslant \Big(\int_{\Omega} \sum_i |f_i|^{6/5} \, dx \Big)^{5/6} \Big(\int_{\Omega} \sum_i |\Phi_i|^6 \, dx \Big)^{1/6} \leqslant C \|\mathbf{\Phi}\|_H .$$

2. If Ω is an arbitrary domain and if

$$\int_{\Omega} |x - y|^2 \sum_i |f_i(x)|^2 \, dx$$

converges for some y, then

$$\left| \int_{\Omega} \mathbf{f} \cdot \mathbf{\Phi} \, dx \right| \leqslant \Big(\int_{\Omega} |x - y|^2 \sum_i |f_i(x)|^2 \, dx \Big)^{1/2}$$

$$\times \left(\int_{\Omega} \sum_i \frac{|\Phi_i(x)|^2}{|x - y|^2} \, dx \right)^{1/2} \leqslant C \|\mathbf{\Phi}\|_H$$

because of the inequality (13) of Chap. 1, Sec 1.

3. Let f_i have the form

$$f_i = \frac{\partial f_{ik}(x)}{\partial x_k},$$

and let $f_{ik}(x) \in L_2(\Omega)$ (see [24]). Then

$$\left| \int_\Omega \mathbf{f} \cdot \boldsymbol{\Phi} \, dx \right| \leqslant \left| - \int_\Omega \sum_{i,k} f_{ik} \, \Phi_{ix_k} \, dx \right| \leqslant C \| \boldsymbol{\Phi} \|_H$$

for any $\boldsymbol{\Phi} \in \dot{J}(\Omega)$. Since $\dot{J}(\Omega)$ is dense in $H(\Omega)$, this inequality will hold for any $\boldsymbol{\Phi}$ in $H(\Omega)$. Here, the domain Ω can be arbitrary.

4. The vector $\mathbf{f}$ need not be a function in the usual sense. It can also be a so-called "generalized function" (see [25, 26] and elsewhere), e. g., a Dirac delta function $\delta(S_1)\,\mathbf{e}$ concentrated on some smooth surface S_1 lying in a bounded region of Ω. For such $\mathbf{f}$, the integral $\int_\Omega \mathbf{f} \cdot \boldsymbol{\Phi} \, dx$ is interpreted as the integral of $\boldsymbol{\Phi} \cdot \mathbf{e}$ over S_1, i.e.,

$$\int_\Omega \mathbf{f} \cdot \boldsymbol{\Phi} \, dx = \int_{S_1} \boldsymbol{\Phi} \cdot \mathbf{e} \, dS.$$

This integral actually defines a linear functional on $H(\Omega)$, because of the familiar inequality (9) of Chap. 1, Sec. 1, which is valid for any function $\boldsymbol{\Phi}$ in $\overset{\circ}{W}{}_2^1(\Omega)$. In the third case listed above, the f_i can also be generalized functions.

Of course, the cases just enumerated do not exhaust all possible situations in which the integral $\int_\Omega \mathbf{f} \cdot \boldsymbol{\Phi} \, dx$ defines a linear functional of $\boldsymbol{\Phi} \in H(\Omega)$. However, there is no need to explore all these possibilities, since in all the theorems on the existence of a generalized solution, proved in Chaps. 2 and 5, we shall not use concrete properties of $\mathbf{f}$, but only the fact that $\int_\Omega \mathbf{f} \cdot \boldsymbol{\Phi} \, dx$ defines a linear functional on $H(\Omega)$.

THEOREM 1. *There exists no more than one generalized solution of the problem* (4), (4a).

Proof: According to (5), if $\mathbf{u}$ were the difference between two possible solutions, we would have $\mathbf{u} \in H(\Omega)$ and

$$\nu \, [\mathbf{u}, \boldsymbol{\Phi}] = 0.$$

Setting $\boldsymbol{\Phi} = \mathbf{u}$ and recalling that [,] is the scalar product in $H(\Omega)$, we find that $\mathbf{u} \equiv 0$.

THEOREM 2. *The problem* (4), (4a) *has a generalized solution if for the given* $\mathbf{f}$, *the integral* $\int_\Omega \mathbf{f} \cdot \boldsymbol{\Phi} \, dx$ *defines a linear functional of* $\boldsymbol{\Phi} \in H(\Omega)$.

Proof: We rewrite the identity (5) in the form

$$\nu\,[\mathbf{v}-\mathbf{a},\boldsymbol{\Phi}] = -\nu\,[\mathbf{a},\boldsymbol{\Phi}] + (\mathbf{f},\boldsymbol{\Phi}) \tag{7}$$

and note that the right-hand side defines a linear functional of $\boldsymbol{\Phi} \in H(\Omega)$. According to Riesz' theorem, this functional can be represented in the form $[\mathbf{u},\boldsymbol{\Phi}]$, where $\mathbf{u}$ is a well-defined element of $H(\Omega)$ which is uniquely specified by $\mathbf{f}$, $\mathbf{a}$ and ν. Obviously, the function $\mathbf{v} = \mathbf{a} + \mathbf{u}$ is the solution we are looking for.

THEOREM 3. *If* $\mathbf{f} \in \mathbf{L}_2(\Omega')$ *and* $\Omega' \subset \Omega$, *then the generalized solution* $\mathbf{v}$ *found in Theorem* 2 *belongs to* $W_2^2(\Omega'')$ *for* $\Omega'' \subset \Omega'$ *and satisfies the system* (4) *almost everywhere in* Ω'', *with* $p \in W_2^1(\Omega'')$.

Proof: Here Ω'' is any subdomain which lies strictly inside Ω'. We choose a fixed Ω''. Without loss of generality, we can regard the function $\mathbf{a}(x)$ in Ω' as being as smooth as we please. In (5), we choose $\boldsymbol{\Phi}$ of the form

$$\boldsymbol{\Phi} = \operatorname{curl}\,[\zeta^2 \operatorname{curl} \mathbf{v}_\varrho]_\varrho,$$

where the index ϱ denotes averaging with the kernel $\omega_\varrho(|x-y|)$, and $\zeta(x)$ is a twice continuously differentiable nonnegative function of compact support in Ω', which equals 1 in $\Omega'' \subset \Omega'$ and does not exceed 1 anywhere in Ω'. We shall assume that the width of the boundary strip in Ω' where $\zeta = 0$ is greater than ϱ. Then, we substitute our $\boldsymbol{\Phi}$ into (5) and carry out a series of transformations, noting that the averaging operation commutes with the differentiation operation. The result is

$$\begin{aligned}\int_{\Omega'} \mathbf{f}\cdot\boldsymbol{\Phi}\,dx &= \nu\int_{\Omega'} \mathbf{v}_{x_k}\cdot\boldsymbol{\Phi}_{x_k}\,dx = \nu\int_{\Omega'} \mathbf{v}_{x_k}\,[\operatorname{curl}\,(\zeta^2\operatorname{curl}\mathbf{v}_\varrho)]_{\varrho x_k}\,dx\\ &= \nu\int_{\Omega'} \mathbf{v}_{\varrho x_k}\,[\operatorname{curl}\,(\zeta^2\operatorname{curl}\mathbf{v}_\varrho)]_{x_k}\,dx\\ &= -\,\nu\int_{\Omega'} \Delta\mathbf{v}_\varrho\,\operatorname{curl}\,(\zeta^2\operatorname{curl}\mathbf{v}_\varrho)\,dx.\end{aligned} \tag{8}$$

But

$$\begin{aligned}\operatorname{curl}\,(\zeta^2\operatorname{curl}\mathbf{v}_\varrho) &= \zeta^2\operatorname{curl}\operatorname{curl}\mathbf{v}_\varrho + \operatorname{grad}\zeta^2\times\operatorname{curl}\mathbf{v}_\varrho\\ &= -\,\zeta^2\,\Delta\mathbf{v}_\varrho + \operatorname{grad}\zeta^2\times\operatorname{curl}\mathbf{v}_\varrho,\end{aligned}$$

since

$$\operatorname{div}\mathbf{v}_\varrho = 0.$$

Therefore, from (8) we obtain

$$\nu\int_{\Omega'} \zeta^2\,(\Delta\mathbf{v}_\varrho)^2\,dx = \int_{\Omega'} [\mathbf{f}_\varrho\cdot\operatorname{curl}\,(\zeta^2\operatorname{curl}\mathbf{v}_\varrho) + \nu\,\Delta\mathbf{v}_\varrho\cdot\operatorname{grad}\zeta^2\times\operatorname{curl}\mathbf{v}_\varrho]\,dx.$$

We estimate the right-hand side by using the inequality

$$2\,a\,b \leqslant \varepsilon\, a^2 + \frac{1}{\varepsilon}\, b^2$$

with arbitrary $\varepsilon > 0$. It is not hard to see that this leads to the inequality

$$\nu \int_{\Omega'} \zeta^2 (\Delta \mathbf{v}_\varrho)^2\, dx \leqslant \varepsilon \int_{\Omega'} \nu\, \zeta^2 (\Delta \mathbf{v}_\varrho)^2\, dx + \frac{C_1}{\varepsilon} \int_{\Omega'} \left(\mathbf{f}^2 \zeta^2 + \sum_{k=1}^{3} \mathbf{v}_{\varrho x_k}^2\right) dx, \tag{9}$$

with a constant C_1 which depends only on the choice of the function $\zeta(x)$. We choose $\varepsilon < 1$ in (9) and use the fact that the estimate

$$\int_{\Omega} \sum_{k=1}^{3} \mathbf{v}_{x_k}^2\, dx \leqslant \text{const}, \tag{10}$$

holds for $\mathbf{v}$, and hence for $\mathbf{v}_\varrho$ also, as follows easily from (5) if we set $\mathbf{\Phi} = \mathbf{v} - \mathbf{a}$.

From (9) and (10), we see that the inequality

$$\int_{\Omega''} (\Delta \mathbf{v}_\varrho)^2\, dx \leqslant \int_{\Omega'} \zeta^2 (\Delta \mathbf{v}_\varrho)^2\, dx \leqslant \text{const}$$

holds for any $\varrho > 0$, with one and the same constant. This in turn implies the following estimate for the second-order derivatives of $\mathbf{v}_\varrho$ (see Chap. 1, Sec. 1):

$$\int_{\Omega''} (D_x^2\, \mathbf{v}_\varrho)^2\, dx \leqslant \text{const}. \tag{11}$$

Since the constant in (11) does not depend on ϱ, the function $\mathbf{v}$ which is the limit of $\mathbf{v}_\varrho$ as $\varrho \to 0$ has second-order derivatives, which also obey the inequality (11) (see [16]). Gathering together all the estimates for $\mathbf{v}$, we obtain

$$\| \mathbf{v} \|_{W_2^2(\Omega'')} \leqslant \text{const}. \tag{12}$$

We can now transform (5) into

$$\int_{\Omega} (\nu\, \Delta \mathbf{v} + \mathbf{f}) \cdot \mathbf{\Phi}\, dx = 0,$$

assuming that $\mathbf{\Phi} \in \dot{J}(\Omega'')$ since $\dot{J}(\Omega'')$ is dense in $\mathring{J}(\Omega'')$, and since $\nu\,\Delta \mathbf{v} + \mathbf{f} \in \mathbf{L}_2(\Omega'')$, it follows that $\nu\,\Delta \mathbf{v} + \mathbf{f}$ is the gradient of a function $p \in W_2^1(\Omega'')$, so that $\nu\,\Delta \mathbf{v} + \mathbf{f} = \operatorname{grad} p$ and p is the pressure we are looking for. This completes the proof of Theorem 3.

To investigate the behavior of $\mathbf{v}$ near S, as will be done in Chap. 3, Sec. 5, more complicated calculations are needed. In all the above theorems, the requirements on the smoothness of $\boldsymbol{\alpha}$ and of the boundary

S reduce to just the fact that it should be possible to continue $\boldsymbol{\alpha}$ inside the domain as a solenoidal field $\mathbf{a}(x)$ with $a_i \in W_2^1(\Omega)$. If $\boldsymbol{\alpha} = 0$, then no smoothness requirements at all are imposed on S.

By using the method of Theorem 3, we can show that if $\mathbf{f} \in W_2^m(\Omega')$, then $\mathbf{v} \in W_2^{m+2}(\Omega'')$ and $p \in W_2^{m+1}(\Omega'')$.

2. The Exterior Three-Dimensional Problem

In this section, we consider linearized problems for unbounded domains Ω. If we have the homogeneous boundary conditions

$$\mathbf{v}\,|_S = 0, \qquad \mathbf{v}^\infty = 0, \tag{13}$$

both on S and at ∞, then the proof that the problem (4), (13) has a unique solution is identical, word for word, with the proofs of Theorems 1 and 2 of the preceding section (here $\mathbf{a}(x) = \boldsymbol{\alpha} = 0$). The boundary conditions are satisfied in the sense that the solution $\mathbf{v}$ belongs to the space $H(\Omega)$. Thus, we have the following theorem:

THEOREM 4. *If* $\int_\Omega \mathbf{f}\cdot\boldsymbol{\Phi}\,dx$ *defines a linear functional of* $\boldsymbol{\Phi} \in H(\Omega)$, *then there exists a unique generalized solution of the problem* (4), (13), *i.e., there exists a function* $\mathbf{v}(x)$ *belonging to* $H(\Omega)$ *which satisfies the identity*

$$\nu[\mathbf{v}, \boldsymbol{\Phi}] = \int_\Omega \mathbf{f}\cdot\boldsymbol{\Phi}\,dx \tag{5}$$

for any $\boldsymbol{\Phi} \in H(\Omega)$. *If, in addition,* $\mathbf{f}$ *is locally square-summable, then* $\mathbf{v}$ *has locally square-summable second-order derivatives and satisfies the system* (4) *almost everywhere, with a pressure* p *which has a locally square-summable gradient. Finally, if* Ω *contains a complete neighborhood of the point at infinity, i.e., a domain* $\{|x| \geqslant R\}$ *and if* $\mathbf{f} \in \mathbf{L}_2\,\{|x| \geqslant R\}$, *then* $\mathbf{v}_{x_i x_j}$ *and* p_{x_i} *are square-summable over the domain* $\{|x| \geqslant R + \varepsilon\}$, $\varepsilon > 0$.

This theorem is proved in just the same way as Theorem 3, if we take into account the inequality of Chap. 1, Sec. 1.4.

We now assume that the boundary conditions at ∞ are nonhomogeneous. In fact, suppose we have n immovable objects of finite size, bounded by surfaces $S_1, \ldots, S_n$, past which there occurs a flow $\mathbf{v}$ that approaches a given vector $\mathbf{v}^\infty = \text{const}$ as $|x| \to \infty$. The problem consists in determining $\mathbf{v}$ and p from the equations (4) and the conditions

$$\mathbf{v}\,\Big|_{S = \sum_{k=1}^{n} S_k} = 0, \qquad \mathbf{v}\,\big|_{|x|=\infty} = \mathbf{v}^\infty. \tag{14}$$

We construct a smooth solenoidal field $\mathbf{a}(x)$, which equals zero on $S = \sum_{k=1}^{n} S_k$ and equals $\mathbf{v}^\infty$ for large $|x|$. For example, we can take $\mathbf{a}(x)$ to be

$$\mathbf{a}(x) = \mathbf{v}^\infty - \mathbf{b}(x),$$

where

$$\mathbf{b}(x) = \operatorname{curl}\big(\zeta(x)\,\mathbf{d}(x)\big), \quad \mathbf{d}(x) = (v_2^\infty x_3,\ v_3^\infty x_1,\ v_1^\infty x_2),$$

and $\zeta(x)$ is a smooth "cutoff" function, equal to 1 on S and near S, and equal to 0 for large $|x|$.

We call the *generalized solution* of the problem (4), (14) the function $\mathbf{v}$ such that $\mathbf{v} - \mathbf{a} \in H(\Omega)$, which satisfies the integral identity (15) for all $\mathbf{\Phi} \in H(\Omega)$. Then the proof of the following theorem is similar to the proofs of Theorems 1 to 4:

THEOREM 5. *All the assertions of Theorem 4 are valid for the problem* (4), (14).

To prove that the problem (4), (14) has a solution, it is enough to verify (see the proof of Theorem 2) that the expression

$$\nu \int_\Omega \mathbf{a}_{x_k} \cdot \mathbf{\Phi}_{x_k}\, dx$$

defines a linear functional of $\mathbf{\Phi} \in H(\Omega)$. But this is certainly the case, since $\mathbf{a}_{x_k} = 0$ for large $|x|$, and hence

$$\left|\nu \int_\Omega \mathbf{a}_{x_k} \cdot \mathbf{\Phi}_{x_k}\, dx\right| \leqslant C\, \|\mathbf{\Phi}\|_H.$$

The differential properties of the solution $\mathbf{v}$, p are improved to the extent that one improves the differential properties of $\mathbf{f}$; in particular, if $\mathbf{f} = 0$, then $\mathbf{v}$ and p are infinitely differentiable. The boundary conditions (14) are understood "in the mean square" [6] on S, and in the sense that

$$\int_\Omega \frac{|\mathbf{v}(x) - \mathbf{a}(x)|^2}{|x - y|^2}\, dx < \infty$$

at infinity.

Using the fundamental singular solution for the Navier-Stokes equations, it is easy to ascertain when the generalized solutions obtained above belong to one or another Hölder space, and at what rate they approach their limits at ∞. The final results are the same as in the Dirichlet problem for the Laplace operator, and will be proved directly for the nonlinear equations in Chap. 4.

The case of boundary conditions which are nonhomogeneous both at ∞ and on S is examined in the same way as the case considered above.

3. Plane-Parallel Flows

For the case of two space variables, the problem (4), (4a) reduces by a familiar argument to the first boundary-value problem for the biharmonic equation. In fact, because of the equation

$$\frac{\partial v_1}{\partial x_1} + \frac{\partial v_2}{\partial x_2} = 0,$$

there exist a "stream function" $\psi(x_1, x_2)$ defined by the equations

$$v_1 = \frac{\partial \psi}{\partial x_2}, \quad v_2 = -\frac{\partial \psi}{\partial x_1}.$$

Taking the curl of both sides of the Navier-Stokes system and replacing v_1 and v_2 by their expressions in terms of ψ, we obtain the following equation for ψ:

$$\nu\, \Delta^2 \varphi = -f_{1x_2} + f_{2x_1}.$$

As is easily seen, the boundary condition $\mathbf{v}|_S = \boldsymbol{\alpha}$ determines the values of ψ and $\frac{\partial \psi}{\partial n}$ on S (the first to within a constant which can be chosen arbitrarily). Thus, for plane-parallel flows, the problem (4), (4a) actually reduces to the well-studied problem of determining ψ. Here, we shall not give the results pertaining to this problem, and we only remark that the methods of the preceding section are of course applicable to the present special case. For bounded domains, these methods lead to the same results as in three-dimensional problems. The situation is otherwise for the problem of flow past an object, i.e., for the problem (4), (14). In fact, in the case of two space variables, it is impossible to satisfy the preassigned conditions (14) at infinity. By analogy with the basic electrostatic problem, the problem of plane-parallel flows past an object takes the following form: Find a solution of the system (4) satisfying a boundary condition which for simplicity is taken to be homogeneous

$$\mathbf{v}|_S = 0, \tag{4a}$$

and which is bounded at infinity. Moreover, it is natural to state the following generalized formulation of this problem: Find a function $\mathbf{v}(x)$ belonging to $H(\Omega)$ which satisfies the identity (5) for all $\boldsymbol{\Phi}$ in

$H(\Omega)$. Theorem 4 guarantees that this problem has a unique solution in $H(\Omega)$ for any linear functional $\mathbf{f}$ on $H(\Omega)$. In particular, if $\mathbf{f} \equiv 0$, then the solution is $\mathbf{v} \equiv 0$, despite the fact that the condition $\mathbf{v}^\infty = 0$ is not assumed to hold at infinity. We note that the fact that $\mathbf{v}$ belongs to $H(\Omega)$ does not compel $\mathbf{v}$ to converge to zero as $|x| \to \infty$ (for example, $\mathbf{v}$ may be constant for large $|x|$), but it does exclude the possibility that $\mathbf{v}$ grows logarithmically as $|x| \to \infty$.

In its classical formulation, the problem of plane flow past an object was discussed by various authors in connection with an analysis of the familiar "Stokes paradox." This paradox consisted in the fact that a solution of the homogeneous system (4) which is equal to 0 on S and to a given $\mathbf{v}^\infty$ at infinity had not been found. It follows from what has been said above that such a solution actually does not exist. In the paper by B. V. Rusanov [27], dealing with the case where Ω is the exterior of a circle, it is shown that the solution $\mathbf{v}(x, t)$ of the nonstationary problem corresponding to a zero force $\mathbf{f}$, a homogeneous boundary condition on S and a nonhomogeneous boundary condition $\mathbf{v}|_{|x|=\infty} = (C_1, 0)$ at infinity, converges to zero as $t \to +\infty$, for any fixed x. The same is also true for the exterior of an arbitrary bounded domain.

Another result pertaining to the Stokes paradox is due to Finn and Noll [28], who proved that the homogeneous system (4) with a zero boundary condition on S has only a zero solution in the class of twice continuously differentiable functions which are bounded at infinity.

4. The Spectrum of Linear Problems

Let Ω be a bounded domain in the Euclidean space of points $x = (x_1, x_2, x_3)$. The linear problem (4), (4a) studied in this chapter corresponds to a linear operator in a Hilbert space, whose properties we now intend to study. We introduce the space $\overset{\circ}{J}(\Omega)$ as the basic Hilbert space, and we introduce the operator $\tilde{\Delta}$ in $\overset{\circ}{J}(\Omega)$, which establishes a correspondence between the solutions $\mathbf{v}(x)$ of the linear problems

$$\left.\begin{aligned} \nu \Delta \mathbf{v} + \operatorname{grad} p &= \boldsymbol{\psi}(x), \\ \operatorname{div} \mathbf{v} = 0, \ \mathbf{v}|_S &= 0 \end{aligned}\right\} \tag{15}$$

and the corresponding free terms $\boldsymbol{\psi}(x)$, i.e., $\tilde{\Delta}\mathbf{v} = \boldsymbol{\psi}$.

In Sec. 1, we proved that to any $\boldsymbol{\psi}$ in $\overset{\circ}{J}(\Omega)$, or even in $\mathbf{L}_2(\Omega)$, there corresponds a unique solution $(\mathbf{v}, p)$, where

$$\mathbf{v} \in W_2^2(\Omega') \cap H(\Omega).$$

In order to justify introducing the operator $\tilde{\Delta}$, we have to show that different functions $\mathbf{v}$ satisfying (15) correspond to different $\boldsymbol{\psi}$ in $\mathring{J}(\Omega)$, or, equivalently, that if the solution of the problem (15) is identically zero, then $\boldsymbol{\psi} \equiv 0$ also. But this is actually so, since for $\mathbf{v} \equiv 0$, it follows from the first of the equations (15) that grad $p = \boldsymbol{\psi}$, and hence $\boldsymbol{\psi} \equiv 0$, since $\boldsymbol{\psi} \in \mathring{J}(\Omega)$ (see Chap. 1, Sec. 2).

Let $D(\tilde{\Delta})$ denote the set of all solutions of the problem (15), corresponding to all possible $\boldsymbol{\psi}$ in $\mathring{J}(\Omega)$. The set $D(\tilde{\Delta})$ is the domain of definition of the operator $\tilde{\Delta}$, and $\tilde{\Delta}$ establishes a one-to-one correspondence between $D(\tilde{\Delta})$ and $\mathring{J}(\Omega)$. We note that the operator $\tilde{\Delta}$ can be regarded as an extension of the operator $\nu\, p_{\mathfrak{J}}\, \Delta$, where $p_{\mathfrak{J}}$ is the operator projecting $\mathbf{L}_2(\Omega)$ onto $\mathring{J}(\Omega)$, defined on $W_2^2(\Omega) \cap H(\Omega)$. Then we have the following theorem:

THEOREM 6. *The operator $\tilde{\Delta}$ is self-adjoint and negative-definite on $D(\tilde{\Delta})$. Its inverse operator $\tilde{\Delta}^{-1}$ is completely continuous.*

Proof: Suppose that $\mathbf{v} \in D(\tilde{\Delta})$ and $\tilde{\Delta}\mathbf{v} = \boldsymbol{\psi}$. Then, by the definition of $\tilde{\Delta}$, the identity

$$\nu \int_\Omega \mathbf{v}_{x_k} \cdot \boldsymbol{\Phi}_{x_k} dx = - \int_\Omega \boldsymbol{\psi} \cdot \boldsymbol{\Phi}\, dx \tag{16}$$

holds for any $\boldsymbol{\Phi} \in H(\Omega)$. If we set $\boldsymbol{\Phi} = \mathbf{v}$, (16) implies the inequality

$$\nu \| \mathbf{v} \|_H^2 = - \int_\Omega \boldsymbol{\psi} \cdot \mathbf{v}\, dx \leqslant \| \boldsymbol{\psi} \| \| \mathbf{v} \| \leqslant C \| \boldsymbol{\psi} \| \| \mathbf{v} \|_1,$$

and also the inequality

$$\| \mathbf{v} \|_1 \leqslant C \| \boldsymbol{\psi} \|, \tag{17}$$

because of the equivalence of the H and W_2^1 norms.

We now show that $\tilde{\Delta}$ is closed on $D(\tilde{\Delta})$. Let $\mathbf{v}^n \in D(\tilde{\Delta})$, $\mathbf{v}^n \Rightarrow \mathbf{v}$ and $\tilde{\Delta}\mathbf{v}^n = \boldsymbol{\psi}^n \Rightarrow \boldsymbol{\psi}$ in $\mathring{J}(\Omega)$ (i.e., in $\mathbf{L}_2(\Omega)$). By (17), $\mathbf{v}^n$ converges to $\mathbf{v}$ in the $H(\Omega)$ norm, and (16) holds for $\mathbf{v}^n$. Letting n approach ∞ in this identity, we arrive at (16) for $\mathbf{v}$ and $\boldsymbol{\psi}$, so that $\mathbf{v}$ actually belongs to $D(\tilde{\Delta})$ and $\tilde{\Delta}\mathbf{v} = \boldsymbol{\psi}$.

Next, we verify that $\tilde{\Delta}$ is symmetric on $D(\tilde{\Delta})$. Let $\mathbf{u}$ and $\mathbf{v}$ belong to $D(\tilde{\Delta})$ (and, *a fortiori*, to $H(\Omega)$). Then (16) will hold for $\mathbf{u}$, with any $\boldsymbol{\Phi} \in H(\Omega)$, and in particular, with $\boldsymbol{\Phi} = \mathbf{v}$, i.e.,

$$\nu [\mathbf{u}, \mathbf{v}] = - (\tilde{\Delta}\mathbf{u}, \mathbf{v});$$

similarly, (16) holds for $\mathbf{v}$, with $\boldsymbol{\Phi} = \mathbf{u}$, i.e.,

$$\nu[\mathbf{v}, \mathbf{u}] = -(\tilde{\Delta}\mathbf{v}, \mathbf{u}).$$

Comparing these equalities, and recalling that we are considering only real spaces, we find that $\tilde{\Delta}$ is symmetric on $D(\tilde{\Delta})$ and negative-definite.

Thus, the operator $\tilde{\Delta}$ is closed and symmetric, and its range fills the entire space $\mathring{J}(\Omega)$. Therefore, $\tilde{\Delta}$ is self-adjoint (see e.g. [16]). The fact that $\tilde{\Delta}^{-1}$ is completely continuous follows from the inequality (17) and the fact that a set of functions which is bounded in $\mathring{W}_2^1(\Omega)$ is compact in $L_2(\Omega)$ (see Chap. 1, Sec. 1). This proves Theorem 6.

The properties just established for the operator $\tilde{\Delta}$ imply a whole series of properties for the eigenfunctions and eigenvalues of $\tilde{\Delta}$ [3, 29], such as the following: The spectrum $\lambda = \lambda_1, \lambda_2, \ldots$ is discrete, negative and of finite multiplicity, λ_k converges to $-\infty$, the eigenfunctions are orthogonal and complete in the metrics of $L_2(\Omega)$ and $H(\Omega)$, etc.

For domains containing a complete neighborhood of the point at infinity, the spectrum of the operator $\tilde{\Delta}$ is continuous and fills the entire negative semi-axis. This is proved in approximately the same way as the analogous fact for the Laplace operator [30, 57].

5. The Positivity of the Pressure

The system (4) determines the pressure $p(x)$ to within an arbitrary additive constant. If we knew that the function $p(x)$ which is obtained had a bounded absolute value, then, by adding a sufficiently large positive constant to $p(x)$, we could see to it that the pressure is positive. However, from Theorem 3 of Sec. 1, it is only known that grad p is summable with exponent 2 over any interior subdomain Ω' of the domain Ω (if $\mathbf{f} \in \mathbf{L}_2(\Omega)$). Moreover, for arbitrary $\mathbf{f} \in \mathbf{L}_2(\Omega)$, the function $p(x) + \text{const}$ will in fact neither be bounded in absolute value nor have constant sign. To see this, we can choose $p(x) + \text{const}$ to be any function in $W_2^1(\Omega)$, and we can choose $\mathbf{v}(x)$ to be any solenoidal vector in $W_2^2(\Omega)$ which vanishes on S; then, the sum $-\Delta\mathbf{v} + \text{grad}\, p$ gives the value of the force $\mathbf{f}$ which corresponds to the chosen values of p and $\mathbf{v}$.

Thus, it is reasonable to relinquish the requirement that $p(x)$ (or, more exactly, $p(x) + \text{const}$) be positive at every point; instead, we replace the physical requirement that the pressure be nonnegative by the requirement that the integrals $\int_\Sigma |p|\, dS$ be bounded over two-dimensional surfaces Σ. This weakened nonnegativity condition is more natural than the condition that $p(x) + \text{const}$ be nonnegative for all x. Actually, the integrals $\int_\Sigma p\, dS$ only have physical meaning for areas Σ whose sizes are not less than a certain positive number (stipulated by the limits of accuracy of measurement and by the discreteness of the liquid medium). If we know that these integrals do not exceed a certain constant in absolute value, then we can add a constant C to $p(x)$ such that the integrals $\int_\Sigma (p + C)\, dS$, giving the pressure on the areas Σ, are nonnegative. Moreover, the finiteness of $\int_\Sigma p\, dS$ and $\int_\Sigma |p|\, dS$ for all planar bounded Σ and all Σ obtained from such Σ by making continuously differentiable transformations $y = y(x)$ with bounded $|\partial y_k/\partial x_m|$, $|\partial x_m/\partial y_k|$ and

$$\frac{\partial(x_1, x_2, x_3)}{\partial(y_1, y_2, y_3)} > 0$$

follows from the finiteness of $\int_\Sigma \text{grad}^2\, p\, dx$. Later, in Chap. 3, Sec. 5, we shall prove that the estimate

$$\| \mathbf{v} \|_{W_2^2(\Omega)} + \| p \|_{W_2^1(\Omega)} \leqslant C \| \mathbf{f} \|_{\mathbf{L}_2(\Omega)}$$

holds for the whole domain Ω.

CHAPTER 3

The Theory of Hydrodynamical Potentials

The linear stationary problem considered in the preceding chapter was originally solved by the methods of potential theory. In fact, Odqvist and Lichtenstein independently constructed hydrodynamical potentials, investigated their properties, and used them to solve the problem (4), (4a). In this chapter, we present this classical method. The method has many advantages over the functional method presented earlier. For example, it allows us to study the differential properties of solutions in the "Hölder norms" $C_{l,h}$ and in the L_p norms, not only inside the domain, but also near its boundary. The weakness of the method is its great complexity as compared to the functional method, and the requirement that the boundary of the domain be sufficiently smooth.

The present theory differs essentially from the widely known theory of electrostatic potentials only in the concrete analytical form of its potentials. However, the properties of these potentials, due to the polarity (singular character) of the kernel, are completely analogous to the properties of electrostatic volume potentials and potentials of single and double layers. Therefore, we shall not give a detailed analysis of the convergence of various improper or singular integrals, and we shall also not give a careful derivation of the integral equations which are satisfied by the hydrodynamical potentials of single and double layers. Moreover, everything which is proved for hydrodynamical potentials in the same way as for ordinary potentials, and is therefore familiar, will be given without proof.

Thus, we now present the formal theory of hydrodynamical potentials, mainly for the case of three-dimensional space.

1. The Volume Potential

First of all, we have to determine the fundamental singular solution of the linearized Navier-Stokes system, or, more exactly, the tensor made up of the solutions corresponding to concentrated forces directed along the various coordinate axes. Thus, consider the problem

$$\left.\begin{aligned} \nu \Delta \mathbf{u}^k (x, y) - \operatorname{grad} q^k (x, y) &= \delta (x - y)\, \mathbf{e}^k, \\ \operatorname{div} \mathbf{u}^k &= 0 \end{aligned}\right\} \tag{1}$$

where $k = 1, 2, 3$. Here, $\mathbf{e}^k$ is a unit vector directed along the kth coordinate axis, and $\delta (x - y)$ is the Dirac delta function. All differentiations are carried out with respect to the variable x, and the point y plays the role of a parameter (the applied force is concentrated at y). The system is supplemented by the requirement that $\mathbf{u}^k$ and q^k approach zero as $|x| \to \infty$.

To find $\mathbf{u}^k$ and q^k, we use Fourier transforms, recalling that the familiar relations

$$f(x) = \frac{1}{(2\pi)^{3/2}} \int_{-\infty}^{\infty} \tilde{f}(\alpha)\, e^{i\alpha x}\, d\alpha = \frac{1}{(2\pi)^3} \iint_{-\infty}^{\infty} f(y)\, e^{i\alpha (x-y)}\, d\alpha\, dy$$

and

$$\Delta \frac{1}{4\pi |x - y|} = -\,\delta (x - y), \quad \Delta^2 \frac{|x - y|}{8\pi} = -\,\delta (x - y)$$

imply that

$$\delta (x - y) = \frac{1}{(2\pi)^3} \int_{-\infty}^{\infty} e^{i\alpha (x-y)}\, d\alpha, \tag{2}$$

$$\frac{1}{4\pi\, |x - y|} = \frac{1}{(2\pi)^3} \int_{-\infty}^{\infty} \frac{e^{i\alpha (x-y)}}{\alpha^2}\, d\alpha, \tag{3}$$

$$\frac{|x - y|}{8\pi} = -\frac{1}{(2\pi)^3} \int_{-\infty}^{\infty} \frac{e^{i\alpha (x-y)}}{\alpha^4}\, d\alpha, \tag{4}$$

where*

$$\alpha^2 = \sum_{k=1}^{3} \alpha_k^2, \quad \alpha x = \sum_{k=1}^{3} \alpha_k x_k.$$

---

* All expressions written here are understood to be generalized functions. The reader can acquaint himself with the theory of these functions in the books [25] and [26]. We shall use such functions formally only to find the concrete form of the basic tensor. After the tensor has been found, we can immediately verify that it has all the required properties.

Let $\tilde{v}(\alpha)$ denote the Fourier transform of the function $v(x)$, i.e.,

$$v(x) = \frac{1}{(2\pi)^{3/2}} \int_{-\infty}^{\infty} \tilde{v}(\alpha)\, e^{i\alpha x}\, d\alpha .$$

Going over to Fourier transforms in equation (1), we obtain

$$-\nu \alpha^2 \tilde{u}_j^k - i\alpha_j \tilde{q}^k = \frac{1}{(2\pi)^{3/2}} \delta_j^k, \quad \alpha_j \tilde{u}_j^k = 0 \qquad (k, j = 1, 2, 3),$$

where δ_j^k is the Kronecker symbol. From this system we can uniquely determine $\tilde{u}_j^k$ and $\tilde{q}^k$:

$$\tilde{u}_j^k = \frac{1}{\nu (2\pi)^{3/2} \alpha^2}\left[-\delta_j^k + \frac{\alpha_j \alpha_k}{\alpha^2}\right], \quad \tilde{q}^k = \frac{i\alpha_k}{(2\pi)^{3/2}\alpha^2}.$$

The inverse Fourier transform and formulas (2), (3) and (4) give

$$u_j^k(x, y) = \frac{1}{(2\pi)^{3/2}} \int_{-\infty}^{\infty} \tilde{u}_j^k(\alpha)\, e^{i\alpha(x-y)}\, d\alpha$$

$$= \frac{1}{\nu}\left[-\frac{\delta_j^k}{4\pi|x-y|} + \frac{\partial^2}{\partial x_j \partial x_k} \frac{|x-y|}{8\pi}\right],$$

$$q^k(x, y) = \frac{1}{(2\pi)^3} \int_{-\infty}^{\infty} \frac{i\alpha_k}{\alpha^2} e^{i\alpha(x-y)}\, d\alpha = \frac{\partial}{\partial x_k} \frac{1}{4\pi|x-y|}.$$

These representations also imply the formulas

$$\left.\begin{aligned} u_j^k(x, y) &= -\frac{1}{8\pi\nu}\left[\frac{\delta_j^k}{|x-y|} + \frac{(x_j - y_j)(x_k - y_k)}{|x-y|^3}\right], \\ q^k(x, y) &= -\frac{x_k - y_k}{4\pi|x-y|^3}. \end{aligned}\right. \tag{5}$$

It is clear from the formulas (5) and the equations (1) that in the argument y, the functions $\mathbf{u}^k(x, y)$ and $q^k(x, y)$ satisfy the adjoint system

$$\left.\begin{aligned} \nu \Delta_y \mathbf{u}^k + \operatorname{grad}_y q^k &= \delta(x-y)\, \mathbf{e}^k, \\ \operatorname{div} \mathbf{u}^k &= 0. \end{aligned}\right\} \tag{6}$$

The solutions $\mathbf{u}^k = (u_1^k, u_2^k, u_3^k)$, q^k allow us to construct the volume potentials

$$\mathbf{U}(x) = \int_{\Omega} \mathbf{u}^k(x, y)\, f_k(y)\, dy,$$

$$P(x) = \int_{\Omega} q^k(x, y)\, f_k(y)\, dy,$$

which, because of (1), satisfy the nonhomogeneous Navier-Stokes system

$$\left.\begin{aligned} \nu\,\Delta\mathbf{U} - \operatorname{grad} P &= \mathbf{f}(x), \\ \operatorname{div}\mathbf{U} &= 0. \end{aligned}\right\} \tag{7}$$

The type of singularity of the kernels $\mathbf{u}_j^k$ and q^k is the same as that of the basic singular solution $1/4\pi\,|x-y|$ of Laplace's equation and of its first derivatives, respectively. This allows us to assert that if $\mathbf{f}$ satisfies a Hölder condition with exponent h, $0<h<1$, and if Ω is bounded, then $\mathbf{U}$, P and $\mathbf{U}_{x_k}$ are continuous on the whole space, and $\mathbf{U}_{x_k x_j}$ and P_{x_i} belong to $C_{0,h}(\Omega')$ in any interior subdomain Ω' of the domain Ω. Moreover, if the boundary S of the domain Ω is a Lyapunov surface of index h(i.e., if $S\in\Lambda_{1,h}$ [18, 19]), then $\mathbf{U}$ and P have the above-mentioned properties in the whole domain Ω. These properties of $\mathbf{U}$ and P are proved in the same way as for the Newtonian potential.

If $\mathbf{f}$ is square-summable over Ω, and if Ω is a bounded domain, then $\mathbf{U}$ and P have generalized derivatives with respect to x_k up to the second and the first orders, respectively, which are square-summable over any bounded domain Ω_1, and $\mathbf{U}$ and P obey the inequalities

$$\begin{aligned} \|\mathbf{U}\|_{W_2^2(\Omega_1)} &\leqslant C\,\|\mathbf{f}\|_{\mathbf{L}_2(\Omega)}, \\ \|P\|_{W_2^1(\Omega_1)} &\leqslant C\,\|\mathbf{f}\|_{\mathbf{L}_2(\Omega)}. \end{aligned} \tag{7a}$$

This follows from the representation given above of the kernels $\mathbf{u}^k$ and q^k and from the relations (27) and (29) of Chap. 1, Sec. 1.

We now give another derivation of the formulas (5) for $\mathbf{u}^k$ and q^k, which is shorter than the first derivation, and what is more important, represents $\mathbf{u}_k$ as the curl of another vector. This representation is useful, for example, in investigating the differential properties of solutions of the Navier-Stokes equations.

Thus, we shall look for $\mathbf{u}^k$ in the form curl curl $\mathbf{U}^k$. Substituting $\mathbf{u}^k = \operatorname{curl}\operatorname{curl}\mathbf{U}^k = -\Delta\mathbf{U}^k + \operatorname{grad}\operatorname{div}\mathbf{U}^k$ into the first of the equations (1), and separating the gradient part from the solenoidal part, we obtain

$$-\nu\,\Delta^2\mathbf{U}^k = \delta(x-y)\,\mathbf{e}^k$$

and

$$q^k = \nu\operatorname{div}\Delta\mathbf{U}^k.$$

It follows that

$$\mathbf{U}^k = \frac{1}{8\pi\nu}|x-y|\,\mathbf{e}^k, \quad q^k = \operatorname{div}\frac{\mathbf{e}^k}{4\pi|x-y|} = \frac{\partial}{\partial x_k}\frac{1}{4\pi|x-y|}. \tag{5a}$$

It is easy to see that these formulas coincide with the formulas (5).

2. Potentials of Single and Double Layers

Before giving a formal definition of the potentials of single and double layers, we write the Green's formulas corresponding to the Navier-Stokes system. These formulas are obtained by integrating by parts, and are valid for any smooth solenoidal vectors **u**, **v** and q, p. They are most simply verified by using the identity

$$\begin{aligned}\frac{\partial}{\partial x_k}[T_{ik}(\mathbf{u})\,v_i] \\ = \frac{\nu}{2}\left(\frac{\partial u_i}{\partial x_k}+\frac{\partial u_k}{\partial x_i}\right)\left(\frac{\partial v_i}{\partial x_k}+\frac{\partial v_k}{\partial x_i}\right)+\left(\nu\,\Delta u_i-\frac{\partial q}{\partial x_i}\right)v_i,\end{aligned} \tag{8}$$

in which

$$T_{ik}(\mathbf{u}) = -\,\delta_i^k q + \nu\left(\frac{\partial u_i}{\partial x_k}+\frac{\partial u_k}{\partial x_i}\right)$$

is the so-called *stress tensor* corresponding to the flow **u**, q. Integrating (8) over Ω, we obtain

$$\begin{aligned}\int_\Omega\left(\nu\Delta u_i-\frac{\partial q}{\partial x_i}\right)v_i\,dx = -\int_\Omega\frac{\nu}{2}\left(\frac{\partial u_i}{\partial x_k}+\frac{\partial u_k}{\partial x_i}\right)\left(\frac{\partial v_i}{\partial x_k}+\frac{\partial v_k}{\partial x_i}\right)dx \\ +\int_S T_{ik}(\mathbf{u})\,v_i\,n_k\,dS,\end{aligned} \tag{9}$$

where $\mathbf{n} = (n_1, n_2, n_3)$ is the exterior (with respect to Ω) normal to S. Interchanging u_i and v_i, and introducing together with q an arbitrary smooth function p, we obtain from (9) the formula

$$\begin{aligned}\int_\Omega\left[\left(\nu\Delta v_i-\frac{\partial p}{\partial x_i}\right)u_i - v_i\left(\nu\,\Delta u_i+\frac{\partial q}{\partial x_i}\right)\right]dx \\ = \int_S[T_{ij}(\mathbf{v})\,u_i\,n_j - T'_{ij}(\mathbf{u})\,v_i\,n_j]\,dS,\end{aligned} \tag{10}$$

where

$$T'_{ik}(\mathbf{u}) = \delta_i^k q + \nu\left(\frac{\partial u_i}{\partial x_k}+\frac{\partial u_k}{\partial x_i}\right). \tag{11}$$

It is natural to call (9) and (10) the *Green's formulas* corresponding to the Stokes problem. By the customary method, using (10) and the fundamental singular solution, we obtain a representation for any solution $\mathbf{v}$, p of the nonhomogeneous system (7) in terms of the free term $\mathbf{f}$ and the values of $\mathbf{v}$ and $T_{ik}(\mathbf{v})$ on S. In fact, letting $\mathbf{u}$, q in (10) be the fundamental singular solution $\mathbf{u}^k(x,y)$, $q^k(x,y)$, and recalling that as a function of y, the singular solution satisfies the system (6), we obtain

$$v_k(x) = \int_\Omega u_i^k(x,y) f_i(y)\,dy + \int_S T'_{ij}\big(\mathbf{u}(x,y)\big)_y v_i n_j\,dS - \int_S u_i^k(x,y)\,T_{ij}(\mathbf{v})\,n_j\,dS \tag{12}$$

for any $x \in \Omega$. The subscript y on $T'_{ij}(\mathbf{u}^k(x,y))$ shows that the differentiation in T'_{ij} is carried out with respect to y. The pressure p corresponding to $\mathbf{v}$ is most easily obtained from the system (7), if we use the expression just derived for $\mathbf{v}$ and the identity

$$\begin{aligned}\Delta_x T'_{ij}\big(\mathbf{u}^k(x,y)\big)_y &= \delta_i^j \Delta_x q^k(x,y) + \nu \frac{\partial}{\partial y_i}\Delta_x u_j^k + \nu \frac{\partial}{\partial y_j}\Delta_x u_i^k \\ &= \delta_i^j \Delta_x q^k(x,y) - \nu \frac{\partial}{\partial x_i}\Delta_x u_j^k - \nu \frac{\partial}{\partial x_j}\Delta_x u_i^k \\ &= -\frac{\partial^2}{\partial x_i\,\partial x_j} q^k - \frac{\partial^2}{\partial x_j\,\partial x_i} q^k = -2\frac{\partial^2}{\partial x_i\,\partial x_j} q^k\end{aligned}$$

(for $x \neq y$), which is obtained from (1). We find $p(x)$ by using the system (7), the representation (12) and the last formula:

$$p(x) = \int_\Omega q^k(x,y) f_k(y)\,dy - \int_S q^k(x,y)\,T_{kj}(\mathbf{v})\,n_j\,dS - 2\nu \int_S \frac{\partial q^k}{\partial x_j} v_k n_j\,dS. \tag{13}$$

Formulas (12) and (13) suggest that it is most convenient to introduce the potentials of single and double layers. In fact, the surface integrals in (12) and (13) give expressions for these potentials. We shall use Greek letters ξ, η, ... to denote points on the surface S.

By the potential of a single layer with density $\boldsymbol{\psi}(\eta)$ we mean the integrals

$$\begin{aligned}\mathbf{V}(x,\boldsymbol{\psi}) &= -\int_S \mathbf{u}^k(x,\eta)\,\psi_k(\eta)\,dS_\eta, \\ Q(x,\boldsymbol{\psi}) &= -\int_S q^k(x,\eta)\,\psi_k(\eta)\,dS_\eta,\end{aligned} \tag{14}$$

and by the potential of a double layer with density $\boldsymbol{\varphi}(\eta)$, we mean the integrals

$$W_k(x,\boldsymbol{\varphi}) = \int_S T'_{ij}\big(\mathbf{u}^k(x,\eta)\big)_\eta\, \varphi_i(\eta)\, n_j(\eta)\, dS_\eta,$$
$$\Pi(x,\boldsymbol{\varphi}) = -2\nu \frac{\partial}{\partial x_j}\int_S q^k(x,\eta)\, n_j(\eta)\, \varphi_k(\eta)\, dS_\eta. \tag{15}$$

If we substitute the explicit expressions for $\mathbf{u}^k$ and q^k from (5) into these formulas, they become

$$V_i(x,\boldsymbol{\psi}) = \frac{1}{8\pi\nu}\int_S \left[\frac{\delta_i^k}{|x-\eta|} + \frac{(x_i-\eta_i)(x_k-\eta_k)}{|x-\eta|^3}\right]\psi_k(\eta)\, dS_\eta,$$
$$Q(x,\boldsymbol{\psi}) = \frac{1}{4\pi}\int_S \frac{x_k-\eta_k}{|x-\eta|^3}\,\psi_k(\eta)\, dS_\eta \tag{16}$$

and

$$W_k(x,\boldsymbol{\varphi}) = -\frac{3}{4\pi}\int_S \frac{(x_i-\eta_i)(x_j-\eta_j)(x_k-\eta_k)}{|x-\eta|^5}\,\varphi_i(\eta)\, n_j(\eta)\, dS_\eta,$$
$$\Pi(x,\boldsymbol{\varphi}) = \frac{\nu}{2\pi}\frac{\partial}{\partial x_j}\int_S \frac{x_k-\eta_k}{|x-\eta|^3}\,\varphi_k(\eta)\, n_j(\eta)\, dS_\eta. \tag{17}$$

In writing these expressions, we have used the relation

$$T_{ij}\big(\mathbf{u}^k(x,y)\big)_x = -T'_{ij}\big(\mathbf{u}^k(x,y)\big)_y = \frac{3}{4\pi}\frac{(x_i-y_i)(x_j-y_j)(x_k-y_k)}{|x-y|^5}, \tag{18}$$

which is easily calculated from the definitions (1), (5) and (11). Formula (12) can now be written in the form

$$v_k(x) = \int_\Omega u_i^k(x,y) f_i(y)\, dy + W_k(x,\mathbf{v}) + V_k(x, \mathbf{T}_j(\mathbf{v})\, n_j), \tag{19}$$

where

$$\mathbf{T}_j(\mathbf{v}) = \big(T_{1j}(\mathbf{v}), T_{2j}(\mathbf{v}), T_{3j}(\mathbf{v})\big).$$

We now introduce a shorter notation, by writing

$$K_{ij}(x,\eta) = -\frac{3}{4\pi}\frac{(x_i-\eta_i)(x_j-\eta_j)(x_k-\eta_k)}{|x-\eta|^5}\, n_k(\eta),$$
$$K_j(x,\eta) = \frac{\nu}{2\pi}\frac{\partial}{\partial x_j}\frac{x_k-\eta_k}{|x-\eta|^3}\, n_k(\eta). \tag{19a}$$

Then the expressions (17) for **W** and Π can be written in the form

$$W_i(x, \varphi) = \int_S K_{ij}(x, \eta)\, \varphi_j(\eta)\, dS_\eta,$$

$$\Pi(x, \varphi) = \int_S K_j(x, \eta)\, \varphi_j(\eta)\, dS_\eta.$$

All the functions **V** and Q, **W** and Π which we have introduced are analytic functions outside S, which satisfy the homogeneous Navier-Stokes system. From the fact that the kernel of the potential in $\mathbf{V}(x, \boldsymbol{\psi})$ has polarity $1/|x - \eta|$, it follows that $\mathbf{V}(x, \boldsymbol{\psi})$ is continuous on the whole space, including the surface S, provided only that $\boldsymbol{\psi}(\eta)$ is not too badly behaved (we shall assume that all densities are continuous). However, the corresponding pressure $Q(x, \boldsymbol{\psi})$ is not continuous in passing through S; in fact, the pressure Q has a discontinuity of the first kind on S. The same is true of W, as we now show.

First, we consider W for a constant density $\boldsymbol{\varphi} = \mathbf{c} = \mathbf{const}$, and we show that W satisfies the formulas

$$\mathbf{W}(x, \mathbf{c}) = \begin{cases} \mathbf{c}, & x \in \Omega, \\ \frac{1}{2}\mathbf{c}, & x \in S, \\ 0, & x \notin \bar{\Omega}. \end{cases} \tag{20}$$

These formulas follow from (10), if we set $\mathbf{v}(y) = \mathbf{c}$, $p = 0$, $\mathbf{u} = \mathbf{u}^k(x, y)$, $q = q^k(x, y)$, and if we locate the parametric point x inside Ω, on S or outside Ω. The last formula follows immediately from (10). The first formula is obtained from (12), if we bear in mind that $\mathbf{u}^k$, q^k is a solution of the system (1), or directly from (10) with $\mathbf{v} = \mathbf{c}$. The second formula can be verified as follows: Cut the point $x \in S$ out of Ω by using a piece of the ball $K(x, \varepsilon)$ with center at x and radius ε, and write formula (10), with the functions indicated above, for Ω_ε, the remaining piece of Ω. This gives

$$0 = \int_{S_\varepsilon + C_\varepsilon} [T_{ij}(\mathbf{c})\, u_i^k\, n_j - T'_{ij}(\mathbf{u}^k)\, c_i\, n_j)]\, dS.$$

Here S_ε is the piece of the surface S remaining after deleting $K(x, \varepsilon)$, and C_ε is the piece of the surface $C(x, \varepsilon)$ of the ball $K(x, \varepsilon)$ bounding Ω_ε. Since $T_{ij}(\mathbf{c}) = 0$, the last formula implies that

$$\lim_{\varepsilon \to 0} \int_{S_\varepsilon} T'_{ij}(\mathbf{u}^k)\, c_i\, n_j\, dS = W_k(x, \mathbf{c}) = -\lim_{\varepsilon \to 0} \int_{C_\varepsilon} T'_{ij}(\mathbf{u}^k)\, c_i\, n_j\, dS.$$

If the integral of $T'_{ij}(\mathbf{u}^k)\, c_i\, n_j \equiv K_{ki}(x, \eta)\, c_i$ were carried out over the whole sphere $C(x, \varepsilon)$, then as the first of the formulas (20) shows, it would equal $-c_k$ (the minus sign appears because the normal $\mathbf{n}$, which is an exterior normal with respect to Ω_ε, is an interior normal with respect to the ball $K(x, \varepsilon)$). Because of the form (19a) for K_{ki}, it is not hard to calculate that the integral of $K_{ki}(x, \eta)\, c_i$ over half of the sphere $C(x, \varepsilon)$ equals $-\frac{1}{2}c_k$, while as $\varepsilon \to 0$, the integral over C_ε approaches the integral over the hemisphere, provided only that the surface S has a tangent plane at the point x. Thus, we see that $W_k(x, \mathbf{c}) = \frac{1}{2} c_k$ if $x \in S$, which completes the proof of the formulas (20).

In a familiar fashion, these formulas allow us to determine the values of the jumps of $W(x, \boldsymbol{\varphi})$ on S for any continuous density $\boldsymbol{\varphi}$. In fact, we first prove that the functions

$$W_i(x, \varphi) - \varphi_j(\xi_0) \int_S K_{ij}(x, \eta)\, dS_\eta$$

are continuous at the point $\xi_0 \in S$, provided only that for the surface S we have*

$$\int_S |K_{ij}(x, \eta)|\, dS_\eta \leqslant \text{const}^*) \tag{21}$$

for any position of the point x. Then, because of (20), we obtain the following relations:

$$\begin{aligned} W_i(\xi)_{(i)} &= \frac{1}{2}\varphi_i(\xi) + W_i(\xi) \\ &= \frac{1}{2}\varphi_i(\xi) + \int_S K_{ij}(\xi, \eta)\, \varphi_j(\eta)\, dS_\eta, \\ W_i(\xi)_{(e)} &= -\frac{1}{2}\varphi_i(\xi) + W_i(\xi) \\ &= -\frac{1}{2}\varphi_i(\xi) + \int_S K_{ij}(\xi, \eta)\, \varphi_j(\eta)\, dS_\eta. \end{aligned} \tag{22}$$

Here, $W_i(\xi)_{(i)}$ and $W_i(\xi)_{(e)}$ denote the limiting values of $W_i(x, \boldsymbol{\varphi})$ on S, as S is approached from inside and outside Ω, respectively, and $W_i(\xi)$ denotes the directly defined value of $W_i(x, \boldsymbol{\varphi})$ on S. All these quantities exist and are continuous functions of ξ on S (we recall that $\boldsymbol{\varphi}$ is continuous, and that S is a Lyapunov surface of index h). The kernel

* By using the method of N. M. Gyunter [18], it can be shown that (21) is certainly true if $S \in \Lambda_{1,h}$.

$K_{ij}(\xi, \eta)$ has polarity

$$\frac{1}{|\xi - \eta|^{2-h}}.$$

We now consider the potential $\mathbf{V}(x, \boldsymbol{\varphi})$ of a single layer for a continuous density $\boldsymbol{\psi}$, and with the same assumptions on S. It is easy to see that $\mathbf{V}(x, \boldsymbol{\psi})$ is continuous everywhere. We form the corresponding stress tensor $T_{ij}(\mathbf{V})$, which is easily seen to have the form

$$T_{ij}(\mathbf{V}) = -\frac{3}{4\pi} \int_S \frac{(x_i - \eta_i)(x_j - \eta_j)(x_k - \eta_k)}{|x - \eta|^5} \psi_k(\eta)\, dS_\eta$$

because of (16). In addition to the first boundary-value problem for the equations (1), where the field $\mathbf{v}$ is specified on S, we shall consider the adjoint second boundary-value problem, where we know

$$T_{ij}(\mathbf{v})\, n_j|_S = b_i \; (i = 1, 2, 3) \tag{23}$$

on S. Accordingly, we investigate the behavior of $T_{ij}(\mathbf{V})\, n_j$ near S. Let ξ be any point on S, and let $\mathbf{n}(\xi)$ be the exterior normal to S at ξ. As x approaches the point ξ along the normal to S either from the interior or the exterior of S, the functions $T_{ij}(\mathbf{V}(x, \boldsymbol{\psi}))\, n_j(\xi)$ have well-defined limiting values which we denote by $T_{ij}(\mathbf{V})_{(i)}\, n_j$ and $T_{ij}(\mathbf{V})_{(e)}\, n_j$, respectively (these two limiting values may be different). Moreover, the directly defined value $T_{ij}(\mathbf{V})\, n_j$ exists on S at the point ξ, and all three values are connected by the relations

$$\begin{aligned} T_{ij}(\mathbf{V})_{(i)}\, n_j &= \frac{1}{2}\psi_i(\xi) + T_{ij}(\mathbf{V})\, n_j \\ &= \frac{1}{2}\psi_i(\xi) - \int_S K_{ji}(\eta, \xi)\, \psi_j(\eta)\, dS_\eta, \\ T_{ij}(\mathbf{V})_{(e)}\, n_j &= -\frac{1}{2}\psi_i(\xi) + T_{ij}(\mathbf{V})\, n_j \\ &= -\frac{1}{2}\psi_i(\xi) - \int_S K_{ji}(\eta, \xi)\, \psi_j(\eta)\, dS_\eta. \end{aligned} \tag{24}$$

The properties just enumerated are deduced by considering the functions

$$\begin{aligned} &T_{ij}(\mathbf{V}(x, \boldsymbol{\psi}))\, n_j(\xi) - W_i(x, \boldsymbol{\psi}) \\ &= -\frac{3}{4\pi} n_j(\xi) \int_S \frac{(x_i - \eta_i)(x_j - \eta_j)(x_k - \eta_k)}{|x - \eta|^5} \psi_k(\eta)\, dS_\eta \\ &+ \frac{3}{4\pi} \int_S \frac{(x_i - \eta_i)(x_j - \eta_j)(x_k - \eta_k)}{|x - \eta|^5} \psi_k(\eta)\, n_j(\eta)\, dS_\eta. \end{aligned}$$

It is not hard to see that as functions of x, they are continuous at the point ξ on S. The relations (24) follow from this fact and from already established properties of the potential $\mathbf{W}(x, \boldsymbol{\psi})$. The integral equations (22) and (24) are the adjoints of each other, and in the next section, we shall explain the conditions under which they have solutions.

3. Investigation of the Integral Equations

We shall consider two problems for the system

$$\left.\begin{aligned} \Delta \mathbf{v} &= \operatorname{grad} p, \\ \operatorname{div} \mathbf{v} &= 0 \end{aligned}\right\} \tag{25}$$

inside and outside S. In the first problem,

$$\mathbf{v}\,|_S = \mathbf{a} \tag{26}$$

is specified, and in the second problem,

$$T_j(\mathbf{v})\, n_j\,|_S = \mathbf{b} \tag{27}$$

is specified. The first problem is the one of interest to us, and we deal with the second problem only insofar as it is the adjoint of the first. Let Ω_i and Ω_e denote the interior and exterior domains, with respect to S (Ω_i was previously denoted by Ω). For simplicity, we assume that S lies in a finite region of space and is connected. In the case of exterior problems, we supplement the conditions (26) and (27) by the condition

$$\mathbf{v}(x) \text{ and } p(x) \to 0 \text{ as } |x| \to \infty. \tag{28}$$

It follows from the very representation of the solutions of these problems that $\mathbf{v}$ behaves like $|x|^{-1}$ for large $|x|$, its derivatives behave like the corresponding derivatives of $|x|^{-1}$, and $p(x)$ behaves like $|x|^{-2}$. Therefore, in order not to hamper our study of the uniqueness of solutions of exterior problems, we assume from the outset that the solution $\mathbf{v}$, which we are looking for, converges to zero like $|x|^{-1}$ as $|x| \to \infty$, that its derivatives converge to zero like $|x|^{-2}$, and that $p(x)$ converges to zero like $|x|^{-2}$. With these assumptions concerning $\mathbf{v}$ and p, formula (9) applied to $\mathbf{u} = \mathbf{v}$, gives

$$\int\limits_{\Omega_i} \frac{\nu}{2}\left(\frac{\partial v_i}{\partial x_k} + \frac{\partial v_k}{\partial x_i}\right)\left(\frac{\partial v_i}{\partial x_k} + \frac{\partial v_k}{\partial x_i}\right) dx = \int\limits_S T_{ik}(\mathbf{v})\, v_i\, n_k\, dS \tag{29}$$

in the domain Ω_i, and

$$\int\limits_{\Omega_e} \frac{\nu}{2}\left(\frac{\partial v_i}{\partial x_k} + \frac{\partial v_k}{\partial x_i}\right)\left(\frac{\partial v_i}{\partial x_k} + \frac{\partial v_k}{\partial x_i}\right) dx = -\int\limits_S T_{ik}(\mathbf{v})\, v_i\, n_k\, dS \tag{30}$$

in the domain Ω_e. In both formulas, the normal $\mathbf{n}$ is taken to be the exterior normal with respect to $\Omega_i = \Omega$. The integral over a large sphere $|x| = R$ containing S vanishes as $R \to \infty$, since $T_{ij}(\mathbf{v})\, v_i$ is of order R^{-3} on this sphere.

It is clear from formula (30) that the first and second boundary-value problems for the exterior domain have no more than one solution. In fact, it follows from (30) that if $\mathbf{v}$ corresponds to homogeneous boundary conditions, then

$$\frac{\partial v_i}{\partial x_k} + \frac{\partial v_k}{\partial x_i} = 0 \qquad (i, k = 1, 2, 3), \tag{31}$$

i.e., the vector $\mathbf{v}(x)$ gives the motion of the fluid as a rigid body. On the other hand, the vector $\mathbf{v}$ vanishes at infinity, and hence it vanishes throughout Ω_e. It follows from the system (25), and the fact that $p \to 0$ as $|x| \to \infty$, that $p(x)$ vanishes. The system (31) has six linearly independent solutions, which we take to be

$$\begin{aligned} \boldsymbol{\varphi}_k &= (\varphi_{1k}, \varphi_{2k}, \varphi_{3k}) = \mathbf{e}^k = (\delta_1^k, \delta_2^k, \delta_3^k) \qquad (k = 1, 2, 3), \\ \boldsymbol{\varphi}_4 &= (0, x_3, -x_2),\ \boldsymbol{\varphi}_5 = (-x_3, 0, x_1),\ \boldsymbol{\varphi}_6 = (x_2, -x_1, 0). \end{aligned} \tag{32}$$

The origin of coordinates is regarded as being inside S. We shall look for a solution of the first boundary-value problem in the form of the potential of a double layer, and for a solution of the second boundary-value problem in the form of the potential of a single layer. For the first boundary-value problem, the field $\mathbf{a}$ cannot be arbitrary in Ω_i. This is clear from

$$0 = \int_{\Omega_i} \operatorname{div} \mathbf{v}\, dx = \int_S \mathbf{v} \cdot \mathbf{n}\, dS,$$

so that a necessary condition for the problem (25), (26) to have a solution in Ω_i is that

$$\int_S \mathbf{a} \cdot \mathbf{n}\, dS = 0. \tag{33}$$

Later, it will be shown that this condition not only necessary, but also sufficient. In fact, the aim of our subsequent considerations is to prove the following theorem:

THEOREM 1. *The first boundary-value problem for* (25) *in* Ω_i *has a unique solution for a continuous field* $\mathbf{a}$ *on* S, *which satisfies the condition* (33). *Moreover, the problem has a unique solution in* Ω_e *for any continuous field* $\mathbf{a}$. *The solutions are analytic inside* S *and continuous up to the boundary* S.

Proof: We look for a solution of the interior problem in the form $\mathbf{W}(x, \boldsymbol{\varphi})$. For the definition of the density $\boldsymbol{\varphi}$, the first of the equations (22) gives

$$a_i(\xi) = \frac{1}{2}\varphi_i(\xi) + \int_S K_{ij}(\xi, \eta)\,\varphi_j(\eta)\,dS_\eta. \tag{34}$$

To prove that (34) has a solution, we have to investigate the corresponding homogeneous adjoint equation

$$\frac{1}{2}\psi_i(\xi) + \int_S K_{ji}(\eta, \xi)\,\varphi_i(\eta)\,dS_\eta = 0. \tag{35}$$

We verify that $\boldsymbol{\psi}(\xi) = \mathbf{n}(\xi)$ satisfies equation (35). Substituting the vector $\mathbf{n}$ for $\boldsymbol{\psi}$ in the left-hand side of (35), and using the representation (19a) for K_{ij}, we obtain

$$\frac{1}{2}n_i(\xi) - \frac{3}{4\pi}\int_S \frac{(\eta_i - \xi_i)(\eta_j - \xi_j)(\eta_k - \xi_k)}{|\xi - \eta|^5}\,n_k(\xi)\,n_j(\eta)\,dS_\eta$$
$$= \frac{1}{2}n_i(\xi) - n_k(\xi)\int_S K_{ik}(\xi, \eta)\,dS_\eta.$$

Because of the second of the formulas (20),

$$\int_S K_{ij}(\xi, \eta)\,c_j\,dS_\eta = \frac{1}{2}c_i$$

for any $\mathbf{c} = \mathbf{const}$, and therefore

$$\frac{1}{2}n_i(\xi) - n_k(\xi)\int_S K_{ik}(\xi, \eta)\,dS_\eta = \frac{1}{2}n_i(\xi) - \frac{1}{2}n_k(\xi)\,\delta_k^i = 0,$$

i.e., $\mathbf{n}$ is actually a solution of the equation (35).

Next, we prove that there are no other solutions of equation (35). Suppose that $\boldsymbol{\psi}(\xi)$ is a solution of (35). Then we use $\boldsymbol{\psi}$ to form the potential $\mathbf{V}(x, \boldsymbol{\psi})$ of a single layer, and we write the corresponding formula (30). The right-hand side vanishes, since the functions $T_{ij}(\mathbf{V}(x, \boldsymbol{\psi}))_{(e)}\,n_j$ equal zero for our potential, because of (35) and the second of the equations (24). Therefore, it follows from (30) that $\mathbf{V}$ is a solution of (31), and since $\mathbf{V}$ vanishes at infinity, we have $\mathbf{V} \equiv 0$. The potential $\mathbf{V}$ also vanishes in the domain Ω_i, since, being continuous everywhere, it vanishes on S. The pressures $Q_{(i)}$ and $Q_{(e)}$ corresponding to $\mathbf{V}$ are constant, because of the equations (25). But in Ω_e the pressure $Q_{(e)} \to 0$ as $|x| \to \infty$, and hence $Q_{(e)} \equiv 0$. The stress tensor in Ω_i is $T_{kj}(\mathbf{V})_{(i)} = -\delta^i_k Q_{(i)}$. If we let $\mathbf{V}^\circ$ denote the potential of a single layer corresponding to $\boldsymbol{\psi} = \mathbf{n}$, then the corresponding tensor is

$$T_{kj}(\mathbf{V}^\circ)_{(i)} = \delta^j_k.$$

This is easily calculated by using the explicit expression for $T_{ik}(\mathbf{V})$ given on p. 56, and the equalities (20) given on p. 54.

We now consider the density $\boldsymbol{\psi}^* = \boldsymbol{\psi} - Q_{(i)}\mathbf{n}$ and the corresponding potential $\mathbf{V}^*$. For $\mathbf{V}^*$, the quantity $T_{ij}(\mathbf{V}(x, \boldsymbol{\psi}^*))$ vanishes as x approaches the surface S either from the interior or from the exterior, and therefore by (24), the density $\boldsymbol{\psi}^* = 0$, i. e., $\boldsymbol{\psi}$ can be expressed linearly in terms of $\mathbf{n}$ by the formula $\boldsymbol{\psi} = Q_{(i)}\, \mathbf{n}$. Thus, we have shown that equation (35) has a unique nontrivial solution $\boldsymbol{\psi} = \mathbf{n}$, and therefore a necessary and sufficient condition for (34) to have a solution is that $\int_\Omega \mathbf{a} \cdot \mathbf{n}\, dS = 0$. This proves the first part of the theorem.

Next, we investigate the exterior problem. To do so, we show that the homogeneous equation

$$-\frac{1}{2}\varphi_i(\xi) + \int_S K_{ij}(\xi, \eta)\, \varphi_j(\eta)\, dS_\eta = 0, \tag{36}$$

corresponding to the nonhomogeneous equation (34) for the exterior problem

$$a_i(\xi) = -\frac{1}{2}\varphi_i(\xi) + \int_S K_{ij}(\xi, \eta)\, \varphi_j(\eta)\, dS_\eta, \tag{37}$$

has the six linearly independent solutions $\boldsymbol{\varphi}^k(\xi), k = 1, 2, \ldots, 6$, defined by the formulas (32). Consider any of the vectors $\boldsymbol{\varphi}^k(\xi), k = 1, 2, ..., 6$, which, together with $p^k(x) \equiv 0$, satisfies the homogeneous system (25). We write formula (19) for $\boldsymbol{\varphi}^k(x)$, recalling that $T_{ij}(\boldsymbol{\varphi}^k) = 0$:

$$\varphi^k(x) = \mathbf{W}(x, \boldsymbol{\varphi}^k), \quad x \in \Omega_i.$$

Letting x approach $\xi \in S$ and using (22), we obtain

$$\varphi^k_i(\xi) = \frac{1}{2}\varphi^k_i(\xi) + \int_S K_{ij}(\xi, \eta)\, \varphi^k_j(\eta)\, dS_\eta,$$

i.e., each $\boldsymbol{\varphi}^k$ is actually a solution of the system (36). We now show that any other solution $\boldsymbol{\varphi}$ of the system (36) depends linearly on $\boldsymbol{\varphi}^k$,

$k = 1, 2, \ldots, 6$. If this were not the case, then the equation

$$-\frac{1}{2}\,\psi_i(\xi) + \int_S K_{ji}(\eta, \xi)\,\psi_j(\eta)\,dS_\eta = 0, \tag{38}$$

which is adjoint to (36), would also have more than six linearly independent solutions $\boldsymbol{\psi}^k(\xi)$, $1 \leqslant k \leqslant k_0$, $k_0 > 6$. To each $\boldsymbol{\psi}^k$, there corresponds a single-layer potential $\mathbf{V}^k = \mathbf{V}(x, \boldsymbol{\psi}^k)$ for which $T_{ij}(\mathbf{V}^k)_{(i)}\,n_j = 0$. But then, because of (30), the $\mathbf{V}^k$ satisfy the system (31), and hence no more than six of the $\mathbf{V}^k$ are linearly independent. The same holds for $\boldsymbol{\psi}^k$, since if $\mathbf{V}(x, \boldsymbol{\psi})$ vanishes in Ω_i, then $\mathbf{V}(x, \boldsymbol{\psi})$ vanishes in Ω_e, and hence the density $\boldsymbol{\psi}$ vanishes. Thus, we have proved that the systems (36) and (38) have precisely six linearly independent solutions, which in the case of the system (36) are given by the vectors (32).

Now we consider the nonhomogeneous system (37), which has a solution only if

$$\int_S \mathbf{a} \cdot \boldsymbol{\psi}^k\,dS = 0 \qquad (k = 1, 2, \ldots, 6). \tag{39}$$

Therefore, a solution of the exterior problem (25), (26), (28) in the form of a potential of a double layer exists only for boundary values $\mathbf{a}(\xi)$ which satisfy the conditions (39). In the general case, where $\mathbf{a}(\xi)$ is arbitrary, we look for a solution of the problem in the form

$$\mathbf{v}(x) = \mathbf{W}(x, \boldsymbol{\varphi}) + \sum_{m=1}^{6} c_m\,\mathbf{V}(x, \boldsymbol{\psi}^m),$$

where the $\boldsymbol{\psi}^m$ are linearly independent solutions of the system (38). For $\boldsymbol{\varphi}$ we obtain the system

$$a_i(\xi) - \sum_{m=1}^{6} c_m\,V_i(\xi, \boldsymbol{\psi}^m) = -\frac{1}{2}\,\varphi_i(\xi) + \int_S K_{ij}(\xi, \eta)\,\varphi_j(\eta)\,dS_\eta \qquad (i = 1, 2, 3), \tag{40}$$

analogous to (37). We choose the constants c_m in such a way that

$$\int_S \left[\mathbf{a} - \sum_{m=1}^{6} c_m\,\mathbf{V}(\xi, \boldsymbol{\psi}^m)\right] \boldsymbol{\psi}^k\,dS = 0 \quad (k = 1, 2, \ldots, 6). \tag{41}$$

If this algebraic system is to have a unique solution, we must show that the corresponding homogeneous system has only the null solution. Thus, let $\mathbf{a} \equiv 0$. Multiplying (41) by c_k and summing over k from 1 to 6, we obtain

$$\int_S \mathbf{V} \cdot \boldsymbol{\psi}\,dS = 0, \tag{42}$$

where

$$\boldsymbol{\psi} = \sum_{m=1}^{6} c_m \boldsymbol{\psi}^m, \quad \mathbf{V} \equiv \mathbf{V}(x, \boldsymbol{\psi}) = \sum_{m=1}^{6} c_m \mathbf{V}(x, \boldsymbol{\psi}^m).$$

If we examine $\mathbf{V}$ in Ω_e, then, because of (24), we obtain

$$T_{ik}(\mathbf{V})_{(e)} n_k = -\frac{1}{2} \psi_i(\xi) - \int_S K_{ji}(\eta, \xi) \psi_j(\eta) \, dS_\eta,$$

so that according to (38), we can transform (42) into

$$\begin{aligned} 0 &= 2 \int_S V_i(\xi) \Big[T_{ik}(\mathbf{V})_{(e)} n_k + \int_S K_{ji}(\eta, \xi) \psi_j(\eta) \, dS_\eta\Big] dS_\xi \\ &= 2 \int_S V_i(\xi) \Big[T_{ik}(\mathbf{V})_{(e)} n_k + \frac{1}{2} \psi_i(\xi)\Big] dS_\xi \\ &= 2 \int_S V_i \, T_{ik}(\mathbf{V})_{(e)} n_k \, dS_\xi. \end{aligned}$$

It follows from this and from formula (30) that $\mathbf{V}$ satisfies the system (31), and therefore V is identically zero. Then its density $\boldsymbol{\psi} \equiv 0$, and all the $c_k = 0$, because of the linear independence of the $\boldsymbol{\psi}^k$.

Thus, finally, we have shown that (40) has a unique solution for any a_i, which proves that the first boundary-value problem for the exterior domain has a unique solution for any vector $\mathbf{a}$. The differential properties of the potentials $\mathbf{V}(x, \boldsymbol{\psi})$ and $\mathbf{W}(x, \boldsymbol{\psi})$, and the methods for studying them, resemble those for electrostatic potentials.

4. The Green's Function

As is well-known, if we can solve the boundary-value problem for a homogeneous equation with nonhomogeneous boundary conditions, then we can construct the matrix Green's function for the given problem. Thus, for example, the matrix Green's function $G_{ij}(x, y)$ for the interior Stokes problem (4), (4a) of Chap. 2, Sec. 1 has the form

$$\begin{aligned} G_{ij}(x, y) &= u_i^j(x, y) - g_i^j(x, y), \\ r_j(x, y) &= q^j(x, y) - g^j(x, y), \end{aligned} \tag{43}$$

where u_i^j and q^j are the fundamental singular solutions of the problem defined by the formulas (5), and the functions $g_j^i(x, y)$ and $g^j(x, y)$ are defined as the solutions of the Stokes problem:

$$\Delta_x g_i^j(x, y) = \frac{\partial}{\partial x_i} g^j(x, y),$$
$$\frac{\partial}{\partial x_i} g_i^j(x, y) = 0, \tag{44}$$
$$g_i^j(x, y)\big|_{x \in S} = u_i^j(x, y)\big|_{x \in S}.$$

For y lying inside S, the functions g_i^j and g^j are analytic functions of x in Ω, which are continuous up to S. Their smoothness in the neighborhood of S is determined by the smoothness of the surface S.

The solution of the nonhomogeneous system with zero boundary values of v is given by the formulas

$$v_i(x) = \int_\Omega G_{ij}(x, y) f_j(y)\, dy,$$
$$p(x) = \int_\Omega r_j(x, y) f_j(y)\, dy. \tag{45}$$

It can be shown that the matrix Green's function and its derivatives can be evaluated in terms of $|x-y|^{-\alpha}$ in approximately the same way as the components of the corresponding fundamental singular solution. These estimates are obvious when the point y is fixed in Ω, and x varies in some subdomain of the domain Ω. However, to obtain estimates which are uniform for x and y in $\bar{\Omega}$ requires a special investigation, i.e., a more careful study of the solutions of the integral equations (22) and (24). The following results are proved in this way:

If S is a Lyapunov surface of index h, $0 < h \leqslant 1$, then

$$|G_{ij}(x, y)| \leqslant \frac{C}{|x-y|};$$
$$\left|\frac{\partial G_{ij}(x, y)}{\partial x_m}\right|, \quad |r_j(x, y)| \leqslant \frac{C}{|x-y|^2};$$
$$\left|\frac{\partial G_{ij}(x, y)}{\partial x_m} - \frac{\partial G_{ij}(x', y)}{\partial x'_m}\right|, \quad |r_j(x, y) - r_j(x', y)|$$
$$\leqslant \begin{cases} C\left[\dfrac{|x-x'|\,|\ln|x-x'||}{R^3} + \dfrac{|x-x'|^h}{R^2}\right], \\ \qquad \text{for } 0 < h < 1, \\ C\left[\dfrac{|x-x'|\,|\ln|x-x'||}{R^3} + \dfrac{|x-x'|\ln^2|x-x'|}{R^2}\right], \\ \qquad \text{for } h = 1. \end{cases} \tag{46}$$

Moreover, if S belongs to $\Lambda_{2,h}$, $0 < h \leqslant 1$, then

$$\left|\frac{\partial^2 G_{ij}(x, y)}{\partial x_k \, \partial x_m}\right|, \quad \left|\frac{\partial r_j(x, y)}{\partial x_m}\right| \leqslant \frac{C}{|x-y|^3};$$

$$\left|\frac{\partial^2 G_{ij}(x, y)}{\partial x_k \, \partial x_m} - \frac{\partial^2 G_{ij}(x', y)}{\partial x_k \, \partial x_m}\right|, \quad \left|\frac{\partial r_j(x, y)}{\partial x_m} - \frac{\partial r_j(x', y)}{\partial x_m}\right|$$

$$\leqslant \begin{cases} C\left[\dfrac{|x-x'|\,|\ln|x-x'||}{R^4} + \dfrac{|x-x'|\ln^2|x-x'|}{R_3} \right. \\ \qquad \left. + \dfrac{|x-x'|^h}{R^2}\right], \text{ for } 0 < h < 1, \\ C\left[\dfrac{|x-x'|\,|\ln|x-x'||}{R^4} + \dfrac{|x-x'|\ln^2|x-x'|}{R^3} \right. \\ \qquad \left. + \dfrac{|x-x'|\,|\ln^3|x-x'||}{R^2}\right], \text{ for } h = 1. \end{cases} \tag{47}$$

Here, we have $R = \min(|x-y|, |x'-y|)$. The estimates (46) and (47) allow us to prove that the differential properties of the solutions of the problems under consideration depend on the data of the problem in the same way as in the case of the solutions of the first boundary-value problem for the Laplace operator. In particular, the results pertaining to volume potentials, given at the end of Sec. 1 of this chapter, are valid for solutions $\mathbf{v}$, p corresponding to zero boundary conditions.

Finally, we give the fundamental singular solution of equation (1) for a planar domain:

$$v_{ij}(x, y) = -\frac{1}{4\pi\nu}\left[\delta_{ij} \ln \frac{1}{|x-y|} + \frac{(x_i - y_i)(x_j - y_j)}{|x-y|^2}\right],$$

$$g_j(x, y) = \frac{1}{2\pi} \frac{\partial}{\partial x_j} \ln \frac{1}{|x-y|}.$$

Using this solution, we can construct a potential theory just as in the case of three-dimensional space, although there are certain differences (as in the theory of the electrostatic potential).

5. Investigation of Solutions in $W_2^2(\Omega)$

We now show that for solutions of the problem

$$\left.\begin{aligned} \Delta \mathbf{v} &= \operatorname{grad} p + \mathbf{f}, \\ \operatorname{div} \mathbf{v} = 0, &\quad \mathbf{v}|_S = 0 \end{aligned}\right\} \tag{48}$$

in a bounded domain Ω, we have a result resembling a corresponding result for operators of elliptic type, in particular, the Laplace operator:

THEOREM 2. *If* $\mathbf{f} \in \mathbf{L}_2(\Omega)$, *then the corresponding solution* $\mathbf{v}$ *belongs to* $W_2^2(\Omega)$; *moreover* $p \in W_2^1(\Omega)$, *and*

$$\|\mathbf{v}\|_{W_2^2(\Omega)} + \|p\|_{W_2^1(\Omega)} \leqslant C\|\mathbf{f}\|_{L_2(\Omega)}. \tag{49}$$

Here, it is assumed that the boundary S *of the domain is twice continuously differentiable.*

In Chap. 2, Sec. 1, it was shown that the solution $\mathbf{v}$ is in $W_2^2(\Omega')$, and that p is in $W_2^1(\Omega')$ for any interior subdomain Ω' of the domain Ω. This fact was proved very simply, and no restrictions were imposed on the smoothness of S. The investigation of $\mathbf{v}$ and p in a closed domain requires more careful arguments, which we now present. In so doing, we shall use the following facts:

1) The estimate (16) of Chap. 1, Sec. 1

$$\|u\|_{W_2^2(\Omega)} \leqslant C\|\Delta u\|_{L_2(\Omega)}, \tag{50}$$

valid for any function in $W_2^2(\Omega)$ which vanishes on the boundary;

2) The estimate (7a) of the present chapter

$$\begin{aligned} \|\mathbf{U}\|_{W_2^2(\Omega)} &\leqslant C\|\mathbf{f}\|_{\mathbf{L}_2(\Omega)}, \\ \|P\|_{W_2^1(\Omega)} &\leqslant C\|\mathbf{f}\|_{\mathbf{L}_2(\Omega)} \end{aligned} \tag{51}$$

for any volume potential $\mathbf{U}$ and P, in terms of its density $\mathbf{f}$;

3) The following result concerning the behavior of functions in $W_2^l(\Omega)$ on the boundary S, when S is smooth:

LEMMA 1. *A necessary and sufficient condition for the function* $u(\xi)$ $(\xi \in S)$ *to be the boundary value of the function* $u(x)$ $(x \in \Omega)$ *in* $W_2^l(\Omega)$, $l \geqslant 1$, *is that the integral*

$$\|u(\xi)\|^2_{W_2^{l-1/2}(S)} \equiv \sum_{k=0}^{l-1} \|D_\xi^k u(\xi)\|^2_{L_2(S)} + \int_S\int_S \frac{|D_\xi^{l-1}u(\xi) - D_{\xi'}^{l-1}u(\xi')|^2}{|\xi-\xi'|^3}\, dS_\xi\, dS_{\xi'}$$

be finite for $u(\xi)$. *If* $u(x) \in W_2^l(\Omega)$, *then*

$$\|u(\xi)\|_{W_2^{l-1/2}(S)} \leqslant C\|u(x)\|_{W_2^l(\Omega)}. \tag{52}$$

Moreover, if the function $u(\xi)$ *specified on* S *has finite norm* $\|u(\xi)\|_{W_2^{l-1/2}(S)}$, *then there exists at least one extension* $\tilde{u}(x)$ *of* $u(x)$ *inside* S, *for which*

$\tilde{u}(x)|_S = u(\xi)$, and

$$\|\tilde{u}(x)\|_{W_2^l(\Omega)} \leqslant C \|u(\xi)\|_{W_2^{l-1/2}(S)}. \tag{53}$$

The surface S is assumed to be continuously differentiable l times.

The reader will find a proof of Lemma 1 in the papers [20—22]. It follows from this lemma and the inequality (50) that the estimate

$$\|u(x)\|_{W_2^2(\Omega)} \leqslant C\left[\|\Delta u\|_{L_2(\Omega)} + \|u(\xi)\|_{W_2^{3/2}(S)}\right] \tag{54}$$

holds for any function $u(x) \in W_2^2(\Omega)$, with a constant C which depends only on the domain Ω. Here, the boundary S is assumed to be twice continuously differentiable. In fact, using the values of $u(x)$ on S, we form the function $\tilde{u}(x)$ indicated in the lemma, and we apply the inequality (50) to the difference $u(x) - \tilde{u}(x)$:

$$\|u(x) - \tilde{u}(x)\|_{W_2^2(\Omega)} \leqslant C \|\Delta u - \Delta\tilde{u}\|_{L_2(\Omega)}.$$

From this, using (53), we obtain

$$\|u(x)\|_{W_2^2(\Omega)} \leqslant C\|\Delta u\|_{L_2(\Omega)} + C\|\Delta\tilde{u}\|_{L_2(\Omega)} + \|\tilde{u}\|_{W_2^2(\Omega)}$$
$$\leqslant C\|\Delta u\|_{L_2(\Omega)} + C_1\|u(\xi)\|_{W_2^{3/2}(S)}.$$

We now turn to the proof of Theorem 2. The solution $\mathbf{v}, p$ can be represented in the form

$$\mathbf{v}(x) = \mathbf{U}(x) + \mathbf{u}(x), \quad p(x) = P(x) + q(x),$$

where $\mathbf{U}$ is the volume potential with density $\mathbf{f}$, and P is the corresponding pressure, i. e.,

$$U_i(x) = \int_\Omega u_i^k(x, y) f_k(y)\, dy, \quad P(x) = \int_\Omega q^k(x, y) f_k(y)\, dy.$$

The functions $\mathbf{u}(x)$ and $q(x)$ will be solutions of the problem

$$\nu\Delta\mathbf{u} = \operatorname{grad} q,$$
$$\operatorname{div}\mathbf{u} = 0, \quad \mathbf{u}|_S = -\mathbf{U}|_S. \tag{55}$$

In Sec. 2 of this chapter, it was shown that $\mathbf{u}$ can be represented as the potential of a double layer, i.e.,

$$u_i(x) = \int_S K_{ij}(x, \eta)\, \varphi_j(\eta)\, dS_\eta \tag{56}$$

and

$$q(x) = \int_S K_j(x, \eta)\, \varphi_j(\eta)\, dS_\eta. \tag{57}$$

The density $\boldsymbol{\varphi}(\eta)$ is determined from the system of integral equations

$$\frac{1}{2}\varphi_i(\xi) + \int_S K_{ij}(\xi, \eta)\varphi_j(\eta)\, dS_\eta = u_i(\xi) = -U_i(\xi). \tag{58}$$

The condition

$$\int_S \mathbf{U} \cdot \mathbf{n}\, dS = 0 \tag{59}$$

which is necessary for this system to have a solution, is satisfied. The estimate (49), or equivalently (51), which we need for the functions $\mathbf{U}$, P has already been proved. Since $U_i \in W_2^2(\Omega)$, then because of Lemma 1, the functions $U_i(\xi)$ belong to $W_2^{3/2}(S)$, i.e., they have finite norm $\| \; \|_{W_2^{3/2}(S)}$. Using this fact, we can show that the solution $\boldsymbol{\varphi}(\xi)$ of the system of integral equations (58) will also belong to $W_2^{3/2}(S)$. In fact, we have the following lemma:

LEMMA 2. *If the free term* $-\mathbf{U}(\xi)$ *in the system of integral equations* (58) *belongs to* $W_2^{3/2}(S)$, *then its solution also belongs to* $W_2^{3/2}(S)$ *and*

$$\sum_{i=1}^{3} \| \varphi_i \|_{W_2^{3/2}(S)} \leqslant C \sum_{i=1}^{3} \| U_i \|_{W_2^{3/2}(S)}. \tag{60}$$

We shall give the proof of this lemma later. For the present, we show how it can be used to obtain the estimate (49).

Thus, suppose the inequality (60) has been proved. We estimate its right-hand side in terms of $\|\mathbf{f}\|_{\mathbf{L}_2(\Omega)}$ by using (52) and (51), so that

$$\sum_{i=1}^{3} \| \varphi_i \|_{W_2^{3/2}(S)} \leqslant C \sum_{i=1}^{3} \| U_i \|_{W_2^{3/2}(S)} \leqslant C_1 \| \mathbf{U} \|_{W_2^2(\Omega)} \leqslant C_2 \| \mathbf{f} \|_{\mathbf{L}_2(\Omega)} \tag{61}$$

Now consider the representation (57) for $q(x)$:

$$\begin{aligned} q(x) &= \int_S K_j(x, \eta)\, \varphi_j(\eta)\, dS_\eta \\ &= \frac{\nu}{2\pi} \frac{\partial}{\partial x_k} \int_S \frac{x_j - \eta_j}{|x - \eta|^3} n_k(\eta)\, \varphi_j(\eta)\, dS_\eta. \end{aligned}$$

The integral appearing in the right-hand side of this equation can be written as follows:

$$\begin{aligned} J &= \frac{\nu}{2\pi} \frac{\partial}{\partial x_k} \int_S \frac{x_j - \eta_j}{|x - \eta|^3} n_k(\eta)\, \varphi_j(\eta)\, dS_\eta \\ &= -\frac{\nu}{2\pi} \frac{\partial^2}{\partial x_k\, \partial x_j} \int_S \frac{1}{|x - \eta|} n_k(\eta)\, \varphi_j(\eta)\, dS_\eta \\ &= \frac{\nu}{2\pi} \frac{\partial}{\partial x_j} \int_S \frac{\partial}{\partial n(\eta)} \frac{1}{|x - \eta|} \varphi_j(\eta)\, dS_\eta. \end{aligned}$$

Thus, J is a sum of derivatives of double-layer potentials, i. e.,

$$J = \nu \sum_{j=1}^{3} \frac{\partial}{\partial x_j} J_j,$$

where

$$J_j(x) = \frac{1}{2\pi} \int_S \frac{\partial}{\partial n(\eta)} \frac{1}{|x-\eta|} \varphi_j(\eta)\, dS_\eta.$$

Each of the $J_j(x)$ is a harmonic function in Ω, with boundary values belonging to $W_2^{3/2}(S)$. In fact, because of familiar properties of the jump of a double-layer potential, the limiting value of J_j from inside can be expressed in terms of the density and the directly-defined value of J_j on the surface:

$$J_j(\xi)_{(i)} = -\varphi_j(\xi) + J_j(\xi).$$

Just as in Lemma 2, it can be proved that $J_j(\xi)_{(i)}$ must belong to $W_2^{3/2}(S)$, if its density $\varphi_j(\eta)$ belongs to $W_2^{3/2}(S)$, and

$$\| J_j(\xi)_{(i)} \|_{W_2^{3/2}(S)} \leqslant C \| \varphi_j(\xi) \|_{W_2^{3/2}(S)}. \tag{62}$$

From (62) and (61), we obtain

$$\| J_j(\xi)_{(i)} \|_{W_2^{3/2}(S)} \leqslant C \| \varphi_j(\xi) \|_{W_2^{3/2}(S)} \leqslant C_1 \| \mathbf{f} \|_{\mathbf{L}_2(\Omega)}.$$

Because of this inequality and the estimate (53) for the harmonic functions $J_j(x)$, we have

$$\| J_j(x) \|_{W_2^2(\Omega)} \leqslant C \| J_j(\xi)_{(i)} \|_{W_2^{3/2}(S)} \leqslant C_1 \| \mathbf{f} \|_{\mathbf{L}_2(\Omega)}.$$

For the function $q(x)$, this gives

$$\| q(x) \|_{W_2^1(\Omega)} \leqslant C \| \mathbf{f} \|_{\mathbf{L}_2(\Omega)}. \tag{63}$$

We now estimate $\mathbf{u}$ from the Navier-Stokes equation $\Delta \mathbf{u} = (1/\nu)\,\mathrm{grad}\, q$ and the boundary condition $\mathbf{u}|_S = -\mathbf{U}|_S$. Knowing (54) and the estimate (63), we obtain

$$\| u_i(x) \|_{W_2^2(\Omega)} \leqslant C \| q \|_{W_2^1(\Omega)} + C \| U_i(\xi) \|_{W_2^{3/2}(S)} \leqslant C_1 \| \mathbf{f} \|_{\mathbf{L}_2(\Omega)}.$$

The inequality (49) follows from this inequality and the inequalities (51) and (63). This completes the proof of Theorem 2.

We now prove Lemma 2. The kernels $K_{ij}(\xi, \eta)$ of the system of integral equations (58) have the estimate

$$|K_{ij}(\xi, \eta)| \leqslant \frac{C}{|\xi - \eta|}. \tag{64}$$

since the surface S is assumed to be twice continuously differentiable. Moreover, the inequalities

$$|K_{ij}(\xi, \eta) - K_{ij}(\xi', \eta)| \leqslant \frac{C\,|\xi - \xi'|}{R^2},$$

$$\left|\frac{\partial K_{ij}(\xi, \eta)}{\partial \xi_\alpha}\right| \leqslant \frac{C}{|\xi - \eta|^2}, \tag{65}$$

$$\left|\frac{\partial K_{ij}(\xi, \eta)}{\partial \xi_\alpha} - \frac{\partial K_{ij}(\xi', \eta)}{\partial \xi'_\alpha}\right| \leqslant \frac{C\,|\xi - \xi'|}{R^3},$$

where $R = \min(|\xi - \eta|, |\xi' - \eta|)$, can immediately be verified. Here, the differentiation is carried out with respect to the tangent directions to S.

The system (58) has an infinite set of solutions, since the corresponding homogeneous problem has the nonzero solution

$$\frac{1}{2}\varphi_i^\circ(\xi) + \int_S K_{ij}(\xi, \eta)\,\varphi_j^\circ(\eta)\,dS_\eta = 0. \tag{66}$$

It was shown in Sec. 3 that the solution $\boldsymbol{\varphi}^\circ$ is unique, to within an arbitrary multiplicative constant. We fix the solution $\boldsymbol{\varphi}$ of the system (58), by imposing the condition

$$\int_S \boldsymbol{\varphi}\cdot\boldsymbol{\varphi}^\circ\,dS = 0.$$

It follows from well-known results on integral equations whose kernels have weak singularities, that the solution $\boldsymbol{\varphi}(\xi)$ will be continuous on S, if the right-hand side of the system (58) is continuous, and if

$$\max_{\xi \in S} |\boldsymbol{\varphi}(\xi)| \leqslant C \max_{\xi \in S} |\mathbf{U}(\xi)|. \tag{67}$$

The potential $\mathbf{U}(x)$ is square-summable together with its derivatives up to the second order, inclusively, over any bounded domain in E_3, and it satisfies the inequality (51), where on the left we can take not only Ω, but also any bounded domain $\Omega_1 \supset \Omega$. This, and the inequality (10) of Chap. 1, Sec. 1.1, give

$$\max_{x \in \bar{\Omega}} |\mathbf{U}(x)| \leqslant C\,\|\mathbf{f}\|_{\mathbf{L}_2(\Omega)}. \tag{68}$$

Next, we show that

$$\int_S \int_S \frac{|\varphi_i(\xi) - \varphi_i(\xi')|^2}{|\xi - \xi'|^{2+2\lambda}} dS_\xi \, dS_{\xi'} \leqslant C \| \mathbf{f} \|^2_{\mathbf{L}_2(\Omega)} \tag{69}$$

for any $\lambda < 1$. To do so, starting from the system (58), we estimate the difference

$$|\varphi_i(\xi) - \varphi_i(\xi')| \leqslant 2\,|U_i(\xi') - U_i(\xi')|$$

$$+ 2 \int |K_{ij}(\xi, \eta) - K_{ij}(\xi', \eta)| \cdot |\varphi_i(\eta)| \, dS_\eta$$

$$\leqslant 2\,|U_i(\xi) - U_i(\xi')| + 2 \max_S |\varphi_j| \int |K_{ij}(\xi, \eta) - K_{ij}(\xi', \eta)| \, dS_\eta .$$

To estimate the last integral for values of ξ and ξ' which are sufficiently close together, we divide S into two parts, the region σ_ξ cut off from S by a sphere of radius $2\,|\xi - \xi'|$ with its center at the point ξ, and the remaining part $S - \sigma_\xi$. According to (65), the integrals over these two parts will not exceed $C\,|\xi - \xi'|$ and $C\,|\xi - \xi'| \cdot |\ln|\xi - \xi'||$, respectively. Therefore, we have

$$|\varphi_i(\xi) - \varphi_i(\xi')| \leqslant 2\,|U_i(\xi) - U_i(\xi')| + C\,|\xi - \xi'| \cdot |\ln|\xi - \xi'|| \cdot \| \mathbf{f} \|_{\mathbf{L}_2(\Omega)} .$$

The estimate (69) follows from this and from the inequalities for $\mathbf{U}(\xi)$ which have already been derived.

We shall carry out further estimates not for the whole surface S at once, but for the separate parts S_k of S, for each of which we can write an explicit equation in local coordinates, referred to some point ξ^k of S_k. Consider one of the S_k, and let ξ^k be a point on S_k. Let (ξ_1, ξ_2, ξ_3) be local coordinates with origin at the point ξ^k, where the axes of ξ_1, ξ_2 lie in the tangent plane to S at the point ξ^k, and ξ_3 is directed along the exterior normal to S. We shall regard all the functions φ_i, U_i and the other functions specified on S as functions of the coordinates ξ_1 and ξ_2, and we shall continue to use the old notation to denote them. Let ξ_1 and ξ_2 vary in the region $D_k : \{(\xi_1 - \xi_1^k)^2 + (\xi_2 - \xi_2^k)^2 \leqslant d^2\}$. We shall denote the derivative with respect to either ξ_1 or ξ_2 by $\partial/\partial\xi_\alpha$.

Now, we write the system (58) in the form

$$\varphi_i(\xi) + \int_S K_{ij}(\xi, \eta)\,[\varphi_j(\eta) - \varphi_j(\xi)]\, dS_\eta = -\,U_i(\xi), \tag{70}$$

which can be done since

$$\int_S K_{ij}(\xi, \eta)\, dS_\eta = \frac{1}{2}\, \delta_i^j \tag{71}$$

(see formula (20) of Sec. 2 of this chapter). Assuming that $\xi \in S_k$, we differentiate (70) with respect to ξ_α. (It follows from the estimates given below that this differentiation can be carried out directly under the integral sign.) Using (20) again, we obtain

$$\frac{1}{2}\frac{\partial \varphi_i(\xi)}{\partial \xi_\alpha} + \int_S \frac{\partial K_{ij}(\xi, \eta)}{\partial \xi_\alpha}[\varphi_j(\eta) - \varphi_j(\xi)]\, dS_\eta = -\frac{\partial U_i(\xi)}{\partial \xi_\alpha}. \tag{72}$$

For the second term, we have

$$\left| \int_S \frac{\partial K_{ij}(\xi, \eta)}{\partial \xi_\alpha}[\varphi_j(\eta) - \varphi_j(\xi)]\, dS_\eta \right|^2$$

$$\leqslant \int_S \sum_{j=1}^{3} \left| \frac{\partial K_{ij}}{\partial \xi_\alpha} \right|^2 |\xi - \eta|^{2+2\lambda}\, dS_\eta \int_S \sum_{j=1}^{3} \frac{|\varphi_j(\eta) - \varphi_j(\xi)|^2}{|\xi - \eta|^{2+2\lambda}}\, dS_\eta$$

$$\leqslant C \int_S \sum_{j=1}^{3} \frac{|\varphi_j(\eta) - \varphi_j(\xi)|^2}{|\xi - \eta|^{2+2\lambda}}\, dS_\eta,$$

because of (65). We integrate this inequality with respect to $\xi \in S_k$, and use the inequality (69), obtaining

$$\int_{S_k} \left| \int_S \frac{\partial K_{ij}}{\partial \xi_\alpha}[\varphi_j(\eta) - \varphi_j(\xi)]\, dS_\eta \right|^2 dS_\xi \leqslant C \| \mathbf{f} \|^2_{\mathbf{L}_2(\Omega)}.$$

This holds for all the pieces S_k ($k = 1, 2, \ldots, N$). From this and from (72), (51) and (52), we obtain

$$\sum_{k=1}^{N} \int_{S_k} \left| \frac{\partial \varphi_i}{\partial \xi_\alpha} \right|^2 dS_\xi \leqslant C \| \mathbf{f} \|^2_{\mathbf{L}_2(\Omega)}. \tag{73}$$

To finish the proof of the theorem, we must still prove that

$$\int_S \int_S \left| \frac{\partial \varphi_i(\xi)}{\partial \xi_\alpha} - \frac{\partial \varphi_i(\xi')}{\partial \xi'_\alpha} \right|^2 |\xi - \xi'|^{-3}\, dS_\xi\, dS_{\xi'} \leqslant C \| \mathbf{f} \|^2_{\mathbf{L}_2(\Omega)}. \tag{74}$$

We shall prove this by assuming that the integration with respect to dS_ξ and $dS_{\xi'}$ is carried out only over one of the pieces S_k. (This does not involve any loss of generality, since the pieces S_k can always be chosen to be overlapping, and the estimate given below can be carried out only for ξ and ξ' which are sufficiently close together. For ξ and ξ' which are far apart, the estimate is not needed, and we can use (73) instead.) Thus, let $\xi, \xi' \in S_k$ be such that (ξ_1, ξ_2) and (ξ_1', ξ_2') are in D_k. We draw a sphere of radius $2|\xi - \xi'|$ with its center at the point ξ, assuming that $|\xi - \xi'| \leqslant d/4$. This sphere cuts off from S a region which we denote by σ_ξ. Because of (72) and the estimate for $\partial U_i/\partial \xi_\alpha$ already available, it is sufficient to examine the second, integral term in (72) instead of $\partial \varphi_i/\partial \xi_\alpha$, and establish the inequality (74) for it. To do this, we first take

$$J^2(\xi, \xi') \equiv \left| \int_S \left\{ \frac{\partial K_{ij}(\xi, \eta)}{\partial \xi_\alpha} [\varphi_j(\eta) - \varphi_j(\xi)] - \frac{\partial K_{ij}(\xi', \eta)}{\partial \xi'_\alpha} [\varphi_j(\eta) - \varphi_j(\xi')] \right\} dS_\eta \right|^2$$

and represent it in the form

$$\begin{aligned} J^2(\xi, \xi') = \Bigg| & \int_{\sigma_\xi} \frac{\partial K_{ij}(\xi, \eta)}{\partial \xi_\alpha} [\varphi_j(\eta) - \varphi_j(\xi)]\, dS_\eta \\ & - \int_{\sigma_\xi} \frac{\partial K_{ij}(\xi', \eta)}{\partial \xi'_\alpha} [\varphi_j(\eta) - \varphi_j(\xi')]\, dS_\eta \\ & + \int_{S-\sigma_\xi} \left(\frac{\partial K_{ij}(\xi, \eta)}{\partial \xi_\alpha} - \frac{\partial K_{ij}(\xi', \eta)}{\partial \xi'_\alpha} \right) [\varphi_j(\eta) - \varphi_j(\xi)]\, dS_\eta \\ & + [\varphi_j(\xi') - \varphi_j(\xi)] \int_{S-\sigma_\xi} \frac{\partial K_{ij}(\xi', \eta)}{\partial \xi'_\alpha}\, dS_\eta \Bigg|^2. \end{aligned}$$

We estimate each of these integrals by using Schwarz' inequality, recalling that the radius of the "cutoff" sphere equals $2|\xi - \xi'|$ and that the inequalities (65) hold for $K_{ij}(\xi, \eta)$. The result is

$$
\begin{aligned}
J^2(\xi, \xi') \leqslant C \Bigg\{ & \int\limits_{\sigma_\xi} \sum_{j=1}^{3} \frac{|\varphi_j(\eta) - \varphi_j(\xi)|^2}{|\xi - \eta|^{2+2\lambda}} dS_\eta \int\limits_{\sigma_\xi} \frac{1}{|\xi - \eta|^{2-2\lambda}} dS_\eta \\
& + \int\limits_{\sigma_\xi} \sum_{j=1}^{3} \frac{|\varphi_j(\eta) - \varphi_j(\xi')|^2}{|\xi' - \eta|^{2+2\lambda}} dS_\eta \int\limits_{\sigma_\xi} \frac{1}{|\xi' - \eta|^{2-2\lambda}} dS_\eta \\
& + \int\limits_{S-\sigma_\xi} \sum_{j=1}^{3} \frac{|\varphi_j(\eta) - \varphi_j(\xi)|^2}{|\xi - \eta|^{2+2\lambda}} dS_\eta \int\limits_{S-\sigma_\xi} \frac{|\xi - \xi'|^2 \, |\xi - \eta|^{2+2\lambda}}{|\xi - \eta|^6} dS_\eta \\
& + \sum_{j=1}^{3} |\varphi_j(\xi') - \varphi_j(\xi)|^2 \Bigg(\int\limits_{S-\sigma_\xi} \frac{1}{|\xi' - \eta|^2} dS_\eta \Bigg)^2 \Bigg\} \\
\leqslant C_1 \Bigg\{ & |\xi - \xi'|^{2\lambda} \int\limits_{\sigma_\xi} \sum_{j=1}^{3} \frac{|\varphi_j(\eta) - \varphi_j(\xi)|^2}{|\xi - \eta|^{2+2\lambda}} dS_\eta \\
& + |\xi - \xi'|^{2\lambda} \int\limits_{\sigma_\xi} \sum_{j=1}^{3} \frac{|\varphi_j(\eta) - \varphi_j(\xi')|^2}{|\xi' - \eta|^{2+2\lambda}} dS_\eta \\
& + |\xi - \xi'|^{2\lambda} \int\limits_{S-\sigma_\xi} \sum_{j=1}^{3} \frac{|\varphi_j(\eta) - \varphi_j(\xi)|^2}{|\xi - \eta|^{2+2\lambda}} dS_\eta \\
& + (\ln^2 |\xi - \xi'|) \sum_{j=1}^{3} |\varphi_j(\xi') - \varphi_j(\xi)| \Bigg\}.
\end{aligned} \tag{75}
$$

Here, as before, λ is any number less than 1.

To obtain the estimate (74), we still have to consider the integrals

$$
I_k = \int\limits_{S_k} \int\limits_{S_k} \frac{J^2(\xi, \xi')}{|\xi - \xi'|^3} dS_\xi \, dS_{\xi'}.
$$

To do this, we use (75):

$$
\begin{aligned}
I_k \leqslant C \sum_{j=1}^{3} \iiint\limits_{S\,S\,S} \Bigg\{ & \frac{|\varphi_j(\eta) - \varphi_j(\xi)|^2}{|\xi - \eta|^{2+2\lambda}} \frac{1}{|\xi - \xi'|^{3-2\lambda}} \\
& + \frac{|\varphi_j(\eta) - \varphi_j(\xi')|^2}{|\xi' - \eta|^{2+2\lambda}} \frac{1}{|\xi - \xi'|^{3-2\lambda}} \\
& + \frac{|\varphi_j(\xi) - \varphi_j(\xi')|^2}{|\xi - \xi'|^{2+2\lambda}} |\xi - \xi'|^{2\lambda-1} \ln^2 |\xi - \xi'| \Bigg\} dS_\xi \, dS_{\xi'} \, dS_\eta.
\end{aligned}
$$

Since λ can be chosen to be larger than 1/2, it follows from this inequality and the inequality (69) that

$$I_k \leqslant C \| \mathbf{f} \|^2_{\mathbf{L}_2(\Omega)},$$

and this in turn proves the inequality (74). Thus, the proof of Lemma 2 is complete.

In just the same way, we can prove the following generalization of Theorem 2:

THEOREM 2′. *If* $\mathbf{f} \in W^l_r(\Omega)$, $r > 1$, *then the corresponding solution* $\mathbf{v}$ *belongs to* $W^{l+2}_r(\Omega)$; *moreover*, $p(x) \in W^{l+1}_r(\Omega)$, *and*

$$\| \mathbf{v} \|_{W^{l+2}_r(\Omega)} + \| p \|_{W^{l+1}_r(\Omega)} \leqslant C \| \mathbf{f} \|_{W^l_r(\Omega)}.$$

CHAPTER **4**

The Linear Nonstationary Problem

In this chapter, we study the boundary-value problem for the nonstationary linearized Navier-Stokes equations. As noted above, the methods of investigation presented in this book can be applied equally well to systems obtained by various kinds of linearization. Therefore, we choose one such system, namely

$$\left.\begin{aligned} \mathbf{v}_t - \nu \Delta \mathbf{v} &= -\operatorname{grad} p + \mathbf{f}, \\ \operatorname{div} \mathbf{v} &= 0 \end{aligned}\right\} \tag{1}$$

and we use it to illustrate our method. For simplicity, we take the boundary conditions to be homogeneous. The case of nonhomogeneous boundary conditions reduces to the homogeneous case, in the way indicated in Chap. 2. The domain Ω can be either bounded or unbounded, but in the latter case, certain restrictions have to be imposed on the behavior of $\mathbf{v}(x, 0)$ as $|x| \to \infty$. In fact, we assume that $\mathbf{v}(x, 0) \in \mathbf{L}_2(\Omega)$, or if $\mathbf{v}(x, 0) \notin \mathbf{L}_2(\Omega)$, that there can be found a function $\boldsymbol{\varphi}(x)$ such that $\mathbf{v}(x, 0) - \boldsymbol{\varphi}(x) \in \mathbf{L}_2(\Omega)$ and $\Delta\boldsymbol{\varphi} \in \mathbf{L}_2(\Omega)$. The function $\mathbf{f}(x, t)$ is assumed to be square-summable over $Q_T \equiv \Omega \times [0, T]$.

The boundary-value problem for (1), i.e., the problem of determining $\mathbf{v}$ and p from the system (1) and from the boundary and initial conditions

$$\mathbf{v}|_S = 0, \qquad \mathbf{v}|_{t=0} = \mathbf{a}(x), \tag{2}$$

can be solved in various ways. From the computational standpoint, it is probably most reasonable to do this by using Galerkin's method, or the method of finite differences. From the theoretical standpoint, the functional method is preferable; we have presented this method in [31, 32] for solving the Cauchy problem for functional equations of the form

$$\frac{du}{dt} + A(t)\,u = f(t), \quad u(0) = u_0, \tag{3}$$

in a Hilbert space, with an unbounded operator $A(t)$. From the results obtained in [32] concerning the problem (3), and from the results on the stationary problem, it follows that the problem (1), (2) has a unique solution. However, in order not to refer the reader to the papers [31, 32] concerning the problem (3), we now present the relevant material, as applied to the present case (this has also been done in A. A. Kiselev's paper [33]). On the other hand, Galerkin's method will be given for the solution of the nonlinear nonstationary problem, since the scheme for carrying it out is identical for the linear problem.

1. Statement of the Problem. Existence and Uniqueness Theorems

First of all, just as in Chap. 2, we avoid the classical statement of the problem (1), (2); instead, we replace it by another statement, which is wider, and, in many respects, simpler and more reasonable. This statement of the problem is susceptible to very wide generalizations. Thus, we can look for a generalized solution $\mathbf{v}(x, t)$ of the problem in the class $\mathbf{L}_2(Q_T)$, with very weak restrictions on $\mathbf{f}$, and we can show that the uniqueness theorem is preserved in this class. Such a solution $\mathbf{v}$ satisfies all the conditions of the problem in a generalized sense. The reader who is familiar with the author's work [2, 31, 32] will understand how to write down all these requirements.

However, here we shall assume that $\mathbf{f} \in \mathbf{L}_2(Q_T)$ and $\mathbf{a} \in H(\Omega)$. Under these conditions, it turns out that the solution will have all the derivatives appearing in the system, and that it will satisfy the equations almost everywhere. Because of this, we do not intend to give here the various permissible extensions of the concept of a solution of the problem (1), (2); rather, we wish to call the reader's attention to the fact that the existence theorem proved below is essentially based on the proof of an existence theorem "for the generalized solution of the problem in the class $\mathbf{L}_2(Q_T)$."

We now prove that the problem (1), (2) has a unique solution. For the time being, we shall assume that Ω is bounded. Let $\mathbf{a}(x) \in H(\Omega)$ and $\mathbf{f}(x, t) \in \mathbf{L}_2(Q_T)$. We decompose the space $\mathbf{L}_2(Q_T)$ into two orthogonal subspaces

$$\mathbf{L}_2(Q_T) = G(Q) \oplus \mathring{J}(Q_T),$$

assuming that the elements of $\overset{\circ}{J}(Q_T)$ belong to the subspace $\overset{\circ}{J}(\Omega)$ and the elements of $G(Q_T)$ belong to the subspace $G(\Omega)$ for almost all t (see Chap. 1, Sec. 2). Without loss of generality, we can assume that $\mathbf{f}$ in the system (1) belongs to $\overset{\circ}{J}(Q_T)$, since its gradient part can be incorporated in $-\operatorname{grad} p$. We shall use the operator $\tilde{\Delta}$ corresponding to the stationary problem ($\tilde{\Delta}$ was introduced in Chap. 2, Sec. 4), and we shall regard the problem (1), (2) as the problem of determining a vector $\mathbf{v}(x, t)$ belonging to $D(\tilde{\Delta})$ for almost all t and satisfying the relations

$$\left.\begin{aligned} L\mathbf{v} \equiv \mathbf{v}_t - \tilde{\Delta}\mathbf{v} = \mathbf{f}, \\ \mathbf{v}\big|_{t=0} = \mathbf{a}. \end{aligned}\right\} \tag{4}$$

With the problem (4), we associate an operator A which assigns the pair of functions $L\mathbf{u}(x, t)$ and $\mathbf{u}(x, 0)$ to each function $\mathbf{u}(x, t)$ in some set $D(A)$:

$$A\mathbf{u} = \big(L\,\mathbf{u};\, \mathbf{u}(x, 0)\big).$$

For the set $D(A)$, we take the set of all vectors $\mathbf{u}(x, t)$ of the form

$$\varphi_0(x) + \int_0^t \boldsymbol{\varphi}(x, \tau)\, d\tau$$

for which $\boldsymbol{\varphi}_0(x)$, $\boldsymbol{\varphi}(x, t)$ belong to $D(\tilde{\Delta})$ for all t, and $\boldsymbol{\varphi}$, $\Delta\tilde{\boldsymbol{\varphi}}$ depend continuously on t as elements of $\mathbf{L}_2(\Omega)$. It is not hard to see (cf. Chap. 1, Sec. 2) that $D(A)$ is dense in the space $\overset{\circ}{J}(Q_T)$. Moreover, the values of the operator A are considered to be elements of the Hilbert space W of pairs of functions $(\mathbf{f}(x, t); \boldsymbol{\varphi}(x))$ with $\mathbf{f} \in \overset{\circ}{J}(Q_T)$, $\boldsymbol{\varphi} \in H(\Omega)$ with the scalar product

$$\{(\mathbf{f}_1; \varphi_1), (\mathbf{f}_2; \varphi_2)\} = \int_0^T (\mathbf{f}_1, \mathbf{f}_2)\, dt + [\boldsymbol{\varphi}_1, \boldsymbol{\varphi}_2].$$

(see Chap. 1, Sec. 2). Just as in $\mathbf{L}_2(Q_T)$, we denote the scalar product in $\overset{\circ}{J}(Q_T)$ by

$$(\mathbf{f}_1, \mathbf{f}_2)_Q = \int_0^T (\mathbf{f}_1, \mathbf{f}_2)\, dt.$$

The domain of the operator A is in the space $\overset{\circ}{J}(Q_T)$ and its range is in W. The object of the considerations which follow is to prove that the operator A can be extended by closure to an operator $\bar{A}$ whose range fills all W. But this means that the problem (4) will have a solution $\mathbf{v}$ for any $\mathbf{f} \in \overset{\circ}{J}(Q_T)$, $\mathbf{a} \in H(\Omega)$, and that this solution $\mathbf{v}$ will belong to $D(\bar{A})$.

First, we show that A has a closure $\bar{A}$, and we characterize the domain of definition $D(\bar{A})$. The first fact is a consequence of the density of the domain of definition of the operator which is the adjoint of A. Instead of verifying this fact, we show directly that A can be extended by closure. Let the sequence $\{\mathbf{u}_n(x,t)\}$ in $D(A)$ be such that $\mathbf{u}_n$ converges to $\mathbf{u}$ in $\mathring{J}(Q_T)$, while $A\mathbf{u}_n$ converges to $(\mathbf{f};\boldsymbol{\varphi})$ in W. If we show that $\mathbf{u} \equiv 0$ implies that $(\mathbf{f};\boldsymbol{\varphi})$ vanishes, then this means that A can be closed and $\bar{A}\mathbf{u} = (\mathbf{f};\boldsymbol{\varphi})$. Thus, let $\mathbf{u}_n \Rightarrow 0$ in $\mathring{J}(Q_T)$, and let $A\mathbf{u}_n = (\mathbf{f}_n;\boldsymbol{\varphi}_n) \Rightarrow (\mathbf{f};\boldsymbol{\varphi})$ in W. We multiply $L\mathbf{u}_n = \mathbf{f}_n$ by an arbitrary smooth vector $\boldsymbol{\Phi}(x,t) \in D(A)$, which vanishes for $t = T$; then we integrate the product over Q_T, and by integrating by parts we change all differentiations of $\mathbf{u}_n$ to differentiations of $\boldsymbol{\Phi}$. The result is

$$\begin{aligned}\int_{Q_T} \mathbf{f}_n \cdot \boldsymbol{\Phi}\, dx\, dt &= \int_{Q_T} (\mathbf{u}_{n\,t} - \tilde{\Delta}\mathbf{u}_n) \cdot \boldsymbol{\Phi}\, dx\, dt \\ &= \int_{Q_T} \mathbf{u}_n \cdot (-\boldsymbol{\Phi}_t - \tilde{\Delta}\boldsymbol{\Phi})\, dx\, dt - \int_{\Omega} \boldsymbol{\varphi}_n(x) \cdot \boldsymbol{\Phi}(x,0)\, dx.\end{aligned} \tag{5}$$

Now let $n \to \infty$. According to our assumptions,

$$\int_{Q_T} \mathbf{f} \cdot \boldsymbol{\Phi}\, dx\, dt = -\int_{\Omega} \boldsymbol{\varphi} \cdot \boldsymbol{\Phi}(x,0)\, dx.$$

But, as is easily verified, the smooth functions $\boldsymbol{\Phi}(x,t)$ in $D(A)$ which vanish for $t = T = 0$ form a dense set in $\mathring{J}(Q_T)$, and hence $\mathbf{f}(x,t) \equiv 0$. Since the values of $\boldsymbol{\Phi}(x,0)$ form a dense set in $H(\Omega)$, it follows that $\boldsymbol{\varphi} \equiv 0$ also. Thus, we have proved that it is possible to close the operator A in $\mathring{J}(Q_T)$.

Next, we characterize the domain of definition of the closed operator $\bar{A}$. To do so, we consider the expression

$$\int_0^t (L\mathbf{u}, L\mathbf{u})\, dt$$

for $\mathbf{u} \in D(\bar{A})$, and we transform it, by integrating by parts, into

$$\begin{aligned}\int_0^t \int_{\Omega} L\mathbf{u} \cdot L\mathbf{u}\, dx\, dt &= \int_{Q_t} [\mathbf{u}_t^2 + (\tilde{\Delta}\mathbf{u})^2 - 2\,\mathbf{u}_t \cdot \tilde{\Delta}\mathbf{u}]\, dx\, dt \\ &= \int_{Q_t} [\mathbf{u}_t^2 + (\tilde{\Delta}\mathbf{u})^2]\, dx\, dt + \nu \int_{\Omega} \sum_{k=1}^{3} u_{x_k}^2(x,t)\, dx \Big|_{t=0}^{t=t},\end{aligned} \tag{6}$$

or equivalently

$$\int_{Q_t} [\mathbf{u}_t^2 + (\tilde{\Delta}\mathbf{u})^2]\, dx\, dt + \nu \int_{\Omega} \sum_{k=1}^{3} \mathbf{u}_{x_k}^2(x, t)\, dx$$
$$= \int_{Q_t} (L\mathbf{u})^2\, dx\, dt + \nu \int_{\Omega} \sum_{k=1}^{3} \mathbf{u}_{x_k}^2(x, 0)\, dx. \tag{7}$$

From this we see that if $A\mathbf{u}_n$ converges to $A\mathbf{u}$ in W, then $\partial u_n/\partial t$ and $\tilde{\Delta}\mathbf{u}_n$ (and, *a fortiori*, $\mathbf{u}_n$) converge in $\mathbf{L}_2(Q_T)$, and $\partial \mathbf{u}_n/\partial x_k$ converges in $\mathbf{L}_2(\Omega)$, uniformly in t. Thus, the elements $\mathbf{u}$ of $D(\bar{A})$ have first-order derivatives with respect to t and $\tilde{\Delta}\mathbf{u} \in \mathbf{L}_2(Q_T)$, while for all $t \in [0, T]$, the derivatives $D_x\mathbf{u}$ belong to $\mathbf{L}_2(\Omega)$ and depend continuously on t in the $\mathbf{L}_2(\Omega)$ norm. The operator $\bar{A}$ can be calculated in the same way as A, i.e.,

$$\bar{A}\mathbf{u} = (\mathbf{u}_t - \tilde{\Delta}\mathbf{u}; \mathbf{u}(x, 0)). \tag{8}$$

The equality (7) also has the following consequence: If $A\mathbf{u}_n$ converges in W, then the $\mathbf{u}_n$ themselves converge in $\mathring{J}(Q_T)$, and in an even stronger sense. This means that $\bar{R}(A) = R(\bar{A})$ i.e., the range of the closure of A is the closure of the range of A; ($R(\bar{A})$ is a closed subspace in W), and the operator $\bar{A}$ has a bounded inverse $\bar{A}^{-1}$ defined on $R(\bar{A})$.

Finally, we show that the equation

$$\bar{A}\mathbf{v} = (\mathbf{f}; \mathbf{a})$$

has a unique solution for any $(\mathbf{f}; \mathbf{a}) \in W$. To prove this, we must still show that $R(\bar{A}) = W$, or equivalently, that there is no element in W orthogonal to $R(\bar{A})$. [Essentially, this assertion is the uniqueness theorem for a generalized solution in $\mathbf{L}_2(Q_T)$.] Assume the opposite, i.e., suppose that there exists an element $(\mathbf{f}; \mathbf{a})$ in W which is orthogonal to all $\mathbf{u}$ in $R(\bar{A})$, or equivalently, to all $\mathbf{u}$ in $R(A)$. Thus, suppose that

$$0 = \{(\mathbf{f}; \mathbf{a}), A\mathbf{u}\} = \int_{Q_T} \mathbf{f}\cdot(\mathbf{u}_t - \tilde{\Delta}\mathbf{u})\, dx\, dt + \int_{\Omega} \mathbf{a}_{x_k}\cdot \mathbf{u}_{x_k}(x, 0)\, dx \tag{9}$$

for all $\mathbf{u} \in D(A)$. From $\mathbf{f}$, we construct the vector

$$\boldsymbol{\psi}(x, t) = \tilde{\Delta}^{-1}\left(\int_T^t \mathbf{f}(x, \tau)\, d\tau\right),$$

where the variable t is regarded as a parameter. Since

$$\int_T^t \mathbf{f}(x, \tau)\, d\tau \in \mathring{J}(\Omega),$$

it follows that $\boldsymbol{\psi}(x, t) \in D(\tilde{\Delta})$ and

$$\tilde{\Delta}\boldsymbol{\psi}(x, t) = \int_T^t \mathbf{f}(x, \tau)\, d\tau .$$

Thus, we have

$$\mathbf{f}(x, t) = \frac{\partial}{\partial t}(\tilde{\Delta}\boldsymbol{\psi}(x, t))$$

for almost all t. We now set

$$\mathbf{u}(x, t) = \int_0^t \boldsymbol{\psi}(x, \tau)\, d\tau$$

in (9), which is possible, since $\mathbf{u}$ belongs to $D(A)$. Then, we obtain

$$0 = \int_{Q_T} (\tilde{\Delta}\boldsymbol{\psi})_t \cdot \left(\boldsymbol{\psi} - \int_0^t \tilde{\Delta}\boldsymbol{\psi}\, d\tau\right) dx\, dt .$$

Integrating by parts with respect to t, and bearing in mind that $\boldsymbol{\psi}|_{t=T} = 0$, we find

$$0 = \int_{Q_T} [-\tilde{\Delta}\boldsymbol{\psi} \cdot \boldsymbol{\psi}_t + (\tilde{\Delta}\boldsymbol{\psi})^2]\, dx\, dt - \int_\Omega \tilde{\Delta}\boldsymbol{\psi} \cdot \boldsymbol{\psi}|_{t=0}\, dx .$$

Further integration by parts with respect to x_k and t gives

$$0 = \frac{1}{2} \int_\Omega \sum_{k=1}^3 \boldsymbol{\psi}_{x_k}^2 (x, t)\, dx \Big|_{t=0}^{t=T} + \int_{Q_T} (\tilde{\Delta}\boldsymbol{\psi})^2\, dx\, dt$$

$$+ \int_\Omega \sum_{k=1}^3 \boldsymbol{\psi}_{x_k}^2 (x, 0)\, dx = \int_{Q_T} (\tilde{\Delta}\boldsymbol{\psi})^2\, dx\, dt + \frac{1}{2} \int_\Omega \sum_{k=1}^3 \boldsymbol{\psi}_{x_k}^2 (x, 0)\, dx ,$$

from which it follows that $\tilde{\Delta}\boldsymbol{\psi} = 0$, and hence $\mathbf{f} \equiv 0$ also.

We now return to the equality (9). According to what was just proved, (9) becomes

$$0 = [\mathbf{a}, \mathbf{u}(x, 0)]$$

for any $\mathbf{u} \in D(A)$, and since for such $\mathbf{u}$, the functions $\mathbf{u}(x, 0)$ are dense in $H(\Omega)$, it follows that $\mathbf{a} \equiv 0$. This proves that $R(\bar{A})$ and W coincide. Thus, everything which has been said in this section leads to the following theorem:

THEOREM 1. *The problem* (1), (2) *has a unique solution* $\mathbf{v}$, p *for any* $\mathbf{f} \in \overset{\circ}{J}(Q_T)$ *and* $\mathbf{a} \in H(\Omega)$. *The solution* $\mathbf{v}(x, t)$ *has derivatives* $\mathbf{v}_t$ *and* $\tilde{\Delta}\mathbf{v}$ *in* $\mathbf{L}_2(Q_T)$ *while* $\mathbf{v}_{x_i x_j}$ *and* p_{x_i} *belong to* $\mathbf{L}_2(\Omega') \times [0, T]$, *where* $\Omega' \subset \Omega$.* *For any*

* Here, as everywhere else in this book, the relation $\Omega' \subset \Omega$ means that Ω' is a strictly interior subdomain of the domain Ω.

$t \in [0, T]$, the solution $\mathbf{v}(x, t)$ itself can be regarded as an element of $H(\Omega)$, which depends continuously on t. Equation (1) is satisfied almost everywhere. If the boundary S is twice continuously differentiable, then $\mathbf{v}_{x_i x_j}$ and p_{x_i} belong to $\mathbf{L}_2(Q_T)$.

The only assertion in the theorem which requires verification is the assertion concerning uniqueness. The rest all follows from the results that have just been proved and the properties of the operator $\tilde{\Delta}$, established in Chaps. 2 and 3. However, the uniqueness of a solution in $D(\bar{A})$ is an easy consequence of equation (7). In fact, if $\mathbf{f} \equiv 0$ and $\mathbf{a} \equiv 0$, while $\mathbf{v}$ is the corresponding solution, then $\mathbf{v}_{x_k}(x, t) \equiv 0$, and hence $\mathbf{v} \equiv 0$ also.

2. Unbounded Domains, Differential Properties of Generalized Solutions, and Behavior of Generalized Solutions as $t \to +\infty$

We proved Theorem 1 with the assumption that the domain Ω is bounded. If Ω is unbounded, and if $\mathbf{a}(x) \in J_{0,1}(\Omega)$, $\mathbf{f}(x, t) \in \mathring{J}(Q_T)$, then the assertions of the theorem are still true. However, the proof given above must be changed; this is only because of the fact that the operator $\tilde{\Delta}$ does not have a bounded inverse on $\mathring{J}(\Omega)$, since if the domain Ω is unbounded, the point $\lambda = 0$ is a point of the continuous spectrum of $\tilde{\Delta}$. Since in general the whole spectrum of the operator $\tilde{\Delta}$ is negative (see Chap. 2, Sec. 4), the operator $\tilde{\Delta}_1 = \tilde{\Delta} - \lambda_0 E$ has a bounded inverse for $\lambda_0 > 0$. Replacing the unknown function $\mathbf{v}$ by $\mathbf{u} = \mathbf{v}\, e^{-\lambda_0 t}$ in (4), we obtain the equation

$$\mathbf{u}_t - \tilde{\Delta}_1 \mathbf{u} = \mathbf{f}\, e^{-\lambda_0 t}$$

for $\mathbf{u}$, where, under the conditions (2), it can be proved that this equation has a unique solution, in just the same way as for bounded Ω.

If the initial distribution of the velocities $\mathbf{a}(x)$ is such that $\mathbf{a} \notin J_{0,1}(\Omega)$, then we first reduce the problem to determining the vector $\mathbf{u}(x, t) = \mathbf{v}(x, t) - \mathbf{b}(x)$, where the solenoidal vector $\mathbf{b}(x)$ is chosen in such a way that

$$\mathbf{b}\,|_S = 0, \qquad \Delta\mathbf{b} \in \mathbf{L}_2(\Omega), \qquad \mathbf{a}(x) - \mathbf{b}(x) \in J_{0,1}(\Omega).$$

If such a $\mathbf{b}(x)$ can be chosen, for example, if $\mathbf{a}(x)$ has the form $\mathbf{a} = \text{const} \neq 0$ for large $|x|$, then, according to the considerations presented in this section, the problem will have a unique solution $\mathbf{u}$.*

---

* We note that the difference $\mathbf{v}(x,t) - \mathbf{a}(x)$ will belong to $J_{0,1}(\Omega)$ for all $t \geqslant 0$.

If in particular, $\mathbf{a}(x) \in H(\Omega)$ but $\notin J_{0,1}(\Omega)$, then the corresponding solution can be found as the limit of solutions $\mathbf{v}^{(n)}(x, t)$ of the same problem corresponding to initial data $\mathbf{a}^{(n)}(x) \in J_{0,1}(\Omega)$ of compact support, approximating $\mathbf{a}(x)$ in the $H(\Omega)$ norm. In view of what has been said above, the solutions $\mathbf{v}^{(n)}(x, t)$ exist, and they satisfy equation (7). The difference $\mathbf{v}^{(n)} - \mathbf{v}^{(m)}$ is a solution of the homogeneous system (1) and hence also satisfies (7). This implies that $\mathbf{v}^{(n)}$ converges to a function $\mathbf{v}$, for which $\mathbf{v}_t$ and $\Delta \mathbf{v}$ are square-summable over Q_T, while $\mathbf{v}_{x_k}$ belongs to $\mathbf{L}_2(\Omega)$ for all $t \in [0, T]$.

In Theorem 1, it was proved that if $\mathbf{f} \in \mathbf{L}_2(Q_T)$ and $\mathbf{a}(x) \in J_{0,1}(\Omega)$, then the corresponding solution $\mathbf{v}(x, t)$ has all derivatives appearing in the system, and that these derivatives are square-summable over Q_T. It is clear that this is a "limiting" result; in the general case, the solution may not have higher-order derivatives or better-behaved derivatives of the same order. However, if $\mathbf{f}(x, t)$ and $\mathbf{a}(x)$ are smoother, then the corresponding solution will be smoother. The simplest "limiting results" are obtained in terms of Hilbert space notions. The procedure for deriving these results is the same as in [2] and [32]. In fact, we first prove that derivatives of the form $D_t^m \mathbf{v}$ and $D_t^m \mathbf{v}_{x_k}$ exist, thereby proving that $\tilde{\Delta}^m \mathbf{v}$ exists, from which it follows that derivatives $D_{x_k}^{2m} \mathbf{v}$ exist. The following result is obtained: If $\mathbf{f}$ has derivatives $D_t^l \mathbf{f}$ and $\tilde{\Delta}^l \mathbf{f}$, $0 \leqslant l \leqslant m$, in $\mathbf{L}_2(Q_T)$, if $\mathbf{a}(x) \in W_2^{2l-1}(\Omega)$, and if $\mathbf{a}(x)$ and $\mathbf{f}(x, t)$ satisfy the necessary consistency condition for $\{x \in S,\ t = 0\}$, then $\mathbf{v}$ has derivatives $D_t^l \mathbf{v}$ and $\tilde{\Delta}^l \mathbf{v}$, $0 \leqslant l \leqslant m + 1$, in $\mathbf{L}_2(Q_T)$, and hence derivatives $D_x^{2l} \mathbf{v}$, $0 \leqslant l \leqslant m + 1$, in $\mathbf{L}_2(\Omega' \times [0, T])$, $\Omega' \subset \Omega$, or in $\mathbf{L}_2(Q_T)$, if S is sufficiently smooth.

For all these derivatives, we can give estimates of the type (7), and we can prove that some norm or other of the solution $\mathbf{v}$ depends continuously on $\mathbf{f}$ and $\mathbf{a}$. We shall not prove these results here, since the reader can easily do this for himself, using the results on the stationary problem in Chaps. 2 and 3.

It is not hard to make a study (in Hilbert space) of how the differential properties of the solution $\mathbf{v}(x, t)$ change as the differential properties of $\mathbf{f}(x, t)$ and $\mathbf{a}(x)$ are made worse. The problem has a unique solution even when $\mathbf{f}(x, t)$ and $\mathbf{a}(x)$ are distributions rather than functions in the usual sense. We shall not give the corresponding results here, since to do so would require description of the concept of a negative norm and knowledge of the elements of the theory of distributions. For studies in this direction, we refer to the literature [7, 58, 59, 25,

26, 60]. We now give the following result, staying within the framework of ordinary functions:

If $\mathbf{a}(x) \in \overset{\circ}{J}(\Omega)$ and $\int_0^t \|\mathbf{f}\|\, dt < \infty$, then for all $t \geqslant 0$, the corresponding solution $\mathbf{v}(x, t)$ is an element of $\overset{\circ}{J}(\Omega)$, which depends continuously on t, and has derivatives $\mathbf{v}_{x_i}$ in $\mathbf{L}_2(Q_T)$. Moreover, $\mathbf{v}(x, t)$ satisfies the inequality (11) given below, and $\|\mathbf{v}(x, t) - \mathbf{a}(x)\|_{\mathbf{L}_2} \to 0$ as $t \to +0$. This solution satisfies the equations of motion (1) in the sense that the integral identity

$$\int_\Omega \mathbf{v}(x, t) \cdot \mathbf{\Phi}(x, t)\, dx - \int_\Omega \mathbf{a}(x) \cdot \mathbf{\Phi}(x, 0)\, dx$$

$$+ \int_0^t \int_\Omega (-\mathbf{v} \cdot \mathbf{\Phi}_t + \nu\, \mathbf{v}_{x_i} \cdot \mathbf{\Phi}_{x_i} - \mathbf{f} \cdot \mathbf{\Phi})\, dx\, dt = 0, \quad 0 \leqslant t \leqslant T,$$

holds for any smooth solenoidal vector $\mathbf{\Phi}(x, t)$ which vanishes on the lateral surface of Q_T.

The existence of $\mathbf{v}(x, t)$ is easily deduced by using Theorem 1 and the inequality (11). In fact, $\mathbf{v}(x, t)$ is given by the limit of the solutions $\mathbf{v}^{(n)}$ for $\mathbf{f}^n$ and $\mathbf{a}^n$ which satisfy the conditions of Theorem 1. As for the uniqueness of solutions like $\mathbf{v}$, in proving Theorem 1, we established a stronger result, i.e., the uniqueness of a generalized solution concerning whose smoothness we only know that it belongs to $\mathbf{L}_2(Q_T)$.

In the case of the general nonlinear problem, just as in the case of the linear problem, it is of interest to study how the differential properties of $\mathbf{v}(x, t)$ depend on the smoothness of $\mathbf{f}$ and $\mathbf{a}$ in a context other than that of Hilbert space. It is particularly important to single out those spaces in which "limiting results" can be obtained. The spaces $\mathbf{L}_r(Q_T)$ and $C_{l,h}(Q_T)$ belong to this category, and for these spaces the following results are true (where the boundary S is assumed to belong to the class $\Lambda_{2,h}$):

1. If $\mathbf{f}(x, t)$ and $\mathbf{a}(x)$ satisfy Hölder conditions with exponents h and $h/2$ in x and t ($h \in (0,1)$), then $\mathbf{v}(x, t)$ is continuous and has derivatives $\mathbf{v}_t$ and $\mathbf{v}_{x_i x_j}$ which satisfy Hölder conditions with the same exponents h and $h/2$ in x and t.

2. If $\mathbf{f}(x, t) \in \mathbf{L}_r(Q_T)$ and $\mathbf{a}(x) \in W_r^{2-(2/r)}(\Omega)$ $(r > 1)$, then $\mathbf{v}_t$ and $\mathbf{v}_{x_i x_j}$ are summable over Q_T with the same exponent r.

The proof of these facts for any domain interior to Q_T is not very complicated, and reduces to the same procedure as in the case of the stationary problem (Chap. 2, Sec. 4). In fact, by using the fundamental singular solutions of the system (1) (see Sec. 5 of this chapter) and a cutoff function, one can easily obtain an integral representation for $\mathbf{v}(x, t)$, from which one can then derive all the conclusions. There is a certain difficulty connected with investigation in $\mathbf{L}_r$ of the singular integrals appearing during differentiation. These integrals are the same as in the Cauchy problem, and in the next section, we shall give one of the possible ways of studying them.

The proof of the two assertions made above is considerably harder for the whole domain Q_T; in this case, one has to use the theory of nonstationary hydrodynamical potentials (see the Comments, beginning on p. 165).

We now discuss the behavior of the solutions of nonstationary problems as $t \to +\infty$. Let $\mathbf{v}$ be a solution of the problem (1), (2). Then $\mathbf{v}$ satisfies equation (7). Moreover, by examining the equality

$$\int_\Omega \mathbf{f} \cdot \mathbf{v}\, dx = \frac{1}{2} \int_\Omega \frac{\partial \mathbf{v}^2}{\partial t} dx + \nu \int_\Omega \sum_{k=1}^{3} \mathbf{v}_{x_k}^2\, dx, \tag{10}$$

we can easily derive

$$\begin{gathered} \int_\Omega \mathbf{v}^2(x, t)\, dx + 2\nu \int_\tau^t \int_\Omega \sum_{k=1}^{3} \mathbf{v}_{x_k}^2\, dx\, dt \\ \leqslant 2 \int_\Omega \mathbf{v}^2(x, \tau)\, dx + 3\left[\int_\tau^t \|\mathbf{f}\|\, dt\right]^2, \quad 0 \leqslant \tau \leqslant t. \end{gathered} \tag{11}$$

In fact, according to (10), we have

$$\|\mathbf{v}\| \frac{d}{dt} \|\mathbf{v}\| \leqslant \|\mathbf{f}\|\, \|\mathbf{v}\|,$$

so that either $\|\mathbf{v}(x, t)\| = 0$ or $\frac{d}{dt}\|\mathbf{v}(x, t)\| \leqslant \|\mathbf{f}(x, t)\|$. But $\|\mathbf{v}(x, t)\|$ is a continuous function of t, and therefore it follows from these inequalities that

$$\|\mathbf{v}(x, t)\| \leqslant \|\mathbf{v}(x, \tau)\| + \int_\tau^t \|\mathbf{f}\|\, dt.$$

Then, integrating (10) with respect to t from τ to t, and using the last inequality, we see that (11) is valid.

THEOREM 2. *If Ω is a bounded domain and if $\mathbf{a}(x) \in H(\Omega)$, then $\|\mathbf{v}(x, t)\|_H$ converges to zero as $t \to \infty$ if the integral $\int_0^\infty \|\mathbf{f}\|^2\, dt$ converges, and $\|\mathbf{v}(x, t)\|$ converges to zero as $t \to \infty$ if the integral $\int_0^\infty \|f\|\, dt$*

converges. If Ω is an arbitrary domain, if $\mathbf{a}(x) \in J_{0,1}(\Omega)$, *and if* $\int_0^\infty (\|\mathbf{f}\| + \|\mathbf{f}\|^2)\, dt < \infty$, *then* $\|\mathbf{v}(x, t)\|_H \to 0$ *as* $t \to \infty$.

Proof: For all $t \geqslant 0$, the two relations (7) and (11) hold for the solution whose existence is assumed. If it is known that $\int_0^\infty \|\mathbf{f}\|\, dt$ converges, then it follows from (11) that $\int_0^\infty \|\mathbf{v}\|_H^2\, dt$ also converges, and hence there exists a sequence $t_k \to \infty$, for which $\|\mathbf{v}(x, t_k)\|_H \to 0$. But for a bounded domain, $\|\mathbf{v}(x, t)\| \leqslant C\|\mathbf{v}(x, t)\|_H$, and hence $\|\mathbf{v}(x, t_k)\| \to 0$ as $t_k \to \infty$. This, together with the inequality

$$\|\mathbf{v}(x, t)\| \leqslant \|\mathbf{v}(x, t_k)\| + \int_{t_k}^t \|\mathbf{f}\|\, dt,$$

satisfied by $\mathbf{v}(x, t)$ for $t \geqslant t_k$ (see (11a)), shows that $\|\mathbf{v}(x, t)\| \to 0$ as $t \to \infty$. The first assertion of the theorem is proved similarly by using (7) and the inequality $\|\mathbf{v}(x, t)\|_H \leqslant C\|\tilde{\Delta}\mathbf{v}(x, t)\|$.

For an arbitrary domain Ω, we are not justified in asserting that the inequalities $\|\mathbf{v}(x, t)\| \leqslant C\|\mathbf{v}(x, t)\|_H$ and $\|\mathbf{v}(x, t)\|_H \leqslant C\|\tilde{\Delta}\mathbf{v}\|$ hold, and therefore, we use both estimates (7) and (11) simultaneously. In fact, let $\mathbf{a} \in J_{0,1}(\Omega)$ and $\int_0^\infty (\|\mathbf{f}\| + \|\mathbf{f}\|^2)\, dt < \infty$. Then, it follows from (11) that there exists a sequence $t_k \to \infty$ for which $\|\mathbf{v}(x, t_k)\|_H \to 0$. Because of (7),

$$\|\mathbf{v}(x, t)\|_H^2 \leqslant \|\mathbf{v}(x, t_k)\|_H^2 + \frac{1}{\nu}\int_{t_k}^t \|\mathbf{f}\|^2\, dt, \quad t \geqslant t_k,$$

and hence $\|\mathbf{v}(x, t)\|_H$ can actually be made arbitrarily small for sufficiently large t. This completes the proof of Theorem 2.

From the relation (10), it is easily deduced (see Chap. 6, Sec. 5) that for a bounded domain Ω, $\|\mathbf{v}(x, t)\|$ falls off like the exponential e^{-ct}, with some $c > 0$, provided only that

$$\int_0^\infty \|\mathbf{f}\| e^{ct}\, dt < \infty.$$

If the force $\mathbf{f}$ does not depend on t, or if it converges rapidly enough to a function $\mathbf{f}_0(x)$ (so that the integrals indicated in Theorem 2 converge for $\mathbf{f} - \mathbf{f}_0$), then the corresponding solution $\mathbf{v}(x, t)$ converges to the solution $\mathbf{v}_0(x)$ of the stationary problem, corresponding to the force $\mathbf{f}_0(x)$, provided this solution exists. (Sufficient conditions for the existence of $\mathbf{v}_0$ were given in Chap. 2.) The validity of this assertion is easily deduced from the theorem just proved; in fact, it is sufficient to apply the theorem to the function $\mathbf{v}(x, t) - \mathbf{v}_0(x)$.

Finally, we consider another case, which, unlike those just considered, has no analogy for plane-parallel flows (see the "Stokes paradox," mentioned above). Thus, let $\mathbf{v}(x, t)$ be the solution of the problem

$$\left.\begin{aligned} \mathbf{v}_t - \nu \Delta \mathbf{v} &= -\operatorname{grad} p, \\ \operatorname{div} \mathbf{v} &= 0, \end{aligned}\right\} \tag{12}$$

$$\mathbf{v}|_S = 0, \quad \mathbf{v}|_{t=0} = \mathbf{a}(x), \quad \mathbf{v}|_{|x|=\infty} = \mathbf{a}^\circ = \mathbf{const}, \tag{13}$$

for a domain Ω which is the exterior of a bounded domain. Let $\mathbf{v}^\circ(x)$ denote the solution of the stationary problem

$$\nu \Delta \mathbf{v}^\circ = \operatorname{grad} q, \quad \operatorname{div} \mathbf{v}^\circ = 0, \quad \mathbf{v}^\circ|_S = 0, \quad \mathbf{v}^\circ|_{|x|=\infty} = \mathbf{a}^\circ$$

in the same domain Ω. It follows from the results of Chap. 2 that $\mathbf{v}^\circ(x)$ exists and that $\mathbf{a}^\circ - \mathbf{v}^\circ(x) \in H(\Omega)$. Moreover, the following theorem holds:

THEOREM 3. *If* $\mathbf{a}(x) - \mathbf{v}^\circ(x) \in J_{0,1}(\Omega)$, *then* $\|\mathbf{v}(x, t) - \mathbf{v}^\circ(x)\|_H \to 0$ *as* $t \to +\infty$.

This theorem is an immediate consequence of Theorem 2, as is obvious if we apply Theorem 2 to the function $\mathbf{v}(x, t) - \mathbf{v}^\circ(x)$.

3. Expansion in Fourier Series

The solution of the nonstationary problem (1), (2) can also be found by using the Fourier method. The proof that the Fourier series representing the solution $\mathbf{v}(x, t)$ and the series obtained by term-by-term differentiation of $\mathbf{v}(x, t)$ with respect to t and x_k converge in $\mathbf{L}_2(\Omega)$ is carried out in the same way as is done for equations of the hyperbolic type (see [2]), by using the corresponding results on the linear stationary problem. We now give without proof one of the results on the convergence of the Fourier series

$$\mathbf{v}(x, t) = \sum_{k=1}^{\infty} a_k e^{-\lambda_k t} \boldsymbol{\varphi}_k(x), \tag{14}$$

representing the solution $\mathbf{v}(x, t)$ of the problem

$$\left.\begin{aligned} \mathbf{v}_t - \tilde{\Delta} \mathbf{v} &= 0, \\ \mathbf{v}|_{t=0} &= \mathbf{a}(x) \end{aligned}\right\} \tag{15}$$

in a bounded domain Ω. In (14), $\boldsymbol{\varphi}_k(x)$ and λ_k are the normalized eigenfunctions and eigenvectors of the problem

$$-\tilde{\Delta}\boldsymbol{\varphi}_k = \lambda_k \boldsymbol{\varphi}_k, \tag{16}$$

and

$$a_k = (\mathbf{a}, \boldsymbol{\varphi}_k).$$

THEOREM 4. *If* $\mathbf{a} \in W_2^2(\Omega) \cap J_{0,1}(\Omega)$, *then the series* (14) *and the series obtained by differentiating* (14) *once term by term with respect to* t *and* x_k *converges in* $\mathbf{L}_2(\Omega)$ *uniformly for* $t \geqslant 0$. *Moreover, the series obtained by differentiating* (14) *twice term by term with respect to* x_k *converges in* $\mathbf{L}_2(\Omega')$ *uniformly for* $t \geqslant 0$ (Ω' *is any strictly interior subdomain of the domain* Ω) *if the boundary* S *is arbitrary, and converges in* $\mathbf{L}_2(\Omega)$ *uniformly for* $t \geqslant 0$ *if the boundary* S *is twice continuously differentiable.*

4. The Limit of Zero Viscosity

In this section, we show that as $\nu \to 0$, the solution $\mathbf{v}^\nu(x, t)$ of the problem (1), (2) converges to the solution $\mathbf{v}^\circ(x, t)$ of the following degenerate problem:

$$\mathbf{v}_t^\circ = -\operatorname{grad} p^\circ + \mathbf{f}(x, t), \quad \mathbf{v}_{t=0}^\circ = \mathbf{a}(x), \quad \mathbf{v}^\circ \in \mathring{J}(\Omega). \tag{17}$$

Roughly speaking, the fact that $\mathbf{v}^\circ$ belongs to $\mathring{J}(\Omega)$ means that $\operatorname{div} \mathbf{v}^\circ = 0$ and $(\mathbf{v}^\circ \cdot \mathbf{n})|_S = 0$. The solution of the problem (17), as is easily seen, can be found naturally and simply as follows: We represent the vector $\mathbf{f}$ as a sum $\mathbf{f}_1 \oplus \mathbf{f}_2$ such that $\mathbf{f}_1 \in \mathring{J}(Q_T)$ and $\mathbf{f}_2 \in G(Q_T)$. Then $\mathbf{f}_2 = \operatorname{grad} p^\circ$ and $\mathbf{f}_1 = \mathbf{v}_t^\circ$, so that

$$\mathbf{v}^\circ(x, t) = \mathbf{a}(x) + \int_0^t \mathbf{f}_1(x, \tau)\, d\tau.$$

We now prove a theorem, in which Ω is assumed to be bounded (for example):

THEOREM 5. *The solution* $\mathbf{v}^\nu(x, t)$ *of the problem* (1), (2) *converges as* $\nu \to 0$ *to the solution of the problem* (17). *Concerning* $\mathbf{f}$ *and* $\mathbf{a}$, *it is assumed that* $\mathbf{f} \in L_2(Q_T)$ *and* $\mathbf{a} \in H(\Omega)$.

Proof: Obviously, the solution $\mathbf{v}^\nu(x, t)$ satisfies the integral identity

$$\int_0^T \int_\Omega \mathbf{f} \cdot \boldsymbol{\Phi}\, dx\, dt = \int_0^T \int_\Omega (\mathbf{v}_t^\nu \cdot \boldsymbol{\Phi} + \nu \mathbf{v}_{x_k}^\nu \cdot \boldsymbol{\Phi}_{x_k})\, dx\, dt \tag{18}$$

for any continuously differentiable solenoidal vector $\mathbf{\Phi}$, equal to zero on S. Moreover, $\mathbf{v}^\nu(x, t)$ satisfies the inequality

$$\int_0^T \int_\Omega \left(\mathbf{v}_t^{\nu 2} + \nu \sum_{k=1}^3 \mathbf{v}_{x_k}^{\nu 2} + \mathbf{v}^{\nu 2} \right) dx\, dt \leqslant C \left(\int_0^T \int_\Omega \mathbf{f}^2\, dx\, dt + \int_\Omega \sum_{k=1}^3 \mathbf{a}_{x_k}^2\, dx \right), \tag{19}$$

which is an immediate consequence of the equality (7) and the inequality (11). Because of (19), we can assert that there exists a sequence $\nu_k \to 0$ such that $\mathbf{v}^{\nu_k}$ and $\mathbf{v}_t^{\nu_k}$ converge weakly in $\mathbf{L}_2(Q_T)$ to some function $\mathbf{v}^\circ$ and to its derivative $\mathbf{v}_t^\circ$, where $\mathbf{v}^\circ|_{t=0} = \mathbf{a}(x)$. Since $\mathbf{v}^{\nu_k}$ and $\mathbf{v}_t^{\nu_k}$ belong to $\mathring{J}(Q_T)$, $\mathbf{v}^\circ$ and $\mathbf{v}_t^\circ$ also belong to $\mathring{J}(\Omega_T)$. If in the identity (18), we pass to the limit with respect to the sequence ν_k, we obtain

$$\int_0^T \int_\Omega \mathbf{f} \cdot \mathbf{\Phi}\, dx\, dt = \int_0^T \int_\Omega \mathbf{v}_t^\circ \cdot \mathbf{\Phi}\, dx\, dt, \tag{20}$$

since

$$\left| \nu \int_0^T \int_\Omega \mathbf{v}_{x_k}^\nu \cdot \mathbf{\Phi}_{x_k}\, dx\, dt \right| \leqslant \sqrt{\nu} \sqrt{\nu \int_0^T \int_\Omega \sum_{k=1}^3 \mathbf{v}_{x_k}^{\nu 2}\, dx\, dt} \sqrt{\int_0^T \int_\Omega \sum_{k=1}^3 \mathbf{\Phi}_{x_k}^2\, dx\, dt} \to 0$$

as $\nu \to 0$. The arbitrary functions $\mathbf{\Phi}$ appearing here form a dense set in $\mathring{J}(Q_T)$, and hence (20) implies that

$$\mathbf{v}_t^\circ = -\operatorname{grad} p^\circ + \mathbf{f},$$

which proves the theorem.

A somewhat more tedious argument is needed to pass to the limit $\nu \to 0$ in the case of the system

$$\left.\begin{aligned} &\mathbf{v}_t - \nu \Delta \mathbf{v} + b_k(x)\, \mathbf{v}_{x_k} = -\operatorname{grad} p + \mathbf{f}, \\ &\operatorname{div} \mathbf{v} = 0, \quad \mathbf{v}|_S = 0, \quad \mathbf{v}|_{t=0} = \mathbf{a}(x), \end{aligned}\right\}$$

where $\mathbf{b}(x)$ is a given vector in $H(\Omega)$.

5. The Cauchy Problem

In this section, we shall show that if the free term $\mathbf{f}(x, t)$ in the linearized Navier-Stokes equations is summable with respect to (x, t) with exponent $r > 1$ in the strip $0 \leqslant t \leqslant T$, then the corresponding solution $\mathbf{v}$ of the Cauchy problem, equal to zero for $t = 0$, has derivatives $\mathbf{v}_t$ and $\mathbf{v}_{x_i x_j}$ which are summable in the strip $0 \leqslant t \leqslant T$ with the same exponent r. The case of nonhomogeneous initial conditions reduces to the given case by subtraction, as usual, with the aid of limit theorems on the extension of functions from the plane $t = 0$ into the half-space $t \geqslant 0$. There is an analogous result concerning solutions of the Navier-Stokes equations for boundary-value problems, provided that the objects past which the flow occurs have regular boundaries; however, the proof of this requires the use of delicate methods from the theory of nonstationary potentials, which we shall not give here. The theorem given below is of interest not only in its own right, but also because of its application to the nonlinear problem, which will be discussed in Chap. 6, Sec. 8. Thus, we now prove the following theorem:

THEOREM 6. *If* $\mathbf{f}(x, t) \in \mathbf{L}_r(0 \leqslant t \leqslant T)$, $r > 1$, *there exists a unique solution* $\mathbf{v}(x, t)$, $p(x, t)$ *of the Cauchy problem for the linearized system* (1) *with zero initial conditions. This solution has derivatives* $\mathbf{v}_{x_i}$, $\mathbf{v}_t$, $\mathbf{v}_{x_i x_j}$, p_{x_i} *in* $\mathbf{L}_r$ $(0 \leqslant t \leqslant T)$.*

Proof: We shall give a proof which is based on the use of Fourier transforms. At the end of this section, we shall discuss another method of proof.

To solve the problem, we take Fourier transforms in x and t. Since we are interested in the solution in a strip $0 \leqslant t \leqslant T$ with some finite height T, we set $\mathbf{f} \equiv 0$ for $t < 0$ and $t > T$. As for the solution $\mathbf{v}$ itself, we set it and p equal to zero for $t \leqslant 0$. Moreover, we replace the unknown functions $\mathbf{v}$ and p by $\mathbf{u} = \mathbf{v}\, e^{-t}$ and $q = p\, e^{-t}$. Then, for $\mathbf{u}$ and q, we obtain the system

$$\left.\begin{aligned} \mathbf{u}_t - \Delta \mathbf{u} + \mathbf{u} + \operatorname{grad} q &= \mathbf{F}, \\ \operatorname{div} \mathbf{u} &= 0, \end{aligned}\right\} \tag{21}$$

where $\mathbf{F} = \mathbf{f}\, e^{-t}$. For convenience, the coefficient ν has been taken to be 1.

We now set

$$\mathbf{u}(x, t) = \frac{1}{(2\pi)^2} \int \tilde{\mathbf{u}}(\alpha, \alpha_0)\, e^{i\alpha x + i\alpha_0 t}\, d\alpha\, d\alpha_0,$$

$$q(x, t) = \frac{1}{(2\pi)^2} \int \tilde{q}(\alpha, \alpha_0)\, e^{i\alpha x + i\alpha_0 t}\, d\alpha\, d\alpha_0,$$

$$\mathbf{F}(x, t) = \frac{1}{(2\pi)^2} \int \tilde{\mathbf{F}}(\alpha, \alpha_0)\, e^{i\alpha x + i\alpha_0 t}\, d\alpha\, d\alpha_0,$$

* In the case of nonhomogeneous initial conditions, we have to require that $\mathbf{a}(x)$ belong to $W_r^{2-(2/r)}$.

where

$$\alpha = (\alpha_1, \alpha_2, \alpha_3), \quad d\alpha = d\alpha_1\, d\alpha_2\, d\alpha_3, \quad \alpha\, x = \sum_{k=1}^{3} \alpha_k\, x_k,$$

α_k and α_0 are real, and the integrals are evaluated between the limits $-\infty < \alpha_k < \infty$, $k = 0, 1, 2, 3$. From (21), in a familiar way, we obtain the algebraic system

$$\left.\begin{aligned} (i\,\alpha_0 + \alpha^2 + 1)\,\tilde{u}_k + i\,\alpha_k\,\tilde{q} &= \tilde{F}_k, \\ i\,\alpha_k\,\tilde{u}_k &= 0, \end{aligned}\right\} \tag{22}$$

where $\alpha^2 = \sum_{k=1}^{3} \alpha_k^2$. The solution of this system is

$$\tilde{u}_k = \frac{\delta_k^j \alpha^2 - \alpha_k\,\alpha_j}{(i\,\alpha_0 + \alpha^2 + 1)\,\alpha^2}\,\tilde{F}_j, \quad \tilde{q} = -\,i\,\frac{\alpha_j\,\tilde{F}_j}{\alpha^2}.$$

Therefore, we find the representations

$$u_k(x, t) = \frac{1}{(2\pi)^2}\int \frac{\delta_k^j \alpha^2 - \alpha_k\,\alpha_j}{(i\,\alpha_0 + \alpha^2 + 1)\,\alpha^2}\,\tilde{F}_j\, e^{i\alpha x + i\alpha_0 t}\, d\alpha\, d\alpha_0, \tag{23}$$

$$q(x, t) = -\frac{1}{(2\pi)^2}\int i\,\frac{\alpha_j}{\alpha^2}\,\tilde{F}_j\, e^{i\alpha x + i\alpha_0 t}\, d\alpha\, d\alpha_0 \tag{24}$$

for the desired solutions **u** and q. The convergence of these integrals can be investigated by using the so-called *Marcinkiewicz lemma* (see [34]), which we shall use in a form applied to Fourier integrals by S. G. Mikhlin (see [35]). The content of the lemma is the following: Let $\varphi(x)$ be a function defined on the whole n-dimensional space of points $x = (x_1, \ldots, x_n)$ and summable over this space with exponent $r > 1$. Let $\tilde{\varphi}(\alpha)$ denote the Fourier transform of $\varphi(x)$, and use $\tilde{\varphi}(\alpha)$ to construct the function

$$A\,\varphi = \frac{1}{(2\pi)^{n/2}}\int \Xi(\alpha)\,\tilde{\varphi}(\alpha)\, e^{i\alpha x}\, d\alpha.$$

The lemma states that if the function $\Xi(\alpha)$ has all "purely mixed" derivatives up to order n with respect to $\alpha_1, \ldots, \alpha_n$, and if

$$|\Xi(\alpha)|, \quad \left|\alpha_k \frac{\partial \Xi(\alpha)}{\partial \alpha_k}\right|, \ldots, \left|\alpha_1\,\alpha_2 \ldots \alpha_n \frac{\partial^n \Xi(\alpha)}{\partial \alpha_1 \ldots \partial \alpha_n}\right| \leqslant M,$$

then the operator A is a bounded operator with domain and range in $L_r(E_n)$.

As is easily verified, this lemma enables us to assert that the formula (23), as well as the formulas for

$$\frac{\partial u_k}{\partial t}, \quad \frac{\partial u_k}{\partial x_i}, \quad \frac{\partial^2 u_k}{\partial x_i \, \partial x_j}, \quad \frac{\partial q}{\partial x_k}$$

obtained from (23) and (24) by formal differentiation, give us functions which are summable over $0 \leqslant t < T$ with exponent r. The fact that $\mathbf{u}$ and q satisfy the system (21) can be verified directly, while the fact that $\mathbf{u}$ vanishes for $t \leqslant 0$ is proved by a method which is familiar from operator calculus. (Essentially, this follows from the fact that in formula (23) the real α_0 axis can be shifted parallel to itself into the half-plane $\alpha_0 = \xi - i\eta$, $\eta > 0$, since the denominator $i\,\alpha_0 + \alpha^2 + 1 = i\,\xi + \eta + \alpha^2 + 1$ does not vanish when this is done. Moreover, $\tilde{F}_j(\alpha, \alpha_0)$ is analytic in α_0 for $\eta > 0$, and for $t = t_1 < 0$, the factor $e^{i\alpha_0 t} = e^{i\xi t + \eta t}$ goes to zero as $\eta \to +\infty$. From the imbedding theorems of S. L. Sobolev [6] and S. M. Nikolski [36], it follows that $\mathbf{u}$ itself and also the derivatives $\mathbf{u}_{x_i}$ are summable with respect to (x, t) with exponents larger than r.

To complete the proof of the theorem, we still have to verify that the problem can have no more than one solution in the class of functions with the same properties as the solution $\mathbf{v} = \mathbf{u}\, e^t$ which we have just found. To show this, we consider the solution $\mathbf{\Phi}(x, t)$, $Q(x, t)$ of the adjoint problem

$$\left.\begin{aligned} -\mathbf{\Phi}_t - \Delta\mathbf{\Phi} - \operatorname{grad} Q &= \mathbf{F}, \\ \operatorname{div} \mathbf{\Phi} = 0, \quad \mathbf{\Phi}(x, T) &= 0 \end{aligned}\right\} \tag{25}$$

in the strip $0 \leqslant t \leqslant T$ for all sufficiently smooth functions $\mathbf{F}(x, t)$ of ocmpact support. It is not hard to verify that for such $\mathbf{F}$, the solution $\mathbf{\Phi}$, Q is given by formulas of the form (23) and (24), where $\mathbf{\Phi}$ and Q will also be sufficiently smooth functions. Moreover, $\mathbf{\Phi}$, $\mathbf{\Phi}_{x_k}$ and Q will fall off like $|x|^{-3}$, $|x|^{-4}$ and $|x|^{-2}$, respectively, as $|x| \to \infty$.*

Let $\mathbf{v}$, p be a solution of the homogeneous linear system of Navier-Stokes equations such that $\mathbf{v}$, $\mathbf{v}_t$, $\mathbf{v}_{x_k}$, $\mathbf{v}_{x_k x_j}$ and p_{x_k} are summable with exponent r in the strip $0 \leqslant t \leqslant T$. We take the scalar product of both sides of the Navier-Stokes equations with $\mathbf{\Phi}$, and then integrate the result over the cylinder
$Q_{T,R} = \{|x| \leqslant R,\ 0 \leqslant t \leqslant T\}$:

$$\iint\limits_{Q_{T,R}} (\mathbf{v}_t - \Delta\mathbf{v} - \operatorname{grad} p) \cdot \mathbf{\Phi}\, dx\, dt = 0.$$

* This can be seen most simply by using the representations (31), (32) given below for the matrix Green's function.

By making some simple transformations and using the system (25), we obtain

$$0 = \iint\limits_{Q_{T,R}} \mathbf{v} \cdot (-\boldsymbol{\Phi}_t - \Delta\boldsymbol{\Phi})\, dx\, dt$$

$$+ \int\limits_{S_{T,R}} \left(-\frac{\partial \mathbf{v}}{\partial n} \cdot \boldsymbol{\Phi} + \mathbf{v} \cdot \frac{\partial \boldsymbol{\Phi}}{\partial n} - p\boldsymbol{\Phi} \cdot \mathbf{n}\right) dS\, dt = \iint\limits_{Q_{T,R}} \mathbf{v} \cdot \mathbf{F}\, dx\, dt$$

$$+ \int\limits_{S_{T,R}} \left(-\frac{\partial \mathbf{v}}{\partial n} \cdot \boldsymbol{\Phi} + \mathbf{v} \cdot \frac{\partial \boldsymbol{\Phi}}{\partial n} - p\,\boldsymbol{\Phi} \cdot \mathbf{n} + Q\,\mathbf{v} \cdot \mathbf{n}\right) dS\, dt, \qquad (26)$$

where $S_{T,R} = \{|x| = R,\ 0 \leqslant t \leqslant T\}$.

We now show that the integral over the surface $S_{T,R}$ converges to zero as R goes to infinity, along some infinite subsequence. To prove this, we first observe that because of

$$\iint\limits_{0 \leqslant t \leqslant T} \left(\sum_{i=1}^{3} |v_i|^r + \sum_{i,j=1}^{3} |v_{ix_j}|^r\right) dx\, dt < \infty,$$

there exists a subsequence $R = R_k$, $k = 1, 2, \ldots$ for which

$$I_k \equiv R_k \int\limits_{S_{T,R_k}} \left(\sum_{i=1}^{3} |v_i|^r + \sum_{i,j=1}^{3} |v_{ix_j}|^r\right) dS\, dt \to 0 \text{ as } k \to \infty.$$

Moreover, without loss of generality, we can assume that $p(0, t) = 0$, and hence that

$$p(x, t) = \int_0^x \frac{\partial p}{\partial \varrho}\, d\varrho,$$

where the integration and differentiation with respect to ϱ are taken along the radius joining the point x and the point $x = 0$. Because of what has been said about $\mathbf{v}$ and p, and because of the rates of decrease of $\boldsymbol{\Phi}$, $\boldsymbol{\Phi}_{x_k}$ indicated above, we have

$$\left| \int\limits_{S_{T,R_k}} \left(-\frac{\partial \mathbf{v}}{\partial n} \cdot \boldsymbol{\Phi} + \mathbf{v} \cdot \frac{\partial \boldsymbol{\Phi}}{\partial n}\right) dS\, dt \right|$$

$$\leqslant \frac{C}{R_k^3} \int\limits_{S_{T,R_k}} \left(\sum_{i=1}^{3} |v_i| + \sum_{i,j=1}^{3} |v_{ix_j}|\right) dS\, dt$$

$$\leqslant \frac{C_1}{R_k^3} \left\{ \int\limits_{S_{T,R_k}} \left(\sum_{i=1}^{3} |v_i|^r + \sum_{i,j=1}^{3} |v_{ix_j}|^r\right) dS\, dt \right\}^{1/r} (4\pi R_k^2)^{1/r'}$$

$$\leqslant C_2 R_k^{-3 + \frac{2}{r'} - \frac{1}{r}} I_k^{\frac{1}{r}} \to 0, \quad k \to \infty,$$

since

$$-3+\frac{2}{r'}-\frac{1}{r}=-4+\frac{3}{r'}<0$$

always holds. Evaluating the integral involving p, we find that

$$\left|\int_{S_{T,R_k}} p\,\mathbf{\Phi}\cdot\mathbf{n}\,dS\,dt\right| \leqslant \frac{C}{R_k^3}\int_{S_{T,R_k}}|p|\,dS\,dt \leqslant \frac{C}{R_k^3}\iint_{Q_{T,R_k}}\left|\frac{\partial p}{\partial \varrho}\right| dx\,dt$$

$$\leqslant \frac{C_1}{R_k^3}\left(\iint_{Q_{T,R_k}}\sum_{i=1}^{3}|p_{x_i}|^r\,dx\,dt\right)^{1/r}\cdot R_k^{3/r'}\to 0,$$

since $-3+\dfrac{3}{r'}<0$. Finally, we have

$$\left|\int_{S_{T,R_k}} Q\,\mathbf{v}\cdot\mathbf{n}\,dS\,dt\right| \leqslant \frac{C}{R_k^2}\left(\int_{S_{T,R_k}}\sum_{i=1}^{3}|v_i|^r\,dS\,dt\right)^{1/r}(4\pi R_k^2)^{1/r'}\to 0,$$

since

$$-2-\frac{1}{r}+\frac{2}{r'}=-3+\frac{3}{r'}<0.$$

Thus, taking the limit in (26) along the subsequence R_k selected above, we obtain

$$\iint_{0<t<T}\mathbf{v}\cdot\mathbf{F}\,dx\,dt=0,$$

from which it follows that $\mathbf{v}\equiv 0$, since $\mathbf{F}$ is an arbitrary smooth vector function of compact support. This proves the required uniqueness, thereby completing the proof of Theorem 6.

For subsequent purposes (Chap. 6, Sec. 8), it is useful to note that the solution $\mathbf{v}=\mathbf{u}\,e^t$ just found, where $\mathbf{u}$ is defined by the formula (23), satisfies the integral identity

$$\iint_{0<t<T}\mathbf{v}\cdot(-\mathbf{\Phi}_t-\Delta\mathbf{\Phi})\,dx\,dt=\iint_{0<t<T}\mathbf{f}\cdot\mathbf{\Phi}\,dx\,dt, \tag{27}$$

where $\mathbf{\Phi}$ is any solution of the problem (25) (for sufficiently smooth $\mathbf{F}$ of compact support). To verify this, we need only show that the integral in the right-hand side is finite. But this follows from Hölder's inequality

$$\left| \iint\limits_{0 \leqslant t \leqslant T} \mathbf{f} \cdot \mathbf{\Phi} \, dx \, dt \right|$$

$$\leqslant \left(\iint\limits_{0 \leqslant t \leqslant T} \sum_{i=1}^{3} |f_i|^r \, dx \, dt \right)^{1/r} \left(\iint\limits_{0 \leqslant t \leqslant T} \sum_{i=1}^{3} |\Phi_i|^{r'} \, dx \, dt \right)^{1/r'},$$

and the fact that $\mathbf{\Phi}$ falls off like $|x|^{-3}$.

Theorem 6 can be proved differently by using the explicit form of the tensor Green's function for the linearized nonstationary Navier-Stokes equations. Let $(\mathbf{u}^k, P^k)$ denote this tensor. The functions $\mathbf{u}^k(x, y, t, \tau)$, $P^k(x, y, t, \tau)$ vanish for $t < \tau$, and for $t > \tau$ satisfy the system

$$\mathbf{u}_t^k - \nu \Delta \mathbf{u}^k = - \operatorname{grad} P^k + \delta(x - y)\, \delta(t - \tau)\, \mathbf{e}^k, \tag{28}$$

$$\operatorname{div} \mathbf{u}^k = 0. \tag{29}$$

Substituting $\mathbf{u}^k$ in the form $\mathbf{u}^k = \operatorname{curl} \operatorname{curl} \mathbf{U}^k = - \Delta \mathbf{U}^k + \operatorname{grad} \operatorname{div} \mathbf{U}^k$ into (28), and separating the potential part from the solenoidal part, we find that $\mathbf{U}^k$ satisfies the system of equations

$$\left(- \frac{\partial}{\partial t} + \nu \Delta \right) \Delta \mathbf{U}^k = \delta(x - y)\, \delta(t - \tau)\, \mathbf{e}^k, \quad \mathbf{U}^k|_{t<\tau} = 0, \tag{30}$$

while P^k satisfies the equation

$$P^k = - \operatorname{div} \left(\frac{\partial}{\partial t} - \nu \Delta \right) \mathbf{U}^k = \operatorname{div} \Delta^{-1} [\delta(x - y)\, \delta(t - \tau)\, \mathbf{e}^k]$$

$$= - \frac{\partial}{\partial x_k} \frac{1}{4\pi |x - y|} \delta(t - \tau). \tag{31}$$

Using the fundamental singular solutions of Laplace's equation and of the equation of heat conduction, we find from (30) that

$$\Delta \mathbf{U}^k(x, y, t, \tau) = - \frac{1}{(4\pi \nu)^{3/2} (t - \tau)^{3/2}} e^{-\frac{|x-y|^2}{4\nu(t-\tau)}} \cdot \mathbf{e}^k,$$

and

$$\mathbf{U}^k(x, y, t, \tau) = \frac{1}{(4\pi)^{5/2} (t - \tau)^{3/2} \nu^{3/2}} \int\limits_{E_3} \frac{1}{|x - z|} e^{-\frac{|z-y|^2}{4\nu(t-\tau)}} dz \cdot \mathbf{e}^k$$

$$= \frac{1}{4\pi^{3/2} \nu^{1/2} (t - \tau)^{1/2} |x - y|} \int\limits_0^{|x-y|} e^{-\frac{\varrho^2}{4\nu(t-\tau)}} d\varrho \cdot \mathbf{e}^k. \tag{32}$$

Using the representations (31) and (32), we can prove the validity of Theorem 6 in approximately the same way as the analogous assertion is proved for the equation of heat conduction.

CHAPTER 5

The Nonlinear Stationary Problem

In this chapter, it is proved that stationary problems for the general nonlinear Navier-Stokes equations have at least one laminar solution for arbitrary Reynolds numbers and for boundaries which need not be smooth. Moreover, the smoother the functions describing the external forces and the boundaries of the objects past which the flow occurs, the better these solutions will be. For small Reynolds numbers, a uniqueness theorem is valid. Here, we shall consider only three-dimensional problems; the special features of two-dimensional problems are the same as in the linearized problems discussed in Chap. 2, Sec. 3. For the reader's convenience, we first treat the case of homogeneous boundary conditions, for which the proof that the problem has a solution is particularly simple, and only later do we treat the general case of nonhomogeneous boundary conditions.

For the most part, our considerations will be carried out in the Hilbert space $H(\Omega)$ (see Chap. 1, Sec. 2), which is the closure of the set $\dot{J}(\Omega)$ of all smooth solenoidal vectors of compact support in Ω, in the norm corresponding to the scalar product

$$[\mathbf{u}, \mathbf{v}] = \int_{\Omega} \sum_{k=1}^{3} \mathbf{u}_{x_k} \cdot \mathbf{v}_{x_k} \, dx. \tag{1}$$

In every case, we shall determine solutions of the system

$$\left.\begin{aligned} -\nu \Delta \mathbf{v} + v_k \mathbf{v}_{x_k} &= -\operatorname{grad} p + \mathbf{f}(x), \\ \operatorname{div} \mathbf{v} &= 0 \end{aligned}\right\} \tag{2}$$

in a domain Ω, with various conditions imposed on the boundary of Ω.

1. The Case of Homogeneous Boundary Conditions

Let the homogeneous boundary condition

$$\mathbf{v}|_S = 0 \tag{3}$$

hold on the boundary S of the domain Ω; if Ω is unbounded, we assume that the same condition is also met at infinity, i.e.,

$$\mathbf{v}\big|_{|x|=\infty} = 0. \tag{4}$$

By a *generalized solution of the problem* (2)—(4), we mean a function $\mathbf{v}(x)$ in $H(\Omega)$ which satisfies the integral identity

$$\int_\Omega (\nu\, \mathbf{v}_{x_k} \cdot \mathbf{\Phi}_{x_k} - v_k\, \mathbf{v} \cdot \mathbf{\Phi}_{x_k})\, dx = \int_\Omega \mathbf{f} \cdot \mathbf{\Phi}\, dx \tag{5}$$

for any $\mathbf{\Phi} \in \mathring{J}(\Omega)$. It is not hard to see that the nonlinear term in (5) can be chosen in the form $\int_\Omega v_k\, \mathbf{v}_{x_k} \cdot \mathbf{\Phi}\, dx$, since

$$\int_\Omega v_k\, \mathbf{v}_{x_k} \cdot \mathbf{\Phi}\, dx = -\int_\Omega v_k\, \mathbf{v} \cdot \mathbf{\Phi}_{x_k}\, dx$$

for $\mathbf{\Phi} \in \dot{J}(\Omega)$ and $\mathbf{v} \in H(\Omega)$.

We begin by proving the following theorem:

THEOREM 1. *The problem* (2), (3) *in a bounded domain Ω has at least one generalized solution for any* $\mathbf{f}$ *such that the integral* $\int_\Omega \mathbf{f} \cdot \mathbf{\Phi}\, dx$ *defines a linear functional of* $\mathbf{\Phi} \in H(\Omega)$.

Proof: According to Riesz' theorem, the linear functional $\int_\Omega \mathbf{f} \cdot \mathbf{\Phi}\, dx$ can be represented in the form

$$\int_\Omega \mathbf{f} \cdot \mathbf{\Phi}\, dx = [\mathbf{F}, \mathbf{\Phi}], \tag{6}$$

where $\mathbf{F}$ is a uniquely determined element of $H(\Omega)$. For fixed $\mathbf{v} \in H(\Omega)$, the integral $\int_\Omega v_k\, \mathbf{v} \cdot \mathbf{\Phi}_{x_k}\, dx$ also defines a linear functional of $\mathbf{\Phi} \in H(\Omega)$; in fact, its linearity in $\mathbf{\Phi}$ is obvious, while its boundedness follows from the estimate

$$\begin{aligned}\left|\int_\Omega v_k\, \mathbf{v} \cdot \mathbf{\Phi}_{x_k}\, dx\right| &\leqslant \sqrt{3}\left(\int_\Omega \sum_{k=1}^{3} v_k^4\, dx\right)^{1/4}\left(\int_\Omega \sum_{i=1}^{3} v_i^4\, dx\right)^{1/4} \\ &\quad\times \left(\int_\Omega \sum_{i,k=1}^{3} \Phi_{ix_k}^2\, dx\right)^{1/2} = \sqrt{3}\left(\int_\Omega \sum_{k=1}^{3} v_k^4\, dx\right)^{1/2} \|\mathbf{\Phi}\|_H \\ &\leqslant \sqrt{3}\, C\, \|\mathbf{v}\|_H^2\, \|\mathbf{\Phi}\|_H .\end{aligned}$$

Here we have used Hölder's inequality and the inequalities (3) and (7) of Chap. 1, Sec. 1. Again according to Riesz' theorem, there exists an element $A\mathbf{v}$ in $H(\Omega)$ such that

$$\int_\Omega v_k\, \mathbf{v} \cdot \mathbf{\Phi}_{x_k}\, dx = [A\mathbf{v}, \mathbf{\Phi}]. \tag{7}$$

Because of (6) and (7), the identity (5) can be rewritten in the form

$$[\nu \mathbf{v} - A\mathbf{v} - \mathbf{F}, \mathbf{\Phi}] = 0,$$

and since $\mathbf{\Phi}$ is an arbitrary element of $\dot{J}(\Omega)$, the problem of determining the generalized solution $\mathbf{v}$ reduces to solving the nonlinear equation

$$\mathbf{v} - \frac{1}{\nu}(A\mathbf{v} + \mathbf{F}) = 0 \tag{8}$$

in the space $H(\Omega)$.

We now show that the operator A is completely continuous in $H(\Omega)$, by proving that A transforms any sequence $\{\mathbf{v}^m\}$ which is weakly convergent in $H(\Omega)$ into a strongly convergent sequence $\{A\mathbf{v}^m\}$. According to the imbedding theorems of Chap. 1, Sec. 1, the $\mathbf{v}^m$ converge strongly in $\mathbf{L}_4(\Omega)$ to their limit $\mathbf{v}$. Using (7), we calculate the quantity

$$[A\mathbf{v}^m - A\mathbf{v}^n, \mathbf{\Phi}] = \int_\Omega (v_k^m \mathbf{v}^m - v_k^n \mathbf{v}^n) \cdot \mathbf{\Phi}_{x_k}\, dx$$

$$= \int_\Omega (v_k^m - v_k^n)\mathbf{v}^m \cdot \mathbf{\Phi}_{x_k}\, dx + \int_\Omega v_k^n(\mathbf{v}^m - \mathbf{v}^n) \cdot \mathbf{\Phi}_{x_k}\, dx.$$

To estimate the right-hand side, we apply Hölder's inequality and also (3) and (7) of Chap. 1, Sec. 1; as before, the result is

$$|[A\mathbf{v}^m - A\mathbf{v}^n, \mathbf{\Phi}]| \leqslant C_1 \| \mathbf{v}^m - \mathbf{v}^n \|_{\mathbf{L}_4(\Omega)} (\| \mathbf{v}^m \|_H + \| \mathbf{v}^n \|_H) \| \mathbf{\Phi} \|_H,$$

whence, setting $\mathbf{\Phi} = A\mathbf{v}^m - A\mathbf{v}^n$ and recalling that $\|\mathbf{v}^m\|_H \leqslant$ const, we obtain

$$\| A\mathbf{v}^m - A\mathbf{v}^n \|_H \leqslant C_2 \| \mathbf{v}^m - \mathbf{v}^n \|_{\mathbf{L}_4(\Omega)} \to 0 \text{ as } m, n \to \infty.$$

Thus, we have shown that A is completely continuous, and hence the operator $A + \mathbf{F}E$, which assigns the function $A\mathbf{v} + \mathbf{F}$ to each function $\mathbf{v}$, is also completely continuous. Therefore, to investigate the solvability of the equation (8), we can apply the Leray-Schauder principle. In fact, it follows from the Leray-Schauder principle (see Chap. 1, Sec. 3) that to prove the existence of at least one solution of the equation (8), it is sufficient to know that the norms of all possible solutions $\mathbf{v}^{(\lambda)}$ of the equation

$$\mathbf{v} - \lambda(A\mathbf{v} + \mathbf{F}) = 0, \tag{9}$$

where $\lambda \in [0, 1/\nu]$, are uniformly bounded. To prove this, we take the scalar product in $H(\Omega)$ of (9) with $\mathbf{v}$, and we write the result in the form

$$\int_\Omega (\mathbf{v}_{x_k}^{(\lambda)} \cdot \mathbf{v}_{x_k}^{(\lambda)} - \lambda v_k^{(\lambda)} \mathbf{v}^{(\lambda)} \cdot \mathbf{v}_{x_k}^{(\lambda)})\, dx = \lambda [\mathbf{F}, \mathbf{v}^{(\lambda)}] = \lambda \int_\Omega \mathbf{f} \cdot \mathbf{v}^{(\lambda)}\, dx, \tag{10}$$

using (7). The nonlinear term vanishes, i.e.,

$$-\lambda \int_\Omega v_k^{(\lambda)} \mathbf{v}^{(\lambda)} \cdot \mathbf{v}_{x_k}^{(\lambda)} \, dx = -\frac{\lambda}{2} \int_\Omega v_k^{(\lambda)} \frac{\partial (\mathbf{v}^{(\lambda)})^2}{\partial x_k} dx = 0,$$

since $\operatorname{div} \mathbf{v}^{(\lambda)} = 0$ and $\mathbf{v}^{(\lambda)}|_S = 0$. Therefore, (10) implies the required a priori estimate

$$\| \mathbf{v}^{(\lambda)} \|_H \leqslant \lambda \| \mathbf{F} \|_H = \lambda \, | \mathbf{f} |,$$

where $|\mathbf{f}|$ is the norm of the linear functional defined by $\mathbf{f}$. This completes the proof of Theorem 1, and for the solution of the problem (2), (3), we have the estimate

$$\| \mathbf{v} \|_H \leqslant \frac{1}{\nu} \| \mathbf{F} \|_H = \frac{1}{\nu} |\mathbf{f}|. \tag{11}$$

Next, we show that for small Reynolds numbers (understood in the generalized sense given below), the problem (2), (3) can have no more than one generalized solution. Suppose that on the contrary, there were two generalized solutions $\mathbf{v}$ and $\mathbf{v}'$. Then the difference $\mathbf{u} = \mathbf{v} - \mathbf{v}'$ would belong to $H(\Omega)$ and would satisfy the identity

$$\int_\Omega (\nu \, \mathbf{u}_{x_k} \cdot \mathbf{\Phi}_{x_k} - u_k \mathbf{v} \cdot \mathbf{\Phi}_{x_k} - v'_k \, \mathbf{u} \cdot \mathbf{\Phi}_{x_k}) \, dx = 0. \tag{12}$$

Since Ω is a bounded domain, we can choose $\mathbf{\Phi}$ to be any element in $H(\Omega)$. If we set $\mathbf{\Phi} = \mathbf{u}$, the identity (12) can be transformed into

$$\begin{aligned} 0 &= \nu \| \mathbf{u} \|_H^2 - \int_\Omega (u_k \mathbf{v} \cdot \mathbf{u}_{x_k} + v'_k \, \mathbf{u} \cdot \mathbf{u}_{x_k}) \, dx \\ &= \nu \| \mathbf{u} \|_H^2 - \int_\Omega u_k \mathbf{v} \cdot \mathbf{u}_{x_k} \, dx. \end{aligned}$$

We use Hölder's inequality and the inequalities (3) and (7) of Chap. 1, Sec. 1 to estimate the last term, obtaining

$$\begin{aligned} \nu \| \mathbf{u} \|_H^2 &= \int_\Omega \sum_{k,i=1}^{3} u_k v_i u_{ix_k} \, dx \leqslant \sqrt{3} \, \| \mathbf{u} \|_H \left(\int_\Omega \sum_{k=1}^{3} u_k^4 \, dx \right)^{1/4} \\ &\times \left(\int_\Omega \sum_{i=1}^{3} v_i^4 \, dx \right)^{1/4} \leqslant 2 \sqrt{3} \mu_1^{-1/4} \| \mathbf{u} \|_H^2 \, \| \mathbf{v} \|_H . \end{aligned}$$

The estimate (11) is valid for the solution $\mathbf{v}$, and hence

$$\nu \| \mathbf{u} \|_H^2 \leqslant 2 \sqrt{3} \, \mu_1^{-1/4} \frac{1}{\nu} \| \mathbf{u} \|_H^2 \, |\mathbf{f}|. \tag{13}$$

If ν, $\mathbf{f}$ and the domain Ω are such that

$$2 \sqrt{3} \, \mu_1^{-1/4} \nu^{-2} \, |\mathbf{f}| < 1,$$

then (13) implies that **u** vanishes, i.e., that **v** and **v**′ coincide. Thus, we have proved the following uniqueness theorem:

THEOREM 2. *If* ν, $\mathbf{f}$ *and* Ω *satisfy the condition*

$$2\sqrt{3}\,\mu_1^{-1/4}\,\nu^{-2}\,|\mathbf{f}| < 1, \tag{14}$$

then the problem (2), (3) *has no more than one generalized solution.*

The condition (14) means that the generalized Reynolds number is not large. Next, we consider the case where the domain Ω is unbounded:

THEOREM 3. *The problem* (2)—(4) *in an unbounded domain* Ω *has at least one generalized solution for any* $\mathbf{f}$ *such that the integral* $\int_\Omega \mathbf{f}\cdot\boldsymbol{\Phi}\,dx$ *defines a linear functional of* $\boldsymbol{\Phi} \in H(\Omega)$.

First, we recall that in Chap. 2, Sec. 1, criteria are given for $\mathbf{f}$ to define a linear functional on $H(\Omega)$. The proof given above is not immediately applicable to the case of an unbounded domain Ω. In fact, in the case of an unbounded domain Ω, the definition of the generalized solution of the problem differs in a certain respect from its definition in the case of a bounded domain Ω, although above we gave a joint definition for both kinds of domain. The point is that in this definition we required that the identity (5) hold for any function $\boldsymbol{\Phi}$ in $\dot{J}(\Omega)$. For a bounded domain, this is equivalent to requiring that (5) be true for any $\boldsymbol{\Phi}$ in $H(\Omega)$, while for an unbounded domain Ω, this is not the case, i.e., (5) will not hold for an arbitrary $\boldsymbol{\Phi}$ in $H(\Omega)$ (because of the presence of the nonlinear term).

We now turn to the proof of Theorem 3. Let Ω_n, $n = 1, 2, \ldots$, be a monotonically increasing sequence of domains which has the whole domain Ω as its limit. It is easy to see that if we extend each of the vectors **v** belonging to $H(\Omega_n)$ over all Ω by setting **v** equal to zero outside Ω_n, then **v** will belong to $H(\Omega)$ and $\|\mathbf{v}\|_{H(\Omega_n)} = \|\mathbf{v}\|_{H(\Omega)}$. Therefore, $\mathbf{f}$ can be regarded as a linear functional on any of the $H(\Omega_n)$, with

$$|(\mathbf{f}, \boldsymbol{\Phi})| \leqslant |\mathbf{f}|\,\|\boldsymbol{\Phi}\|_{H(\Omega)}$$

for $\boldsymbol{\Phi} \in H(\Omega_n)$, where $|\mathbf{f}|$ is the norm of the linear functional $\mathbf{f}$ on $H(\Omega)$. For each of the domains Ω_n, the problem (2), (3) has at least one solution $\mathbf{v}^{(n)}$, and the estimate (11) holds for all the $\mathbf{v}^{(n)}$, with one and the same constant $|\mathbf{f}|$. Therefore, the sequence of solutions $\{\mathbf{v}^{(n)}\}$ is weakly compact in $H(\Omega)$. We now show that any weak limit **v** of $\{\mathbf{v}^{(n)}\}$ is a generalized solution of the problem (2)—(4). To show this, it is sufficient to convince ourselves that **v** satisfies the identity (5) for $\mathbf{\Phi}$ in $\dot{J}(\Omega)$ (but not in $H(\Omega)$!). Thus, take any $\mathbf{\Phi}$ in $\dot{J}(\Omega)$. Since $\mathbf{\Phi}$ is of compact support, the identity (5) will hold with this $\mathbf{\Phi}$ and all $\mathbf{v}^{(n)}$ for all sufficiently large n. Passing to the limit in (5) along a subsequence n_k for which $\{\mathbf{v}^{(n_k)}\}$ is weakly convergent in $H(\Omega)$ to $\mathbf{v}$ (and hence is strongly convergent in $\mathbf{L}_4(|x| \leqslant \text{const})$), we see that $\mathbf{v}$ actually satisfies (5) with the chosen $\mathbf{\Phi}$. This proves Theorem 3. It should be noted that no smoothness conditions whatsoever have been imposed on S.

In Sec. 4 of this chapter, it will be shown that each of the generalized solutions which we have found will have increasingly better differential properties as the external perturbation $\mathbf{f}$ and the boundary S of the domain Ω are made smoother. This dependence has a local character, i.e., the solution becomes better in the part of the region Ω in which $\mathbf{f}$ is improved, and the same is true of the boundary S. The final results (as concerns the smoothness of solutions) are the same as in the case of boundary-value problems for the Laplace operator. Theorems 1—3 are also valid for two-dimensional flows (except that in (14) we must replace $\sqrt{3}$ by $\sqrt{2}$), and the proofs are the same as in the three-dimensional case.

2. The Interior Problem with Nonhomogeneous Boundary Conditions

We now look for a generalized solution of the system (2) in a bounded domain Ω whose boundary S (which may consist of separate surfaces, i.e., $S = S_1 + \cdots + S_n$) satisfies the boundary condition

$$\mathbf{v}|_S = \mathbf{a}|_S. \tag{15}$$

The assumptions which we make concerning the regularity of the boundary S and of the field $\mathbf{a}$ reduce to just the following two conditions:

I. The field $\mathbf{a}|_S$ can be extended inside the domain Ω in the form $\mathbf{a}(x) = \operatorname{curl} \mathbf{b}(x)$, with $\mathbf{b}(x) \in W_2^2(\Omega)$ (see Chap. 1, Sec. 2).

II. There exists a sequence of twice continuously differentiable "cutoff" functions $\zeta(x, \delta)$, where $\delta \in (0, \delta_1]$, equal to 1 near S and to 0 at all points of Ω with distances from the boundary S exceeding δ, which are such that

$$|\zeta(x, \delta)| \leqslant C, \quad \left|\frac{\partial \zeta(x, \delta)}{\partial x_i}\right| \leqslant \frac{C}{\delta},$$

with the same constant C for all $\delta \in (0, \delta_1]$.

In addition to a certain smoothness of **a** and S, the first requirement implies that the condition

$$\int_{S_k} \mathbf{a} \cdot \mathbf{n}\, dS = 0 \qquad (k = 1, \ldots, n) \tag{15a}$$

is met. The second requirement involves only the properties of S, and it is not hard to see that this requirement is satisfied by piecewise smooth boundaries with nonzero angles. We shall write

$$\mathbf{a}(x, \delta) = \operatorname{curl}\left(\mathbf{b}(x)\, \zeta(x, \delta)\right).$$

Then it is obvious that $\mathbf{a}(x, \delta)|_S = \mathbf{a}|_S$.

By a *generalized solution of the problem* (2), (15), we mean a function $\mathbf{v}(x)$ which satisfies the integral identity (5) for any $\mathbf{\Phi} \in \dot{J}(\Omega)$ and which is such that $\mathbf{u}(x, \delta) = \mathbf{v}(x) - \mathbf{a}(x, \delta) \in H(\Omega)$. It is not hard to see that if $\mathbf{u}(x, \delta)$ belongs to $H(\Omega)$ for any $\delta \in (0, \delta_1]$, then it also belongs to $H(\Omega)$ for any other $\delta \in (0, \delta_1]$ (since $\mathbf{a}(x, \delta') - \mathbf{a}(x, \delta'') \in \dot{J}(\Omega)$).

The theorem which we now prove is also true for two-dimensional flows:

THEOREM 4. *The problem* (2), (15) *has at least one generalized solution for any* $\mathbf{f}$ *such that the integral* $\int_\Omega \mathbf{f} \cdot \mathbf{\Phi}\, dx$ *defines a linear functional of* $\mathbf{\Phi} \in H(\Omega)$, *provided only that the conditions* I *and* II *are met.*

Proof: To prove the theorem, we follow the same plan as used to prove Theorem 1 of the preceding section. Choosing one of the $\mathbf{a}(x, \delta)$, we note that the identity (5)

$$\int_\Omega [\nu(\mathbf{u}_{x_k} + \mathbf{a}_{x_k}) \cdot \mathbf{\Phi}_{x_k} - (u_k + a_k)(\mathbf{u} + \mathbf{a}) \cdot \mathbf{\Phi}_{x_k}]\, dx = (\mathbf{f}, \mathbf{\Phi}) \tag{16}$$

is equivalent to the operator equation

$$\nu\, \mathbf{u} - A_1 \mathbf{u} - \mathbf{F} = 0 \tag{17}$$

in the space $H(\Omega)$. The nonlinear operator A_1 in (17) is defined by the relation

$$[A_1 \mathbf{u}, \mathbf{\Phi}] = \int_\Omega [-\nu\, \mathbf{a}_{x_k} + (u_k + a_k)(\mathbf{u} + \mathbf{a})] \cdot \mathbf{\Phi}_{x_k}\, dx.$$

In the same way as before, we prove that A_1 is a completely continuous operator in $H(\Omega)$. Therefore, to prove that (17) has a solution, it suffices to show that all possible solutions of the equation

$$\mathbf{u} - \lambda(A_1 \mathbf{u} + \mathbf{F}) = 0 \tag{18}$$

for $\lambda \in [0, 1/\nu]$ are uniformly bounded in $H(\Omega)$.

Thus, let $\mathbf{u}$ be any solution of (18). Then $\mathbf{u}$ satisfies the identity (16) with $\nu\, \mathbf{u}_{x_k} \cdot \mathbf{\Phi}_{x_k}$ replaced by $(1/\lambda)\, \mathbf{u}_{x_k} \cdot \mathbf{\Phi}_{x_k}$. Setting $\mathbf{\Phi} = \mathbf{u}$ in (16) (which is possible, since Ω is finite), and using the fact that

$$\int_\Omega (u_k + a_k)\, \mathbf{u} \cdot \mathbf{u}_{x_k}\, dx = \frac{1}{2} \int_\Omega (u_k + a_k) \frac{\partial \mathbf{u}^2}{\partial x_k}\, dx = 0,$$

we obtain

$$\int_\Omega [(\mathbf{u}_{x_k} + \lambda \nu\, \mathbf{a}_{x_k}) \cdot \mathbf{u}_{x_k} - \lambda (u_k + a_k)\, \mathbf{a} \cdot \mathbf{u}_{x_k}]\, dx = \lambda (\mathbf{f}, \mathbf{u}).$$

This relation implies the inequality

$$\| \mathbf{u} \|_H^2 \leqslant \lambda \left| \int_\Omega u_k\, \mathbf{a} \cdot \mathbf{u}_{x_k}\, dx \right| + \| \mathbf{a} \|_H \| \mathbf{u} \|_H + \lambda\, C_3 \| \mathbf{a} \|_H^2 \| \mathbf{u} \|_H + \lambda |\mathbf{f}| \| \mathbf{u} \|_H, \tag{19}$$

if we note that

$$\left| \int_\Omega \mathbf{a}_{x_k} \cdot \mathbf{u}_{x_k}\, dx \right| \leqslant \| \mathbf{a} \|_H \| \mathbf{u} \|_H,$$

$$|(\mathbf{f}, \mathbf{u})| \leqslant |\mathbf{f}| \| \mathbf{u} \|_H,$$

$$\left| \int_\Omega a_k\, \mathbf{a} \cdot \mathbf{u}_{x_k}\, dx \right| \leqslant \sqrt{3} \left(\int_\Omega \sum_{k=1}^{3} a_k^4\, dx \right)^{1/2} \| \mathbf{u} \|_H \leqslant C_3 \| \mathbf{a} \|_H^2 \| \mathbf{u} \|_H .$$

Suppose now that the $\| \mathbf{v} \|_H$, and hence the $\| \mathbf{u} \|_H$ as well, are not uniformly bounded for all $\lambda \in [0, 1/\nu]$. Then there exists a sequence $\lambda = \lambda_1, \lambda_2, \ldots$ in $[0, 1/\nu]$ which converges to some number λ_0, such that the corresponding solutions $\mathbf{u}^n \equiv \mathbf{u}(x, \lambda_n)$ of the equation (15) have norms $N_n = \| \mathbf{u}^n \|_H$ converging to ∞. The inequality (19) holds for all the $\mathbf{u}^n$, with the same constant C_3. Dividing both sides of (19) by N_n^2, and writing the result as an inequality for the function $\mathbf{w}^n \equiv (1/N_n)\, \mathbf{u}^n$, we find that

$$1 \leqslant \lambda_n \left| \int_\Omega w_k^n\, \mathbf{a} \cdot \mathbf{w}_{x_k}^n\, dx \right| + \frac{1}{N_n} \| \mathbf{a} \|_H + \frac{\lambda_n C_3}{N_n} \| \mathbf{a} \|_H^2 + \frac{\lambda_n}{N_n} |\mathbf{f}| . \tag{20}$$

The set of functions $\{\mathbf{w}^n\}$ is uniformly bounded in $H(\Omega)$ (in fact, $\| \mathbf{w}^n \|_H = 1$), and hence is strongly compact in $\mathbf{L}_4(\Omega)$. Without loss of generality, we can assume that the whole sequence $\{\mathbf{w}^n\}$ converges strongly in $\mathbf{L}_4(\Omega)$ and weakly in $H(\Omega)$ to some function $\mathbf{w}$, where the limit function $\mathbf{w}$ belongs to $H(\Omega)$. It is not hard to see that the integral $\int_\Omega w_k^n\, \mathbf{a} \cdot \mathbf{w}_{x_k}^n\, dx$ converges to $\int_\Omega w_k\, \mathbf{a} \cdot \mathbf{w}_{x_k}\, dx$.

We now let $n \to \infty$ in (20). In the limit, (20) goes into the inequality

$$1 \leqslant \lambda_0 \left| \int_\Omega w_k \mathbf{a} \cdot \mathbf{w}_{x_k} dx \right|. \tag{21}$$

We have obtained this inequality for one of the $\mathbf{a}(x, \delta)$, which was chosen at the very beginning of the argument. However, $\mathbf{w}$ does not depend on which $\delta \in (0, \delta_1]$ was chosen in $\mathbf{a}(x, \delta)$. In fact,

$$\mathbf{w}^n = \frac{1}{N_n} \mathbf{u}(x, \lambda_n) = \frac{1}{N_n} \mathbf{v}(x, \lambda_n) - \frac{1}{N_n} \mathbf{a}(x, \delta),$$

and since we chose the sequence $\{\lambda_n\}$ converging to λ_0, by starting only with solutions $\mathbf{v}(x, \lambda_n)$ of the problem (2), (15) which do not depend on the choice of δ, and since $(1/N_n)\,\mathbf{a}(x, \delta) \to 0$ as $n \to \infty$, then

$$\mathbf{w} = \lim_{n\to\infty} \mathbf{w}^n = \lim_{n\to\infty} \frac{1}{N_n} \mathbf{v}(x, \lambda_n)$$

also does not depend on δ. Thus, the inequality (21) will be valid for this limit function $\mathbf{w}(x)$, for all $\delta \in (0, \delta_1]$. We now show that this is impossible.

Because of the conditions I and II (see p. 100), the inequality

$$|\mathbf{a}(x, \delta)| \leqslant C_4 \left(\frac{1}{\delta} + \sum_{k=1}^{3} |\mathbf{b}_{x_k}(x)| \right)$$

holds for $\mathbf{a}(x, \delta)$. (We recall that it follows from $\mathbf{b} \in W_2^2(\Omega)$ that the magnitude of $\mathbf{b}$ is bounded; see formula (10) of Chap. 1, Sec. 1.) Therefore, (21) implies

$$\begin{aligned} 1 &\leqslant \lambda_0 \left| \int_{\Omega_\delta} w_k \mathbf{w}_{x_k} \cdot \mathbf{a}(x, \delta)\, dx \right| \leqslant C_4 \lambda_0 \int_{\Omega_\delta} \sum_{i,k=1}^{3} |w_k w_{ix_k}| \\ &\times \left(\frac{1}{\delta} + \sum_{l=1}^{3} |\mathbf{b}_{x_l}| \right) dx \leqslant \frac{C_4 \lambda_0 \sqrt{3}}{\delta} \left(\int_{\Omega_\delta} \sum_{k=1}^{3} w_k^2\, dx \right)^{1/2} \\ &\times \left(\int_{\Omega_\delta} \sum_{i,k=1}^{3} w_{ix_k}^2\, dx \right)^{1/2} + C_5 \left(\int_{\Omega_\delta} \sum_{k=1}^{3} w_k^4\, dx \right)^{1/4} \\ &\times \left(\int_{\Omega_\delta} \sum_{i,k=1}^{3} w_{ix_k}^2\, dx \right)^{1/2} \left(\int_{\Omega_\delta} \sum_{i,k=1}^{3} b_{ix_k}^4\, dx \right)^{1/4}, \end{aligned} \tag{22}$$

where Ω_δ is a boundary strip of width δ, and C_4, C_5 are absolute constants, determined only by the domain Ω. Since $\mathbf{w} \in H(\Omega)$, it satisfies the inequality

$$\left(\int_{\Omega_\delta} \mathbf{w}^2\, dx\right)^{1/2} \leqslant C_6\, \delta \left(\int_{\Omega_\delta} \sum_{k=1}^{3} \mathbf{w}_{x_k}^2\, dx\right)^{1/2}, \tag{23}$$

as is easily deduced from the representation

$$\mathbf{w}(x) = \mathbf{w}(y)\big|_{y \in S} + \int_y^x \frac{\partial \mathbf{w}}{\partial n}\, dn,$$

by using Schwarz' inequality, if we bear in mind that $\mathbf{w}|_S = 0$ and that the boundary is not too bad. Because of (23), it follows from (22) that

$$1 \leqslant \lambda_0\, C_7 \int_{\Omega_\delta} \sum_{k=1}^{3} \mathbf{w}_{x_k}^2\, dx$$

with a constant C_7 which does not depend on δ. But this inequality is impossible, since

$$\int_{\Omega_\delta} \sum_{k=1}^{3} w_{x_k}^2\, dx \to 0$$

as $\delta \to 0$. This contradiction proves the uniform boundedness of $\| \mathbf{u}(x, \lambda)\|_H$ for $\lambda \in [0, 1/\nu]$, and completes the proof of Theorem 4.

3. Flows in an Unbounded Domain

Suppose we have a system of n immovable bounded objects, past which there occurs a flow $\mathbf{v}(x)$ with a known value $\mathbf{v}_\infty = \mathbf{const}$ at infinity. Let $\mathbf{a}(x)$ denote any solenoidal, locally square-summable vector function, with generalized first derivatives that are square-summable over Ω, which vanishes on S and equals $\mathbf{v}_\infty$ for large $|x|$ ($|x| \geqslant R_0$). The formal definition of the generalized solution $\mathbf{v}$ of the problem of flow past the system of objects is just like that of the problem (2), (15) of the preceding section. As we know, the requirement that $\mathbf{v}(x) - \mathbf{a}(x)$ should belong to $H(\Omega)$ guarantees that the integral

$$\int_\Omega \frac{[\mathbf{v}(x) - \mathbf{a}(x)]^2}{|x - y|^2}\, dx$$

converges, which in turn means that $\mathbf{v}(x)$ converges in a definite sense to $\mathbf{v}_\infty$ as $|x| \to \infty$ (see Chap. 1, Sec. 1). Regarding $\mathbf{f}$, we make the same assumptions as in Sec. 2, and the restrictions on S just reduce to the possibility of constructing "cutoff function" $\zeta(x, \delta)$, $\delta \in (0,\delta_1]$, i.e., functions equal to 1 near S and to 0 at points of Ω whose distance from S is greater than δ, and which obey the inequalities

$$|\zeta| \leqslant C, \qquad \left|\frac{\partial \zeta}{\partial x_k}\right| \leqslant \frac{C}{\delta}.$$

Without loss of generality, we can assume that these functions are twice continuously differentiable (this can always be achieved by extra averaging of the ζ). If we define the vector $\mathbf{b} = (\alpha_2 x_3, \alpha_3 x_1, \alpha_1 x_2)$, where $\boldsymbol{\alpha} = \mathbf{v}_\infty$, it is obvious that the vector $\mathbf{e}(x, \delta) = \operatorname{curl}(\mathbf{b}(x)\,\zeta(x, \delta))$ coincides with $\mathbf{v}_\infty$ near S and equals 0 outside the boundary strip Ω_δ. In defining the generalized solution, we can take for the function $\mathbf{a}(x)$ any of the functions $\mathbf{a}(x, \delta) = \mathbf{v}_\infty - \mathbf{e}(x, \delta)$, and this fact will be used subsequently.

The following theorem holds:

THEOREM 5. *The problem of flow past a system of n objects, where the velocity equals* $\mathbf{v}_\infty = \boldsymbol{\alpha}$ *at infinity, always has at least one generalized solution for any* $\mathbf{f}$ *such that the integral* $\int_\Omega \mathbf{f} \cdot \boldsymbol{\Phi}\, dx$ *defines a linear functional on* $H(\Omega)$, *in particular, for* $\mathbf{f} \equiv 0$.

Proof: A generalized solution can be found in just the same way as in Theorem 2 of Sec. 1, as follows: We construct a sequence of domains Ω_n converging to Ω, and in each Ω_n we take a solution $\mathbf{v}^n$ of the system (2) satisfying the boundary conditions

$$\mathbf{v}^n|_S = 0, \qquad \mathbf{v}^n|_{\Gamma_n} = \mathbf{a}(x)|_{\Gamma_n},$$

where $S + \Gamma_n$ is the boundary of Ω_n. Then we show that the norms of all the $\mathbf{u}^n = \mathbf{v}^n - \mathbf{a}$ in $H(\Omega_n)$ are uniformly bounded (in n):

$$\|\mathbf{u}^n\|_{H(\Omega_n)} \leqslant C_8. \tag{24}$$

The estimate (24) allows us to choose a subsequence from $\{\mathbf{u}^n\}$ converging to a function $\mathbf{u}(x) \in H(\Omega)$, which determines the desired generalized solution $\mathbf{v} = \mathbf{u} + \mathbf{a}$. The argument is the same, word for word, as that given in Sec. 1, and hence we shall not repeat it here.

Thus, it only remains to show that (24) holds. This is done in essentially the same way as we proved the uniform boundedness in λ of $\|\mathbf{v}(x, \lambda)\|_H$ in the preceding section. In fact, suppose that on the contrary,

$$N_n = \|\mathbf{u}^n\|_{H(\Omega_n)} \to \infty \quad \text{as} \quad n \to \infty.$$

The identity (16) holds for each of the $\mathbf{u}^n$. In (16) and below, we take $\mathbf{a}(x)$ to be the function $\mathbf{a}(x, \delta) = \mathbf{v}_\infty - \mathbf{e}(x, \delta)$. Then we set $\mathbf{u} = \mathbf{u}^n$,

$\mathbf{\Phi} = \mathbf{u}^n$ in (16), and estimate the right-hand side of the resulting equality in just the same way as before, noting only that since $\mathbf{a}(x, \delta)$ equals the constant vector $\mathbf{v}_\infty$ outside the boundary strip Ω_δ, then

$$\left| \int_{\Omega_n} a_k \, \mathbf{a} \cdot \mathbf{u}^n_{x_k} \, dx \right| = \left| \int_{\Omega_n} a_k \, \mathbf{a}_{x_k} \cdot \mathbf{u}^n \, dx \right| = \left| \int_{\Omega_\delta} a_k \, \mathbf{a}_{x_k} \cdot \mathbf{u}^n \, dx \right|$$
$$\leqslant C_9 \| \mathbf{a} \|^2_{H(\Omega_\delta)} \| \mathbf{u}^n \|_{H(\Omega_n)},$$

with the same constant C_9 for all n and $\delta \in (0, \delta_1]$. As a result, instead of (19), we obtain

$$\| \mathbf{u}_n \|^2_{H(\Omega_n)} \leqslant \left| \int_{\Omega_n} \mathbf{u}^n_{x_k} \cdot \mathbf{a} \, u^n_k \, dx \right| + \| \mathbf{a} \|_{H(\Omega_\delta)} \| \mathbf{u}^n \|_{H(\Omega_n)}$$
$$+ C_9 \| \mathbf{a} \|^2_{H(\Omega_\delta)} \| \mathbf{u}^n \|_{H(\Omega_n)} + |\mathbf{f}| \, \| \mathbf{u}^n \|_{H(\Omega_n)}. \qquad (25)$$

We now extend each of the $\mathbf{u}^n(x)$ onto all Ω by setting $\mathbf{u}^n(x)$ equal to zero outside Ω_n, and we introduce the functions

$$\mathbf{w}^n(x) = \frac{\mathbf{u}^n(x)}{N_n}, \quad \text{where} \quad N_n = \| \mathbf{u}^n \|_{H(\Omega_n)}.$$

The functions $\mathbf{w}^n(x)$ can be regarded as elements of $H(\Omega)$, which are uniformly bounded in $H(\Omega)$, and which satisfy (25), or equivalently

$$1 \leqslant \left| \int_{\Omega_\delta} w^n_k \, \mathbf{e} \cdot \mathbf{w}^n_{x_k} \, dx \right| + \frac{1}{N_n} \| \mathbf{a} \|_{H(\Omega_\delta)} + \frac{C_9}{N_n} \| \mathbf{a} \|^2_{H(\Omega_\delta)} + \frac{1}{N_n} |\mathbf{f}|,$$

if we bear in mind that

$$\int_{\Omega_n} u^n_k \, \mathbf{a} \cdot \mathbf{u}^n_{x_k} \, dx = - \int_{\Omega_\delta} u^n_k \, \mathbf{e}(x, \delta) \cdot \mathbf{u}^n_{x_k} \, dx.$$

Then, repeating the argument of the preceding section, word for word, we arrive at a contradiction with our assumption that $N_n \to \infty$ as $n \to \infty$. This establishes (24), and thereby proves Theorem 5.

Of course, the method used here to prove that the problem of flow past a system of objects has a solution is also applicable to the case where nonhomogeneous boundary conditions $\mathbf{v}|_{S_k} = \mathbf{a}|_{S_k}$ are specified on the boundaries S_k of the objects, provided only that

$$\int_{S_k} \mathbf{a} \cdot \mathbf{n} \, dS = 0, \qquad (k = 1, 2, \ldots, n).$$

For two-dimensional flows in domains of the kind considered here, Theorem 4 holds instead of Theorem 5, where $\mathbf{a}$ does not have to satisfy the conditions (15a).

4. Effective Estimates of Solutions

We can also give an explicit estimate $\|\mathbf{u}\|_{H(\Omega)}$ of the solutions of equation (18), by constructing the cutoff function $\zeta(x)$ in a special way. This is done as follows: As before, suppose the field $\mathbf{a}|_S$ can be extended inside the domain Ω as an expression of the form curl $\mathbf{b}(x)$, with $\mathbf{b} \in W_2^2(\Omega)$. Let the boundary S of the domain Ω be piecewise smooth with nonzero angles. More precisely, we make the following assumptions about S:

1. S and some neighborhood of S can be covered by a finite number of balls $K_i(r)$, $i = 1, \ldots, N$, of small radius r, such that in each $K_i(2r)$,* we can introduce nondegenerate coordinates $y^i = y^i(x)$, with continuously differentiable $y^i(x)$ and $x^i = x^i(y)$, relative to which the equations of the piece of boundary $S \cap K_i(2r)$ has the form

$$y_3^i = \omega^i(y_1^i, y_2^i),$$

where (y_1^i, y_2^i) vary over a bounded domain D_i, and ω^i is a continuous, piecewise smooth function with derivatives $\omega^i_{y_1^i}$, $\omega^i_{y_2^i}$ bounded by some number m_i.

2. The region

$$\{\omega^i(y_1^i, y_2^i) \leq y_3^i \leq \omega^i(y_1^i, y_2^i) + \delta_i,\ (y_1^i, y_2^i) \in D_i\},$$

where $\delta_i > 0$, belongs to $\bar{\Omega}$ and contains $K_i(2r) \cap \bar{\Omega}$, but the region

$$\{\omega^i(y_1^i, y_2^i) - \delta_i \leq y_3^i \leq \omega^i(y_1^i, y_2^i)\}$$

must have no points in common with $\bar{\Omega}$.

Next, we introduce a "partition of unity"

$$1 \equiv \sum_{i=1}^{N} \varphi_i(x),$$

where φ_i $(i = 1, \ldots, N)$ is a smooth nonnegative function which vanishes outside of $K_i(2r)$, so that $\sum_{i=1}^{N} \varphi_i(x)$ equals 1 in a two-sided neighborhood of S of width r. Consider the function

$$\eta(t, \varepsilon, \varrho) = \begin{cases} 1 & , -\infty < t \leq 2\varrho\left(1 + e^{-\frac{1}{\varepsilon}}\right), \\ -\varepsilon \ln \dfrac{t - 2\varrho}{2\varrho} & , 2\varrho\left(1 + e^{-\frac{1}{\varepsilon}}\right) \leq t \leq 4\varrho, \\ 0 & , 4\varrho \leq t < \infty, \end{cases}$$

This function is piecewise smooth, and

$$\frac{d\eta}{dt} = \eta' = \begin{cases} 0 & , -\infty < t \leq 2\varrho\left(1 + e^{-\frac{1}{\varepsilon}}\right), \\ -\dfrac{\varepsilon}{t - 2\varrho} & , 2\varrho\left(1 + e^{-\frac{1}{\varepsilon}}\right) \leq t \leq 4\varrho, \\ 0 & , 4\varrho \leq t < \infty, \end{cases}$$

* $K_i(2r)$ is concentric with $K_i(r)$.

so that

$$|\eta'(t, \varepsilon, \varrho)| \leqslant \frac{\varepsilon}{t}.$$

Using η, we construct the functions

$$\zeta_i(y^i, \varepsilon, \varrho) = \begin{cases} \eta[y_3^i - \omega^i(y_1^i, y_2^i), \varepsilon, \varrho]\, \varphi_i(x(y^i)) & \text{in } K_i(2r), \\ 0 & \text{outside } K_i(2r), \end{cases}$$

which we denote by $\hat{\zeta}_i(x, \varepsilon, \varrho)$ in the old coordinates x, i. e.,

$$\hat{\zeta}_i(x, \varepsilon, \varrho) = \zeta_i(y^i(x), \varepsilon, \varrho).$$

The function

$$\hat{\zeta}(x, \varepsilon, \varrho) = \sum_{i=1}^{N} \hat{\zeta}_i(x, \varepsilon, \varrho)$$

has the following properties:

1. It is continuous and has piecewise continuous derivatives, and its values lie between 0 and 1.

2. It equals 1 in a two-sided neighborhood of S, whose width is of order ϱ, say $C_1 \varrho$.

3. It vanishes outside a neighborhood of S of width $C_2 \varrho$.

4. Moreover

$$\left|\frac{\partial \hat{\zeta}}{\partial x^i}\right| \leqslant C_3 \frac{\varepsilon}{d(x)},$$

where $d(x)$ is the distance from x to S, and the constant C_3, like C_1 and C_2, does not depend on ε and ϱ.

We now average the function $\hat{\zeta}(x, \varepsilon, \varrho)$, using the "averaging radius" $\frac{1}{2} C_1 \varrho$ and a nonnegative infinitely differentiable kernel (see Chap. 1, Sec. 3). This new function, denoted by $\zeta(x, \varepsilon, \varrho)$, will have the same properties as $\hat{\zeta}$, except that unlike $\hat{\zeta}$, it will be infinitely differentiable. In the boundary strip of width $\frac{1}{2} C_1 \varrho$, ζ equals 1, and ζ vanishes outside the strip of width $(C_2 + \frac{1}{2} C_1)\varrho$. The function $\zeta(x, \varepsilon, \varrho)$ is just the cutoff function with the properties we require. In what follows, we shall choose the numbers ε and ϱ to be suitably small.

Returning to the problem of estimating $\|\mathbf{u}\|_{H(\Omega)}$, we note that in the inequality (19), it only remains to estimate the first term

$$I = \lambda \left| \int_{\Omega} u_k \mathbf{a} \cdot \mathbf{u}_{x_k}\, dx \right|,$$

where $\mathbf{a} = \operatorname{curl}(\mathbf{b}\,\zeta)$. Taking ζ to be the function $\zeta(x, \varepsilon, \varrho)$ just constructed, we estimate I, recalling that $\lambda \in [0,1/\nu]$:

$$
\begin{aligned}
I &\leqslant \frac{C_4}{\nu} \|\mathbf{u}\|_H \sum_{k,l=1}^{3} \sqrt{\int_\Omega u_k^2 a_l^2\, dx} \\
&\leqslant C_5 \|\mathbf{u}\|_H \sum_{k,l,i} \sqrt{\int_{D_i} dy_1^i\, dy_2^i \int_{\omega^i(y_1^i, y_2^i)}^{\omega^i(y_1^i, y_2^i)+C_6\varrho} u_k^2 a_l^2\, dy_3^i} \\
&\leqslant C_7 \|\mathbf{u}\|_H \sum_{k,l,i} \left(\sqrt{\int_{D_i} \int_{\omega^i}^{\omega^i + C_6\varrho} u_k^2 \frac{\varepsilon^2}{(y_3^i - \omega^i)^2}\, dy^i} \right. \\
&\qquad \left. + \sqrt{\int_{D_i} \int_{\omega^i}^{\omega^i + C_6\varrho} u_k^2\, |\operatorname{grad} \mathbf{b}|^2\, dy^i} \right).
\end{aligned}
\tag{26}
$$

For any smooth function w, equal to zero for $t = 0$,

$$
\begin{aligned}
j &= \int_{D_i} \int_0^{C_6\varrho} \frac{w^2(y_1, y_2, t)}{t^2}\, dy_1\, dy_2\, dt \\
&= \int\!\!\int_{D_i} \frac{2 w w_t}{t}\, dy_1\, dy_2\, dt - \int_{D_i} \frac{w^2(y_1, y_2, C_6\varrho)}{C_6\varrho}\, dy_1\, dy_2 \\
&\leqslant 2 \sqrt{\int\!\!\int \frac{w^2}{t^2}\, dy_1\, dy_2\, dt}\, \sqrt{\int\!\!\int |\operatorname{grad} w|^2\, dy_1\, dy_2\, dt},
\end{aligned}
$$

from which we obtain the familiar inequality

$$
j \leqslant 4 \int_{D_i} \int_0^{C_6\varrho} |\operatorname{grad} w|^2\, dy_1\, dy_2\, dt, \tag{27}
$$

which, by closure, is also true for the components of the vector $\mathbf{u}$, since $\mathbf{u} \in H(\Omega)$. Moreover,

$$
\begin{aligned}
&\int_{D_i} dy_1^i\, dy_2^i \int_{\omega^i(y_1, y_2)}^{\omega^i(y_1, y_2) + C_6\varrho} u_k^2\, |\operatorname{grad} \mathbf{b}|^2\, dy_3^i \\
&\qquad \leqslant \sqrt{\int\!\!\int u_k^4\, dy^i}\, \sqrt{\int\!\!\int |\operatorname{grad} \mathbf{b}|^4\, dy^i} \leqslant C^2(\varrho)\, \|\mathbf{u}\|^2_{H(\Omega)},
\end{aligned}
\tag{28}
$$

where $C(\varrho) \to 0$ as $\varrho \to 0$. It follows from (26)—(28) that

$$
I \leqslant [C_8\, \varepsilon + C(\varrho)]\, \|\mathbf{u}\|^2_H .
$$

If we now choose the numbers ε and ϱ so small that

$$
C_8\, \varepsilon + C(\varrho) \leqslant \frac{1}{2},
$$

then this inequality, together with (19), gives an effective estimate of $\|\mathbf{u}\|_{H(\Omega)}$ which depends only on known quantities and not on $\lambda \in [0, 1/\nu]$.

We can also give an effective estimate of $\|\mathbf{u}\|_{H(\Omega)}$ for flows in an unbounded domain Ω. In this case, we have to use a cutoff function $\zeta(x, \varepsilon, \varrho)$ of the same type as that just constructed for the case of a bounded domain. Then the function

$$\mathbf{a}(x, \varepsilon, \varrho) = \mathbf{v}_\infty - \mathbf{e} = \mathbf{v}_\infty - \operatorname{curl}(\mathbf{b}(x)\, \zeta(x, \varepsilon, \varrho))$$

equals $\mathbf{v}_\infty$ in the whole region Ω, except for a strip $\Omega_{C_9 \varrho}$ of width $C_9\, \varrho$ near S, and in this strip $\mathbf{a}$ satisfies the estimate

$$|\mathbf{a}(x, \varepsilon, \varrho)| \leqslant C_{10}\left(|\mathbf{b}(x)| \frac{\varepsilon}{d(x)} + |\operatorname{grad} \mathbf{b}| + 1\right),$$

where $d(x)$ is the distance from x to S. This allows us to estimate the quantity

$$\begin{aligned} I_n = \int_{\Omega_n} u_k^n \mathbf{a} \cdot \mathbf{u}_{x_k}^n \, dx &= - \int_{\Omega_n} \mathbf{u}_{x_k}^n \cdot \operatorname{curl}(\mathbf{b}\, \zeta)\, u_k^n \, dx \\ &= - \int_{\Omega_{C_9 \varrho}} \mathbf{u}_{x_k}^n \cdot \operatorname{curl}(\mathbf{b}\, \zeta)\, u_k^n \, dx, \end{aligned}$$

i. e., the only integral in the right-hand side of (25) which has not yet been estimated. In fact, we have the same estimate

$$|I_n| \leqslant (C_{10}\, \varepsilon + C(\varrho))\, \|\mathbf{u}^n\|_{H(\Omega_n)} \leqslant \frac{1}{2} \|\mathbf{u}^n\|^2_{H(\Omega_n)}$$

given at the end of Sec. 2 for a bounded domain. Together with (25), this gives an effective estimate of $\|\mathbf{u}^n\|_{H(\Omega_n)}$, in terms of known quantities, which is independent of n. The estimate is also valid for the limit function $\mathbf{u}(x)$ in the domain Ω.

5. The Differential Properties of Generalized Solutions

We now show that the differential properties of generalized solutions become better to the extent that the data of the problem become better, and that this improvement is of a local character. For the case of plane parallel flows, this can be done by familiar methods, since in this case, solving the boundary-value problems under consideration is equivalent to solving the first boundary-value problem for the function $\psi(x_1, x_2)$ (see Chap. 2, Sec. 3). In fact, the stream function ψ satisfies the equation

$$\nu\, \Delta^2 \psi + \psi_{x_1} \Delta \psi_{x_2} - \psi_{x_2} \Delta \psi_{x_1} = - f_{1x_2} + f_{2x_1},$$

and we know the boundary values of ψ and $\partial\psi/\partial n$. For the case of three space variables, it is not possible to make such a simple reduction of the problems being considered to the case of problems which have already been studied. However, we shall show that the following theorem holds (for example):

THEOREM 6. *If* $\mathbf{v}(x)$ *is a generalized solution of one of the problems considered in this chapter, and if* $\mathbf{f}(x)$ *is square-summable over a finite part* Ω_1 *of the domain* Ω, *then* $\mathbf{v}(x)$ *is continuous in* Ω_1 *and has second-order derivatives in* Ω_1, *which are square-summable over* Ω_2, *where* Ω_2 *is any interior subdomain of* Ω_1. *Moreover, if* $\mathbf{f}$ *satisfies a Hölder condition in* Ω_1, *then* $\mathbf{v}$ *has second-order derivatives which satisfy a Hölder condition in* Ω_2 *with the same exponent.*

Proof: Let $\mathbf{v}(x)$ be a generalized solution of one of the problems considered above. Then $\mathbf{v}(x)$ satisfies the identity

$$\int_\Omega (\nu\, \mathbf{v}_{x_k} \cdot \mathbf{\Phi}_{x_k} - v_k\, \mathbf{v} \cdot \mathbf{\Phi}_{x_k})\, dx = (\mathbf{f}, \mathbf{\Phi}) \tag{5}$$

and certainly belongs to $W_2^1(\Omega_1)$. If we were to choose $\mathbf{\Phi}(x)$ in (5) to be the basic singular solution $\mathbf{u}^k(x, y)$ of the homogeneous linearized system, then, for such a $\mathbf{\Phi}$, the integral $\int_\Omega \nu\, \mathbf{v}_{x_i} \cdot \mathbf{\Phi}_{x_i}\, dx$ would give the value of v_k at the point y, and from (5) we would obtain a representation of $v_k(y)$ in terms of volume and surface integrals from which we could easily obtain the required properties of the solution $\mathbf{v}$. However, in (5), $\mathbf{\Phi}$ must not only be solenoidal, but must also vanish on S and be square-summable over Ω, together with its first-order derivatives, and $\mathbf{u}^k$ does not have the last two properties. Thus, we "fix up" $\mathbf{u}^k$ in such a way that it becomes acceptable, i.e., belongs to $H(\Omega)$. To do so, we recall that $\mathbf{u}^k(x, y)$ can be represented in the form

$$\mathbf{u}^k(x, y) = \operatorname{curl}_x \mathbf{V}^k(x, y), \quad \mathbf{V}^k(x, y) = \frac{1}{8\pi\nu} \operatorname{curl}\,(|x - y|\, \mathbf{e}^k), \tag{29}$$

where $\mathbf{e}^k = (\delta_k^1, \delta_k^2, \delta_k^3)$ (see Chap. 3, Sec. 1).

Now, let $\Omega_2, \Omega_3, \ldots$ denote subdomains of the domain Ω_1, each containing the next (i.e., $\Omega_1 \supset \Omega_2 \supset \Omega_3 \supset \ldots$), and such that the distance from Ω_n to the boundary of Ω_{n-1} is positive. In (5), let $\mathbf{\Phi}$ equal

$$\mathbf{\Phi}(x) = \operatorname{curl}_x [\zeta^2(x)\, \mathbf{V}^k(x, y)]_\varrho, \tag{30}$$

where $\zeta(x)$ is a nonnegative continuously differentiable function, equal to 1 in Ω_3 and to 0 outside Ω_2. Moreover, let the symbol $\{\psi\}_\varrho$ denote averaging of ψ "with radius ϱ" (see Chap. 1, Sec. 1). We take the radius ϱ to be less than the distance from Ω_2 to the boundary of Ω_1, and we choose $y \in \Omega_3$. It is clear that $\boldsymbol{\Phi} \in H(\Omega)$ and even that $\boldsymbol{\Phi} \in H(\Omega_1)$. We substitute this $\boldsymbol{\Phi}$ into (5), and bear in mind that the averaging operation commutes with differentiation and that

$$\int_\Omega u(x)\, v_\varrho(x)\, dx = \int_\Omega u_\varrho(x)\, v(x)\, dx,$$

provided only that one of the functions is of compact support in Ω and ϱ is less than the distance from its support to S. This gives

$$\begin{aligned}(\mathbf{f}, \boldsymbol{\Phi}) &= \int_{\Omega_1} \mathbf{f}_\varrho \cdot \operatorname{curl}_x [\zeta^2 \mathbf{V}^k(x, y)]\, dx \\ &= \int_{\Omega_1} \{\nu\, \mathbf{v}_{\varrho x_i} \cdot [\operatorname{curl}_x (\zeta^2 \mathbf{V}^k)]_{x_i} - (v_i\, \mathbf{v})_\varrho \cdot \operatorname{curl}_x (\zeta^2 \mathbf{V}^k)_{x_i}\}\, dx.\end{aligned} \tag{31}$$

Using the equation for $\mathbf{u}^k$, we transform the first integral in the right-hand side into

$$\int_{\Omega_1} \nu\, \mathbf{v}_{\varrho x_i} \cdot [\operatorname{curl}_x (\zeta^2 \mathbf{V}^k)]_{x_i}\, dx = \lim_{\varepsilon\to 0} \int_{\substack{\Omega_1\\ |x-y|\geq\varepsilon}} \nu\, \mathbf{v}_{\varrho x_i} \cdot [\operatorname{curl}_x (\zeta^2 \mathbf{V}^k)]_{x_i}\, dx$$

$$= \lim_{\varepsilon\to 0} \int_{\substack{\Omega_1\\ |x-y|\geq\varepsilon}} -\nu\, \mathbf{v}_\varrho \cdot \Delta(\zeta^2 \operatorname{curl}_x \mathbf{V}^k + \operatorname{grad} \zeta^2 \times \mathbf{V}^k)\, dx$$

$$- \lim_{\varepsilon\to 0} \int_{r=|x-y|=\varepsilon} \nu\, \mathbf{v}_\varrho \cdot \frac{\partial}{\partial r} \operatorname{curl} \mathbf{V}^k\, dS = \lim_{\varepsilon\to 0} \Bigg\{ - \int_{\substack{\Omega_1\\ |x-y|\geq\varepsilon}} \mathbf{v}_\varrho \cdot [\zeta^2 \operatorname{grad} q^k$$

$$+ 2\nu(\zeta^2)_{x_i} \mathbf{u}^k_{x_i} + \nu\, \mathbf{u}^k \Delta(\zeta^2) + \nu \Delta(\operatorname{grad} \zeta^2 \times \mathbf{V}^k)]\, dx \Bigg\} - \lim_{\varepsilon\to 0} \int_{r=\varepsilon} \nu\, \mathbf{v}_\varrho \cdot \frac{\partial \mathbf{u}^k}{\partial r}\, dS$$

$$= \int_{\Omega_1} \{\operatorname{div}(\zeta^2 \mathbf{v}_\varrho)\, q^k - \nu\, \mathbf{v}_\varrho \cdot [4\, \zeta \zeta_{x_i} \mathbf{u}^k_{x_i} + \mathbf{u}^k \Delta(\zeta^2) + \Delta(\operatorname{grad} \zeta^2 \times \mathbf{V}^k)]\}\, dx$$

$$- \lim_{\varepsilon\to 0} \int_{r=\varepsilon} \left(\nu\, \mathbf{v}_\varrho \cdot \frac{\partial \mathbf{u}_k}{\partial r} - q^k\, \mathbf{v}_\varrho \cdot \frac{\mathbf{x}-\mathbf{y}}{|x-y|} \right) dS.$$

The last integral gives $v_{k\varrho}(y)$ in the limit, because of the basic property of the solution $\mathbf{u}^k$, q^k, or equivalently, because of equation (1) of Chap. 3. We substitute all this into (31), bearing in mind that $\operatorname{div} \mathbf{v}_\varrho = 0$;

the result is

$$\int_{\Omega_1} \mathbf{f}_\varrho \cdot \operatorname{curl}_x (\zeta^2 \mathbf{V}^k)\, dx = -v_{k\varrho}(y) + \int_{\Omega_1} \nu\, \mathbf{v}_\varrho \cdot \big((1/\nu)\, q^k \operatorname{grad} \zeta^2 - 4\, \zeta\, \zeta_{x_i} \mathbf{u}^k_{x_i}$$
$$- \mathbf{u}^k \Delta(\zeta^2) - \Delta(\operatorname{grad} \zeta^2 \times \mathbf{V}^k)\big)\, dx - \int_{\Omega_1} (v_i \mathbf{v})_\varrho \cdot \operatorname{curl}_x (\zeta^2 \mathbf{V}^k)_{x_i} dx \tag{32}$$

for $y \in \Omega_3$. If we introduce the notation

$$\mathbf{L}_1^k(x, y) = -\operatorname{curl}_x (\zeta^2 \mathbf{V}^k),$$

$$\mathbf{L}_2^k(x, y) = \frac{1}{\nu} q^k \operatorname{grad} \zeta^2 - 4\, \zeta \zeta_{x_i} \mathbf{u}^k_{x_i} - \mathbf{u}^k \Delta(\zeta^2) - \Delta(\operatorname{grad} \zeta^2 \times \mathbf{V}^k),$$

then formula (32) can be written in the form

$$v_{k\varrho}(y) = \nu \int_{\Omega_1} \mathbf{L}_2^k(x, y) \cdot \mathbf{v}_\varrho(x)\, dx$$
$$+ \int_{\Omega_1} \mathbf{L}^k_{1 x_i}(x, y) \cdot (v_i \mathbf{v})_\varrho\, dx + \int_{\Omega_1} \mathbf{L}_1^k(x, y) \cdot \mathbf{f}_\varrho(x)\, dx. \tag{33}$$

We now pass to the limit as $\varrho \to 0$ in (33). One cannot expect convergence for arbitrary y, since all we know about $\mathbf{v}(y)$ is that it belongs to $H(\Omega)$ and hence is summable over Ω_1 with an exponent no greater than 6 (see Chap. 1, Sec. 1). It follows from this and from the property of the averaging operator that $\mathbf{v}_\varrho(y)$ will converge to $\mathbf{v}(y)$ in the $\mathbf{L}_6(\Omega_3)$ norm.

Next, we consider the different integrals in (33). For the kernels $\mathbf{L}_j^k(x, y)$, the estimates

$$|\mathbf{L}_1^k(x, y)| \leqslant \frac{C}{|x-y|}, \quad |\mathbf{L}^k_{1 x_i}(x, y)| \leqslant \frac{C}{|x-y|^2},$$
$$|\mathbf{L}_2^k(x, y)| \leqslant \frac{C}{|x-y|^2} \tag{34}$$

hold for any $x \in \Omega_1$, $y \in \Omega_3$. The densities $\mathbf{f}_\varrho$, $(v_i \mathbf{v})_\varrho$ and $\mathbf{v}_\varrho$ multiplying these kernels are uniformly bounded for any ϱ in the spaces $\mathbf{L}_2(\Omega_2)$, $\mathbf{L}_3(\Omega_2)$ and $\mathbf{L}_6(\Omega_2)$, respectively, and converge in these spaces to the limits $\mathbf{f}$, $v_i \mathbf{v}$ and $\mathbf{v}$, as $\varrho \to 0$. The inequalities (11) and (12) of Chap. 1, Sec. 1, together with the estimates (34), allow us to assert that $\int_{\Omega_1} \mathbf{L}_2^k \cdot \mathbf{v}_\varrho\, dx$ and $\int_{\Omega_1} \mathbf{L}_1^k \cdot \mathbf{f}_\varrho\, dx$ converge to $\int_{\Omega_1} \mathbf{L}_2^k \cdot \mathbf{v}\, dx$ and $\int_{\Omega_1} \mathbf{L}_1^k \cdot \mathbf{f}\, dx$ uniformly in Ω_3, while $\int_{\Omega_1} \mathbf{L}^k_{1 x_i} \cdot (v_i \mathbf{v})_\varrho\, dx$ converges to $\int_{\Omega_1} \mathbf{L}^k_{1 x_i} \cdot v_i \mathbf{v}\, dx$ in the

$\mathbf{L}_q(\Omega_3)$ norm, for any $q < \infty$. Thus, taking the limit $\varrho \to 0$ in (33), we obtain for almost all y

$$v_k(y) = \nu \int_{\Omega_1} \mathbf{L}_2^k(x, y) \cdot \mathbf{v}(x)\, dx$$
$$+ \int_{\Omega_1} \mathbf{L}_{1x_i}^k(x, y) \cdot v_i \mathbf{v}\, dx + \int_{\Omega_1} \mathbf{L}_1^k(x, y) \cdot \mathbf{f}(x)\, dx. \tag{35}$$

Since the right-hand side of this equality is summable over Ω_3 with any finite exponent, it follows that $\mathbf{v}(y) \in \mathbf{L}_q(\Omega_3)$ with any $q < \infty$. The domain Ω_3 is any interior subdomain of the domain Ω_1; similarly, let Ω_4 be any interior subdomain of the domain Ω_3. Then, for $y \in \Omega_4$ and $x \in \Omega_3$, a representation of the form (35) holds, which we denote by $(35)_{4,3}$. In this representation, the integration is carried out over Ω_3, and the same estimates (34) are valid for the kernels $\mathbf{L}_l^k$, but with another constant C. Using (34), we deduce from $(35)_{4,3}$ that $\mathbf{v}(y)$ is a continuous function in Ω_4, and even satisfies a Hölder condition in Ω_4. Thus, by successively making the domains Ω_k smaller, we prove that $\mathbf{v}(y)$ has derivatives of the first and second order, which are square-summable over any interior subdomain $\Omega_k \subset \ldots \subset \Omega_2 \subset \Omega_1$.

If the representation (35) did not contain the term

$$J(y) = \int_{\Omega_1} \mathbf{L}_1^k(x, y) \cdot \mathbf{f}(x)\, dx,$$

corresponding to the external force $\mathbf{f}$, then we could convince ourselves step by step that $\mathbf{v}(y)$ has derivatives of higher and higher order, i.e., that $\mathbf{v}(y)$ is infinitely differentiable. The term J imposes a limit on such an improvement. We now consider the term J in more detail for the case where $\mathbf{f} \in \mathbf{L}_2(\Omega_1)$:

$$J(y) = \int_{\Omega_1} \mathbf{f}(x) \cdot \big(\zeta^2 \operatorname{curl}_x \mathbf{V}^k(x, y)$$
$$+ \operatorname{grad} \zeta^2 \times \mathbf{V}^k(x, y)\big)\, dx \equiv J_1(y) + J_2(y).$$

The integral

$$J_2(y) = \int_{\Omega_1} \mathbf{f}(x) \cdot \operatorname{grad} \zeta^2 \times \mathbf{V}^k(x, y)\, dx$$

has a bounded kernel, can be directly differentiated twice with respect to y, and is square-summable together with its derivatives up to order 2, inclusively, over any bounded domain, because of Lemma 5 of Chap. 1, Sec. 1.

Since $\mathbf{f}\,\zeta^2 \in \mathbf{L}_2(\Omega_1)$, the integral

$$J_1(y) = \int\limits_{\Omega_1} \mathbf{f}\cdot\zeta^2 \operatorname{curl}_x \mathbf{V}^k\,dx = \int\limits_{\Omega_1} \mathbf{f}\cdot\zeta^2\,\mathbf{u}^k\,dx$$

$$= -\frac{1}{4\pi\nu}\int\limits_{\Omega_1}\frac{f_k\,\zeta^2}{|x-y|}\,dx + \frac{1}{8\pi\nu}\frac{\partial^2}{\partial x_j\,\partial x_k}\int\limits_{\Omega_1}|x-y|\,f_j\,\zeta^2\,dx,$$

also has derivatives up to order 2, inclusively, which are square-summable over any bounded domain (see Chap. 1, Sec. 1). The domains Ω_k, $k = 1, 2, \ldots$, are only subject to the condition that each contains the next ($\Omega_1 \supset \Omega_2 \supset \ldots$) and that the distance between their boundaries is positive. Therefore, we have proved that any generalized solution $\mathbf{v}$ has generalized derivatives in Ω_1 up to order 2, inclusively, which are square-summable over any interior subdomain Ω_1' of the domain Ω_1. This implies that $\mathbf{v}$ is continuous inside Ω_1 (Chap. 1, Sec. 1). Moreover, it follows from these considerations that $\mathbf{v}$ satisfies the estimate

$$\|\mathbf{v}\|_{W_2^2(\Omega_2)} \leqslant C\left(\|\mathbf{v}\|^2_{W_2^1(\Omega_1)} + \|\mathbf{f}\|_{\mathbf{L}_2(\Omega_1)}\right). \tag{36}$$

This estimate and the estimates given for $\|\mathbf{v}\|_{W_2^1(\Omega)}$ in the preceding sections imply an estimate for $\|\mathbf{v}\|_{W_2^2(\Omega_2)}$ in terms of nothing but the data of the problem, i.e., $\mathbf{f}$ and the boundary values of $\mathbf{v}$.

If $\mathbf{f}$ satisfies a Hölder condition in Ω_1, then $J(y)$ and hence $\mathbf{v}$ also, has second-order derivatives which satisfy a Hölder condition with the same exponent in $\Omega_2 \subset \Omega_1$. We omit the proof of this assertion, since it is carried out in just the same way as for the Newtonian potential. This completes the proof of Theorem 6, which shows how to investigate the differential properties of a generalized solution inside its domain of existence.

To study the behavior of the solution near the boundary, we can proceed as follows: Let any piece S' of the surface S be a Lyapunov surface. Without loss of generality, we can assume that the boundary values of $\mathbf{v}$ are homogeneous on S'. Let Ω_1 be a small subdomain contained in Ω, whose boundary S_1 is a Lyapunov surface with $S_1 \cap S \in S'$, such that the ϱ-neighborhood of Ω_1 (i. e., the domain $\Omega_{1(\varrho)}$ which is the union of Ω_1 and all balls of radius ϱ with centers in Ω_1) belongs to Ω for all $\varrho \leqslant \varrho_0$, when shifted by $\varrho\,\boldsymbol{l}$, where $\boldsymbol{l}$ is a fixed vector chosen for Ω_1. Let

$$\mathbf{G}_k(x, y) = (G_{k1}(x, y), G_{k2}(x, y), G_{k3}(x, y)), \qquad r_k(x, y)$$

For fixed x, the sum

$$w_i^k(x, y) = u_i^k(x, y) + \tilde{u}_i^k(x, y),$$
$$q^k(x, y) = p^k(x, y) + \tilde{p}^k(x, y)$$

of these two solutions satisfies the system

$$\begin{aligned} \nu \Delta_y w_i^k(x, y) + \frac{\partial q^k(x, y)}{\partial y_i} &= \delta_i^k \, \delta(x - y) \quad (i, k = 1, 2, 3), \\ \frac{\partial w_i^k}{\partial y_i} &= 0, \end{aligned} \tag{39}$$

and the boundary condition

$$w_i^k(x, y)\big|_{y \in |x-y| = R} = 0. \tag{40}$$

Next, we apply Green's formula (10) of Chap. 3, Sec. 2 to $\mathbf{u}(y) = \mathbf{v}(y) - \boldsymbol{\alpha}$, $p(y)$ and $\mathbf{w}^k = (w_1^k, w_2^k, w_3^k)$, q^k as functions of y in the region $|x - y| \leqslant \varrho$, assuming that $|x| > R_0 + 1$ and $\varrho \leqslant 1$. This gives

$$u_k(x) = \int_{|x-y| \leqslant \varrho} w_i^k(x, y) \left(\nu \, \Delta u_i - \frac{\partial p}{\partial y_i}\right) dy + \int_{|x-y| = \varrho} T'_{ij}(\mathbf{w}^k) \, u_i \, n_j \, dS_y,$$

or the formula

$$u_k(x) = \int_{|x-y| \leqslant \varrho} w_i^k(x, y) (u_l + \alpha_l) \, u_{i y_l} \, dy + \int_{|x-y| = \varrho} T'_{ij}(\mathbf{w}^k) \, u_i \, n_j \, dS_y, \tag{41}$$

where

$$T'_{ij}(\mathbf{w}^k) = \delta_i^j q^k + \nu \left(\frac{\partial w_i^k}{\partial y_j} + \frac{\partial w_j^k}{\partial y_i}\right),$$

because of the Navier-Stokes equations for $\mathbf{v}$, p and the fact that $\mathbf{f} \equiv 0$ in $|x - y| \leqslant \varrho$. It follows at once from the form of $\mathbf{w}^k$ and q^k that

$$\begin{aligned} |w_i^k(x, y)| \leqslant \frac{C}{|x - y|}, \quad & |q^k(x, y)|\big|_{|x-y| = \varrho} \leqslant \frac{C}{\varrho^2}, \\ \left|\frac{\partial w_i^k(x, y)}{\partial y_i}\right|\Bigg|_{|x-y| = \varrho} &\leqslant \frac{C}{\varrho^2}. \end{aligned} \tag{42}$$

We now estimate the right-hand side of (41), by using the inequalities (42) and Schwarz' inequality:

$$|u_k(x)| \leqslant C \int\limits_{|x-y|\leqslant \varrho} \sum_{i,l=1}^{3} \frac{|u_l+\alpha_l|\,|u_{iy_l}|}{|x-y|}\,dy + \frac{C}{\varrho^2}\int\limits_{|x-y|=\varrho}\sum_{j=1}^{3}|u_j|\,dS \leqslant C\sum_{i,l=1}^{3}\Bigg(\int\limits_{|x-y|\leqslant\varrho}\frac{|u_l+\alpha_l|^2}{|x-y|^2}\,dy\Bigg)^{1/2} \times\Bigg(\int\limits_{|x-y|\leqslant\varrho} u_{iy_l}^2\,dy\Bigg)^{1/2} + \frac{C}{\varrho^2}\int\limits_{|x-y|=\varrho}\sum_{j=1}^{3}|u_j|\,dS.$$

We integrate both sides of this inequality with respect to ϱ from 1/2 to 1, and bear in mind that

$$\int\limits_{|x-y|\leqslant 1}\frac{|u_l+\alpha_l|^2}{|x-y|^2}\,dy \leqslant \text{const},$$

because of (38); the result is

$$|u_k(x)| \leqslant C_1\Bigg(\int\limits_{|x-y|\leqslant 1}\sum_{i,l=1}^{3} u_{iy_l}^2\,dy\Bigg)^{1/2} + 4C\int\limits_{|x-y|\leqslant 1}\sum_{j=1}^{3}|u_j(y)|\,dy.$$

From this, applying Schwarz' inequality again to the last term, we obtain

$$|u_k(x)| \leqslant C_1\Bigg(\int\limits_{|x-y|\leqslant 1}\sum_{i,l=1}^{3} u_{iy_l}^2\,dy\Bigg)^{1/2} + C_2\Bigg(\int\limits_{|x-y|\leqslant 1}\sum_{j=1}^{3} u_j^6(y)\,dy\Bigg)^{1/6}. \tag{43}$$

The function $\mathbf{u}(x)$ satisfies the inequality (38), from which it immediately follows that the right-hand side of (43) is less than an arbitrarily small $\varepsilon > 0$, provided only that $|x| \gg R_2 \gg 1$. This proves the theorem.

CHAPTER 6

The Nonlinear Nonstationary Problem

1. Statement of the Problem. The Uniqueness Theorem

In this chapter, we study the boundary-value problem for the general system of Navier-Stokes equations

$$\left.\begin{aligned} L\mathbf{v} \equiv \mathbf{v}_t - \nu \Delta \mathbf{v} + v_k \mathbf{v}_{x_k} &= -\operatorname{grad} p + \mathbf{f}(x, t), \\ \operatorname{div} \mathbf{v} = 0, \quad \mathbf{v}|_S = 0, \quad \mathbf{v}|_{t=0} &= \mathbf{a}(x) \end{aligned}\right\} \tag{1}$$

in the domain $Q_T = \Omega \times [0, T]$. The boundary conditions are taken to be homogeneous only in order to simplify matters somewhat. Without loss of generality, we assume that the force $\mathbf{f}$ belongs to $\mathring{J}(\Omega)$, and we incorporate its gradient part in $-\operatorname{grad} p$. Then, the condition $\mathbf{f} \equiv 0$ will mean that the external forces can be derived from a potential. Concerning $\mathbf{a}(x)$, we assume that

$$\operatorname{div} \mathbf{a}(x) = 0, \quad \mathbf{a}|_S = 0. \tag{2}$$

The basic results concerning the solution of the problem (1) are the following: If all the data of the problem are independent of one of the coordinates x_1, x_2, x_3 (i.e., if we are concerned with plane-parallel two-dimensional flows), then the problem has a unique solution "in the large," i.e., at all instants of time, with no restrictions whatsoever on the smallness of $\mathbf{f}$, $\mathbf{a}$ or the domain [38]. The same is true in the three-dimensional problem if there is axial symmetry and if the axis of symmetry does not belong to the domain occupied by the fluid [38]. In the general three-dimensional case, it has been shown that the problem has a unique solution for all $t \geqslant 0$ under the condition that the forces $\mathbf{f}$ are derivable from a potential and that the "generalized Reynolds number" is less than 1 at the initial instant of time. However, if these conditions are not met, then it has been proved only that the problem has a unique solution for a certain time interval $t \in [0, T]$, whose size can be estimated from below, by starting from the data of the problem [39].

These results were preceded by results of Leray and Hopf (concerning which, see the Introduction and the Comments). In Sec. 6, we present Hopf's results, i.e., we prove the existence for all $t \geqslant 0$ of a "weak solution" of the general three-dimensional problem (1). The question of whether a uniqueness theorem holds for "weak solutions," and hence whether such an extension of the concept of solution is justified, remains open.

In Sec. 8, we use the example of the Cauchy problem to show that the "weak solution" has derivatives $\mathbf{v}_t$ and $\mathbf{v}_{x_i x_j}$ which are summable with respect to (x_1, x_2, x_3, t) with exponent 5/4, and that it satisfies the Navier-Stokes system almost everywhere. A similar result is also true for the boundary-value problem. However, even this supplementary information on the weak solution in the general case does not enable us to prove the uniqueness of such a solution. Nevertheless, it is our opinion that the problem (1) has a unique solution "in the large" without any smallness restrictions, even in the general case.

Before becoming involved with precise formulations, we call the reader's attention to the fact that the statement "it has been proved that the problem has a unique solution" can have very different meanings depending on the function space in which one looks for the solution. The form in which the requirements of the problem must be satisfied is different for different spaces, and different extensions of the concept of a solution of a problem, i.e., different "generalized solutions," present themselves. In fact, for every problem there are infinitely many "generalized solutions," and in this book, we select from this set the kind of solution introduced in the paper [39], for which it was first proved that boundary-value problems have unique solutions in the large.

After the publication of [38] and [39], a series of papers appeared (see the Comments) in which generalized solutions in other spaces were considered. For these solutions, the principal results concerning the solvability of the problem (1) are the same as in [38] and [39], and no one has yet succeeded in improving them. In the present book, we have chosen the generalized solutions given in [39], since the basic results on the unique solvability of the problem are most easily proved for such solutions, without recourse to any special branches of functional analysis, and in a way which is uniform for both the two-dimensional and the three-dimensional cases.

The nicest results concerning the way in which the differential properties of the solutions of the problem (1) depend on the differential properties of the data of the problem are obtained in the Hölder spaces. For example, it has been proved that in all the above cases where the problem has a unique solution, the derivatives of the solution which appear in the system are Hölder-continuous inside the domain, and that the solution itself is Hölder-continuous in the closed domain, provided only that $\mathbf{f}$ and $\mathbf{a}$ satisfy a Hölder condition. The proof of these assertions requires rather painstaking and delicate arguments (see the Comments). Consequently, we prefer to begin our study of problems involving solvability in the context of the Hilbert space $\mathbf{L}_2(Q_T)$, just as was done in the linear case. The comparative simplicity of the investigations in this case is explained by the fact that it is just the Hilbert spaces which are organically related to the variational form of the problems of hydrodynamics, and it is in the norms of these spaces that one can express the basic law of energy dissipation and the other laws obeyed by moving fluids (see Lemmas 1—6). In other words, the basic a priori estimates on which our entire study is based are stated in terms of the norms of these spaces.

We now begin our study of the problem (1): We define a *generalized solution of the problem* (1)* in the domain $Q_T = \Omega \times [0, T]$ to be the vector function $\mathbf{v}(x, t)$ for which the integrals

$$\int_\Omega \sum_{k=1}^{3} v_k^4(x, t)\, dx$$

are bounded for all $t \in [0, T]$ by the same constant C_T, and for which the derivatives $\mathbf{v}_{x_k}$, $\mathbf{v}_t$ exist and are square-summable over Q_T, and which satisfies the conditions

$$\operatorname{div} \mathbf{v} = 0, \quad \mathbf{v}|_S = 0, \quad \mathbf{v}|_{t=0} = \mathbf{a}(x) \tag{3}$$

and the identity

$$\int_0^T \int_\Omega (\mathbf{v}_t \cdot \mathbf{\Phi} + \nu\, \mathbf{v}_{x_k} \cdot \mathbf{\Phi}_{x_k} - v_k \mathbf{v} \cdot \mathbf{\Phi}_{x_k} - \mathbf{f} \cdot \mathbf{\Phi})\, dx\, dt = 0 \tag{4}$$

for all possible $\mathbf{\Phi}(x, t)$ in $\mathbf{L}_2(Q_T)$ with

$$\mathbf{\Phi}_{x_k} \in \mathbf{L}_2(Q_T), \quad \operatorname{div} \mathbf{\Phi} = 0, \quad \mathbf{\Phi}|_S = 0.$$

The fact that the classical solution is a generalized solution in this sense is easily proved. To do so, it is sufficient to carry out integration

* In the paper [39], in Sec. 6 of this chapter, and in the Comments, we also give other definitions of generalized solutions, and we prove uniqueness theorems for them.

by parts in the identity

$$\int_0^T \int_\Omega (\mathbf{v}_t - \nu \Delta \mathbf{v} + v_k \mathbf{v}_{x_k} + \operatorname{grad} p - \mathbf{f}) \cdot \boldsymbol{\Phi} \, dx \, dt = 0$$

while taking into account (3) and the fact that grad p and $\boldsymbol{\Phi}$ are orthogonal. The identity obtained in this way coincides with (4). The converse is also true. More precisely, if $\mathbf{v}(x, t)$ is a generalized solution and if, in addition, it has derivatives $\mathbf{v}_{x_k x_l}$ in $\mathbf{L}_2(\Omega' \times [0, T])$, where Ω' is any interior subdomain of Ω, then $\mathbf{v}(x, t)$ satisfies the system (1) almost everywhere. In fact, taking $\boldsymbol{\Phi}$ to be 0 near the lateral surface of the cylinder Q_T, we can use integration by parts to reduce (4) to the identity

$$\int_0^T \int_\Omega (\mathbf{v}_t - \nu \Delta \mathbf{v} + v_k \mathbf{v}_{x_k} - \mathbf{f}) \cdot \boldsymbol{\Phi} \, dx \, dt = 0 .$$

It then follows from Theorem 1 of Chap. 1, Sec. 2 that the expression in parentheses is the gradient of some function, which, except possibly for sign, coincides with the pressure p.

The uniqueness theorem holds for classical solutions. We now show that this theorem also holds for a wider class of functions, i.e., for the generalized solutions just defined.

THEOREM 1. *The problem* (1) *has no more than one generalized solution.*

Proof: Let $\mathbf{v}$ and $\mathbf{v}'$ be two generalized solutions of the problem (1), and subtract from the identity (4) for $\mathbf{v}$ the same identity for $\mathbf{v}'$. Then in the equality so obtained, we set

$$\boldsymbol{\Phi} = \begin{cases} \mathbf{v} - \mathbf{v}' \equiv \mathbf{u}, & 0 \leqslant t \leqslant t_1, \\ 0, & t_1 \leqslant t \leqslant T, \end{cases}$$

and as a result we have

$$\int_0^{t_1} \int_\Omega [\mathbf{u}_t \cdot \mathbf{u} + \nu \mathbf{u}_{x_k} \cdot \mathbf{u}_{x_k} - (u_k \mathbf{v}' + v_k \mathbf{u}) \cdot \mathbf{u}_{x_k}] \, dx \, dt = 0 .$$

This equality can be transformed into

$$\frac{1}{2} \| \mathbf{u}(x, t_1) \|^2 + \nu \int_0^{t_1} \sum_{k=1}^3 \| \mathbf{u}_{x_k} \|^2 \, dt - \int_0^{t_1} \int_\Omega u_k \mathbf{v}' \cdot \mathbf{u}_{x_k} \, dx \, dt = 0, \qquad (5)$$

if we bear in mind that div $\mathbf{v} = 0$. To estimate the last term, we use the inequality (5) of Chap. 1, Sec. 1 and the fact that

$$\int_\Omega \sum_{k=1}^3 (v_k'(x, t))^4 \, dx \leqslant C_T .$$

If we write

$$\varphi^2(t) = \int_\Omega \sum_{k=1}^{3} \mathbf{u}_{x_k}^2(x, t)\, dx,$$

then

$$\left| \int_\Omega u_k \mathbf{v}' \cdot \mathbf{u}_{x_k} dx \right|$$

$$\leqslant \sqrt{3}\, \varphi(t) \left(\int_\Omega \sum_{k=1}^{3} u_k^4\, dx \right)^{1/4} \left(\int_\Omega \sum_{k=1}^{3} (v_k')^4\, dx \right)^{1/4}$$

$$\leqslant \sqrt{3}\, C_T^{1/4} \varphi(t) \left[\varepsilon\, \varphi(t) + C_\varepsilon \left(\int_\Omega \mathbf{u}^2\, dx \right)^{1/2} \right]$$

$$\leqslant 2 \sqrt{3}\, C_T^{1/4} \varepsilon\, \varphi^2(t) + \frac{\sqrt{3}\, C_T^{1/4} C_\varepsilon^2}{4\varepsilon} \| \mathbf{u} \|^2.$$

This estimate allows us to derive the inequality

$$\frac{1}{2} \| \mathbf{u}(x, t_1) \|^2 + \nu \int_0^{t_1} \varphi^2(t)\, dt \leqslant C_1 \int_0^{t_1} \left[2\,\varepsilon\, \varphi^2(t) + \frac{C_\varepsilon^2}{4\,\varepsilon} \| \mathbf{u} \|^2 \right] dt$$

from (5), where $C_1 = \sqrt{3}\, C_T^{1/4}$.

If we set $\varepsilon = \nu / 2 C_1$, then

$$\frac{1}{2} \| \mathbf{u}(x, t_1) \|^2 \leqslant C_2 \int_0^{t_1} \| \mathbf{u} \|^2 dt.$$

Writing

$$\int_0^{t_1} \| \mathbf{u} \|^2 dt = y(t_1),$$

we can transform the last inequality into

$$\frac{dy(t_1)}{dt_1} \leqslant 2\, C_2\, y(t_1),$$

or equivalently, into

$$\frac{d}{dt_1} \left(e^{-2C_2 t_1} y(t_1) \right) \leqslant 0. \tag{6}$$

The number t_1 is arbitrary in $[0, T]$, and hence, bearing in mind that $y(t_1)$ is nonnegative and that $y(0) = 0$, we conclude from (6) that $y(t) \equiv 0$, i.e., that the solutions $\mathbf{v}$ and $\mathbf{v}'$ coincide. This proves the theorem.

For the case of plane-parallel flows, there is a uniqueness theorem for the "weak solution" (Hopf's solution; see Sec. 6). This is because of the inequality (1) of Chap. 1 for functions of two independent variables.

2. A Priori Estimates

Suppose that the solution of the system (1) has generalized derivatives of the form $\mathbf{v}_{t\,x_k\,x_l}$ and of all lower orders (from which $\mathbf{v}_{t\,x_k\,x_l}$ can be obtained), belonging to $\mathbf{L}_2(Q_T)$. Then, $\mathbf{v}$ satisfies the two equalities

$$(\mathbf{f}, \mathbf{v}) = \frac{1}{2}\frac{d}{dt}\|\mathbf{v}\|^2 + \nu \sum_{k=1}^{3} \|\mathbf{v}_{x_k}\|^2 \tag{7}$$

and

$$(\mathbf{f}_t, \mathbf{v}_t) = \frac{1}{2}\frac{d}{dt}\|\mathbf{v}_t\|^2 + \nu \sum_{k=1}^{3} \|\mathbf{v}_{tx_k}\|^2 + \int_\Omega v_{k\,t}\,\mathbf{v}_{x_k}\cdot\mathbf{v}_t\,dx, \tag{8}$$

which are derived from

$$\int_\Omega L\,\mathbf{v}\cdot\mathbf{v}\,dx = \int_\Omega (-\operatorname{grad} p + \mathbf{f})\cdot\mathbf{v}\,dx = \int_\Omega \mathbf{f}\cdot\mathbf{v}\,dx,$$

$$\int_\Omega (L\,\mathbf{v})_t\cdot\mathbf{v}_t\,dx = \int_\Omega (-\operatorname{grad} p_t + \mathbf{f}_t)\cdot\mathbf{v}_t\,dx = \int_\Omega \mathbf{f}_t\cdot\mathbf{v}_t\,dx$$

by integrating by parts and bearing in mind that $\operatorname{div}\mathbf{v} = 0$, $\mathbf{v}|_S = 0$. We now introduce the notation

$$\varphi^2(t) = \sum_{k=1}^{3} \|\mathbf{v}_{x_k}(x, t)\|^2,$$

$$\psi^2(t) = \|\mathbf{v}_t(x, t\|^2,$$

$$F^2(t) = \sum_{k=1}^{3} \|\mathbf{v}_{tx_k}(x, t)\|^2,$$

where $\|\ \|$, as always, is the $\mathbf{L}_2(\Omega)$ norm, i.e.,

$$\|\mathbf{u}(x, t)\| = \Big(\int_\Omega \mathbf{u}^2(x, t)\,dx\Big)^{1/2}.$$

Then, for the function $\mathbf{v}$, we obtain a series of estimates, where instead of assuming that $\mathbf{v}$ must be a solution of the problem (1), we only use the following properties of $\mathbf{v}$:

I. The functions $\varphi(t)$, $F(t)$ and $(d/dt)\,\psi^2(t)$ involving $\mathbf{v}$ exist for $t \in [0, T]$, where $\varphi(t)$ and $\psi(t)$ are absolutely continuous, and $F^2(t)$ and $(d/dt)\,\psi^2(t)$ are summable over $[0, T]$.

II. The function $\mathbf{v}$ satisfies the relations (7) and (8), and $\mathbf{v}(x, 0) = \mathbf{a}(x)$.

First, we have the following lemma, which generalizes somewhat the familiar energy conservation law:

LEMMA 1. *If the function* $\mathbf{v}$ *meets the conditions* I *and* II, *then it satisfies the estimates*

$$\| \mathbf{v}(x, t) \| \leqslant \| \mathbf{a}(x) \| + \int_0^t \| \mathbf{f}(x, \tau) \| \, d\tau \tag{9}$$

and

$$\begin{aligned} &\| \mathbf{v}(x, t) \|^2 + 2\nu \int_0^t \varphi^2(\tau)\, d\tau \\ &\qquad \leqslant \| \mathbf{a}(x) \|^2 + 2 \| \mathbf{a}(x) \| \int_0^t \| \mathbf{f}(x, \tau) \| \, d\tau \\ &\qquad + 2 \left(\int_0^t \| \mathbf{f}(x, \tau) \| \, d\tau \right)^2 \equiv A(t). \end{aligned} \tag{10}$$

Proof: Both estimates are easily deduced from formula (7). In fact, according to (7), we have

$$\| \mathbf{v} \| \frac{d}{dt} \| \mathbf{v} \| \leqslant \| \mathbf{f} \| \| \mathbf{v} \|,$$

so that either $\| \mathbf{v}(x, t) \| = 0$ or $\dfrac{d}{dt} \| \mathbf{v}(x, t) \| \leqslant \| \mathbf{f}(x, t) \|$. But $\| \mathbf{v}(x, t) \|$. is a continuous function of t, and hence these relations imply that

$$\| \mathbf{v}(x, t) \| \leqslant \| \mathbf{a}(x) \| + \int_0^t \| f(x, \tau) \| \, dt.$$

Moreover, integrating (7) with respect to t from 0 to t, we obtain

$$\frac{1}{2} \| \mathbf{v}(x, t) \|^2 - \frac{1}{2} \| \mathbf{v}(x, 0) \|^2 + \nu \int_0^t \varphi^2(\tau)\, d\tau = \int_0^t (\mathbf{f}, \mathbf{v})\, dt,$$

which, because of Schwarz' inequality and the estimate just obtained for $\| \mathbf{v}(x, t) \|$, gives the estimate (10):

$$\begin{aligned} \| \mathbf{v}(x, t) \|^2 + 2\nu \int_0^t \varphi^2(\tau)\, d\tau &\leqslant \| \mathbf{a} \|^2 + 2 \int_0^t \| \mathbf{f} \| \| \mathbf{v} \| \, dt \\ &\leqslant \| \mathbf{a} \|^2 + 2 \int_0^t \| \mathbf{f} \| \left(\| \mathbf{a} \| + \int_0^\tau \| \mathbf{f} \| \, d\tau \right) dt \\ &\leqslant \| \mathbf{a} \|^2 + 2 \| \mathbf{a} \| \int_0^t \| \mathbf{f} \| \, dt + 2 \left(\int_0^t \| \mathbf{f} \| \, dt \right)^2. \end{aligned}$$

This proves the lemma.

To prove the lemmas which follow, we use the inequalities

$$\left(\int_\Omega u^4\,dx\right)^{1/4} \leqslant C_\Omega \left(\int_\Omega \sum_{k=1}^{3} u_{x_k}^2\,dx\right)^{1/2}, \quad u|_S = 0 \tag{11}$$

and

$$\left(\int_\Omega u^4\,dx\right)^{1/4} \leqslant C_\varepsilon \left(\int_\Omega u^2\,dx\right)^{1/2} + \varepsilon \left(\int_\Omega \sum_{k=1}^{3} u_{x_k}^2\,dx\right)^{1/2}, \tag{12}$$

given in Chap. 1, Sec. 1, valid for any functions $\mathbf{u} \in \mathring{W}_2^1(\Omega)$ and any $\varepsilon > 0$. In general, the constant C_Ω appearing in the first inequality grows without limit as the domain Ω is made larger and larger. However, the constant C_ε does not depend on the size of Ω, but approaches infinity as $\varepsilon \to 0$.

Now let Ω be such that the inequality (11) holds with $C_\Omega < \infty$. Then we have the following lemma:

LEMMA 2. *If* $\mathbf{v}$ *satisfies the conditions* I *and* II, *if*

$$\nu - \beta \sqrt{\frac{\|\mathbf{a}\|\;\|\mathbf{v}_t(x, 0)\|}{\nu}} = \gamma > 0, \quad \beta = \sqrt{3}\, C_\Omega^2, \tag{13}$$

and if $(\mathbf{f}, \mathbf{v}) = (\mathbf{f}_t, \mathbf{v}_t) = 0$, *then the estimates*

$$\varphi^2(t) \leqslant \frac{1}{\nu}\|\mathbf{a}\|\,\|\mathbf{v}_t(x, 0)\|,$$

$$\|\mathbf{v}_t(x, t)\|^2 + 2\gamma \int_0^t F^2(\tau)\,d\tau \leqslant \|\mathbf{v}_t(x, 0)\|^2 \tag{14}$$

hold for all $t \geqslant 0$.

Proof: To prove this lemma, we use the equalities (7) and (8). We estimate the last term in (8) by using Hölder's inequality and the inequality (11):

$$|J| = \left|\int_\Omega v_{kt}\,\mathbf{v}_{x_k} \cdot \mathbf{v}_t\,dx\right| \leqslant \left\{\int_\Omega \sum_{k,l=1}^{3} (v_{kt} v_{lt})^2\,dx\right\}^{1/2}$$

$$\times \left\{\int_\Omega \sum_{k,l=1}^{3} v_{lx_k}^2\,dx\right\}^{1/2} \leqslant \sqrt{3}\,\varphi(t) \left\{\int_\Omega \sum_{l=1}^{3} v_{lt}^4\,dx\right\}^{1/2}$$

$$\leqslant \beta \sum_{k=1}^{3} \|\mathbf{v}_{tx_k}\|^2 \varphi(t) = \beta\,\varphi(t)\,F^2(t).$$

Then it follows from the relation (8) that

$$\frac{1}{2}\frac{d}{dt}\|\mathbf{v}_t\|^2 + (\nu - \beta\,\varphi(t))\,F^2(t) \leqslant 0. \tag{15}$$

On the other hand, the equality (7) gives

$$\nu\,\varphi^2(t) = -\frac{1}{2}\frac{d}{dt}\|\mathbf{v}\|^2 = -\int_\Omega \mathbf{v}\cdot\mathbf{v}_t\,dx \leqslant \|\mathbf{v}(x,t)\|\,\|\mathbf{v}_t(x,t)\|$$

and

$$\|\mathbf{v}(x,t)\| \leqslant \|\mathbf{a}\|,$$

so that

$$\varphi(t) \leqslant \frac{1}{\sqrt{\nu}}\sqrt{\|\mathbf{a}\|\,\|\mathbf{v}_t(x,t)\|}\,. \tag{16}$$

Because of (13) and (16), we have

$$\nu - \beta\,\varphi(0) \geqslant \nu - \beta\frac{1}{\sqrt{\nu}}\sqrt{\|\mathbf{a}\|\,\|\mathbf{v}_t(x,0)\|} = \gamma > 0$$

at the initial instant of time. Since the function $\nu - \beta\,\varphi(t)$ is continuous for $t \geqslant 0$ and positive at the point $t = 0$, there are two possibilities: Either $\nu - \beta\varphi(t)$ is positive for all $t \geqslant 0$, or else there exists a $T > 0$ such that $\nu - \beta\varphi(t)$ is positive for $t < T$, but vanishes for $t = T$. We now show that the second case is impossible. In fact, if

$$\nu - \beta\,\varphi(t) > 0$$

for $t \in [0, T)$, then it follows from (15) that $(d/dt)\,\|\mathbf{v}_t\|^2 \leqslant 0$ for such t, i.e.,

$$\|\mathbf{v}_t(x,t)\| \leqslant \|\mathbf{v}_t(x,0)\|.$$

But then from (16), we have

$$\varphi(t) \leqslant \frac{1}{\sqrt{\nu}}\sqrt{\|\mathbf{a}\|\,\|\mathbf{v}_t(x,0)\|}\,. \tag{17}$$

Because of the continuity of $\varphi(t)$, this inequality is also valid for $t = T$, and hence

$$\nu - \beta\varphi(T) \geqslant \nu - \frac{\beta}{\sqrt{\nu}}\sqrt{\|\mathbf{a}\|\,\|\mathbf{v}_t(x,0)\|} = \gamma > 0. \tag{18}$$

But this contradicts our assumption that $\nu - \beta\varphi(T) = 0$, and thus, the inequality $\nu - \beta\varphi(t) > 0$ holds for all $t \geqslant 0$. In this case, the inequalities (17) and (18) hold for all $t \geqslant 0$, as well as

$$\frac{1}{2}\frac{d}{dt}\|\mathbf{v}_t\|^2 + \gamma\,F^2\,(t) \leqslant 0$$

(because of (15)). This implies

$$\| \mathbf{v}_t(x,t) \|^2 + 2\gamma \int_0^t F^2(\tau)\, d\tau \leqslant \| \mathbf{v}_t(x,0) \|^2,$$

and the lemma is proved.

In the two lemmas that follow, the domain Ω can be either bounded or unbounded:

Lemma 3. *If* $\mathbf{v}$ *satisfies the conditions* I *and* II, *and if*

$$A^2 = \left(\| \mathbf{a} \| + \int_0^T \| \mathbf{f} \|\, dt \right) \times \left(\max_{0 \leqslant t \leqslant T} \| \mathbf{f} \| + \| \mathbf{v}_t(x,0) \| + \int_0^T \| \mathbf{f}_t \|\, dt \right) < \frac{\nu^3}{\beta^2}, \tag{19}$$

then the following estimate holds for $t \in [0, T]$:

$$\int_0^T F^2(t)\, dt \leqslant \frac{\sqrt{\nu}}{\nu^{3/2} - \beta A} \left[\int_0^T \| f_t \| \left(\| \mathbf{v}_t(x,0) \| + \int_0^T \| \mathbf{f}_t \|\, d\tau \right) dt + \frac{1}{2} \| \mathbf{v}_t(x,0) \|^2 \right] \equiv C_3. \tag{20}$$

Proof: First of all, we take account of the fact that the relation (7) implies the inequality (9) and the inequality

$$\begin{aligned} \nu \varphi^2(t) &\leqslant (\| \mathbf{f}(x,t) \| + \| \mathbf{v}_t(x,t) \|)\, \| \mathbf{v}(x,t) \| \\ &\leqslant (\| \mathbf{f}(x,t) \| + \| \mathbf{v}_t(x,t) \|) \left(\| \mathbf{a} \| + \int_0^t \| \mathbf{f} \|\, dt \right). \end{aligned} \tag{21}$$

On the other hand, the relation (8) and the estimate for J obtained above imply that

$$\begin{aligned} (\nu - \beta \varphi(t))\, F^2(t) &\leqslant \| \mathbf{f}_t \| \| \mathbf{v}_t \| - \frac{1}{2} \frac{d}{dt} \| \mathbf{v}_t \|^2 \\ &= \| \mathbf{v}_t \| \left(\| \mathbf{f}_t \| - \frac{d}{dt} \| \mathbf{v}_t \| \right), \end{aligned}$$

from which, because of (21), we have

$$B(t)\, F^2(t) \leqslant \| \mathbf{v}_t(x,t) \| \left(\| \mathbf{f}_t(x,t) \| - \frac{d}{dt} \| \mathbf{v}_t \| \right), \tag{22}$$

where

$$B(t) = \nu - \frac{\beta}{\sqrt{\nu}} \left(\max_{0 \leqslant \tau \leqslant t} (\| \mathbf{f}(x, \tau) \| + \| \mathbf{v}_\tau (x, \tau) \|)^{1/2} \right) \times \left(\| \mathbf{a} \| + \int_0^t \| \mathbf{f} \| \, d\tau \right)^{1/2}.$$

It follows from the condition (19) that $B(0) > 0$. The function $B(t)$ is continuous for $t \geqslant 0$, and falls off monotonically as t increases.

We now estimate from below the interval $0 \leqslant t \leqslant T_1$ for which the inequality $B(t) > 0$ is preserved. Let $B(t) > 0$ for $t \in [0, T_1]$, and let $B(T_1) = 0$. Then, for $t \in [0, T_1]$, we have

$$0 \leqslant \| \mathbf{v}_t(x, t) \| \left(\| \mathbf{f}_t(x, t) \| - \frac{d}{dt} \| \mathbf{v}_t(x, t) \| \right),$$

because of (22), which implies that

$$\| \mathbf{v}_t(x, t) \| \leqslant \| \mathbf{v}_t(x, 0) \| + \int_0^t \| \mathbf{f}_t \| \, dt. \tag{23}$$

Therefore,

$$B(t) \geqslant \nu - \frac{\beta}{\sqrt{\nu}} \left(\max_{0 \leqslant \tau \leqslant t} \| \mathbf{f} \| + \| \mathbf{v}_t(x, 0) \| + \int_0^t \| \mathbf{f}_t \| \, dt \right)^{1/2} \times \left(\| \mathbf{a} \| + \int_0^t \| \mathbf{f} \| \, dt \right)^{1/2} \tag{24}$$

for $t \in [0, T_1]$. If now we take account of the condition (19), which can be written in the form

$$\nu - \beta \nu^{-1/2} A > 0,$$

then from (24) we obtain

$$B(T) \geqslant \nu - \beta \nu^{-1/2} A > 0.$$

On the other hand, $B(T_1) = 0$ and $B(t)$ is a monotonically decreasing function of t, and hence $T_1 > T$. Thus, we have established that

$$B(t) \geqslant \nu - \beta \nu^{-1/2} A > 0$$

for $t \in [0, T]$. Therefore, it follows from (23) and (22) that

$$\frac{1}{2} \| \mathbf{v}_t \|^2 \Big|_{t=0}^{t=t} + \left(\nu - \beta \nu^{-1/2} A \right) \int_0^t F^2(\tau) \, d\tau$$

$$\leqslant \int_0^t \| \mathbf{f}_t \| \, \| \mathbf{v}_t \| \, dt \leqslant \int_0^t \| \mathbf{f}_t \| \left(\| \mathbf{v}_t(x, 0) \| + \int_0^t \| \mathbf{f}_t \| \, d\tau \right) dt$$

for $t \in [0, T]$, and Lemma 3 follows from these inequalities.

Next, we consider the general case where no restrictions whatsoever are imposed on the size of the initial perturbation and **f**. Thus, we show that the following lemma is valid:

LEMMA 4. *If* v *satisfies the conditions* I *and* II, *then there exists a positive number* $T \leqslant T_1$ *such that for* $0 \leqslant t \leqslant T$ *the estimates*

$$\int_0^T F^2(t)\, dt \leqslant C \text{ and } \| \mathbf{v}_t(x, t) \| \leqslant C_5, \tag{25}$$

hold, where the quantities T, C_4 *and* C_5 *are determined by the data of the problem, i.e., by* ν, $\varphi(0)$, $\|\mathbf{v}_t(x, 0)\|$ *and* $\int_0^{T_1} \|\mathbf{f}_t\|\, dt$. *The domain* Ω *can also be unbounded.*

Proof: We take three positive numbers k, γ, ε such that

$$\nu - 2\sqrt{3}\,\varepsilon^2 [\varphi(0) + k] \geqslant \frac{\gamma}{2} > 0, \tag{26}$$

and we denote by T the smallest value of t for which

$$\varphi(t) = \varphi(0) + k. \tag{27}$$

Obviously, it is sufficient to consider only the case where such a T exists and is finite. Next, we consider the equality (8), and we use (12) to estimate the last nonlinear term in (8), where in (12), we fix ε in the way indicated in (26). The result is

$$\begin{aligned} |J| &\leqslant \sqrt{3}\,\varphi(t) \sqrt{\int_\Omega \sum_{k=1}^{3} v_{kt}^4\, dx} \\ &\leqslant 2\sqrt{3}\,\varphi(t)\, [C_\varepsilon^2 \| \mathbf{v}_t \|^2 + \varepsilon^2 F^2(t)]. \end{aligned}$$

Writing $2\sqrt{3}\, C_\varepsilon^2 = C_6$ and substituting the resulting estimate into (8), we obtain

$$\begin{aligned} &\frac{1}{2}\frac{d}{dt}\| \mathbf{v}_t \|^2 + \left(\nu - 2\sqrt{3}\,\varepsilon^2 \varphi(t)\right) F^2(t) \\ &\qquad \leqslant C_6\, \varphi(t) \| \mathbf{v}_t \|^2 + \| \mathbf{f}_t \| \| \mathbf{v}_t \|. \end{aligned}$$

Because of the assumptions (26) and (27), it follows from this inequality that

$$\begin{aligned} \frac{1}{2}\frac{d}{dt}\| \mathbf{v}_t \|^2 + \frac{\gamma}{2} F^2(t) &\leqslant C_6\, [\varphi(0) + k] \| \mathbf{v}_t \|^2 + \| \mathbf{f}_t \| \| \mathbf{v}_t \| \\ &\equiv C_7 \| \mathbf{v}_t \|^2 + \| \mathbf{f}_t \| \| \mathbf{v}_t \| \end{aligned} \tag{28}$$

for $t \leqslant T$. From this, by a familiar method, we deduce estimates for $\|\mathbf{v}_t\|$ and $F(t)$, i.e., we first drop the nonnegative term $(\gamma/2)\, F^2(t)$ in the left-hand side of (28), obtaining

$$\|\mathbf{v}_t\| \left[\frac{d}{dt}\|\mathbf{v}_t\| - C_7 \|\mathbf{v}_t\|\right] \leqslant \|\mathbf{f}_t\| \|\mathbf{v}_t\|,$$

from which we easily conclude that

$$\begin{aligned} \|\mathbf{v}_t(x,t)\| &\leqslant e^{C_7 t}\left[\|\mathbf{v}_t(x,0)\| + \int_0^t e^{-C_7\tau}\|\mathbf{f}_\tau(x,\tau)\|\,d\tau\right] \\ &\equiv D(t) \leqslant D(T) \equiv C_5. \end{aligned} \tag{29}$$

We now return to the inequality (28). Integrating (28) with respect to t from 0 to T, dropping the nonnegative term $\|\mathbf{v}_t(x, T)\|^2$ in the left-hand side of (28), and dividing the resulting inequality by $\gamma/2$, we find that

$$\begin{aligned} \int_0^T F^2(t)\,dt \leqslant \frac{1}{\gamma}\Big[&\|\mathbf{v}_t(x,0)\|^2 + 2\,C_7\,TD^2(T) \\ &+ 2\,D(T)\int_0^T \|\mathbf{f}_t\|\,dt\Big] \equiv C_4. \end{aligned}$$

On the other hand,

$$\frac{1}{2}\frac{d}{dt}\varphi^2(t) = \varphi(t)\,\varphi_t(t) \leqslant \varphi(t)\,F(t),$$

because of the definition of φ and F, and therefore

$$\left|\int_0^t \varphi_t(\tau)\,d\tau\right| = |\varphi(t) - \varphi(0)| \leqslant \int_0^t F(\tau)\,d\tau \leqslant \sqrt{t\int_0^t F^2(\tau)\,d\tau}.$$

From this and from the estimate obtained for F, we have

$$\varphi(0) + k = \varphi(T) \leqslant \varphi(0) + \sqrt{T\int_0^T F^2(t)\,dt} \leqslant \varphi(0) + \sqrt{C_4\,T},$$

and this inequality gives a lower bound for T, i.e.,

$$C_4 T \geqslant k^2 > 0,$$

which concludes the proof of Lemma 4.

We now show that in the case of plane-parallel flow, we can estimate

$$\int_0^t \int_\Omega \sum_{k=1}^2 \mathbf{v}_{tx_k}^2\,(x_1, x_2, t)\,dx_1\,dx_2\,dt$$

for all $t \geqslant 0$, without any restrictions whatsoever on the size of the initial perturbation. Thus, suppose that all the data of the problem are independent of x_3, and suppose that $f_3 = v_3 \equiv 0$. Let Ω denote the domain of the space of points $x = (x_1, x_2)$ in which the solution is being studied, and let S denote the boundary of Ω. This time, the Navier-Stokes system consists of three equations for $\mathbf{v} = (v_1, v_2)$ and p. We retain the same notation $\| \; \|$, φ, ψ, F for the various integrals, and merely bear in mind that the integration with respect to x is now over the two-dimensional domain Ω. Obviously, the estimates (9) and (10) in Lemma 1 are also valid in the present case. Instead of the other lemmas, we now prove the following lemma:

LEMMA 5. *If the vector function* $\mathbf{v} = (v_1(x_1, x_2, t), v_2(x_1, x_2, t))$ *satisfies the inequalities* (9), (10) *and the equality* (8), *and if the integrals*

$$\int_\Omega [\mathbf{v}^2(x, 0) + \mathbf{v}_t^2(x, 0)]\, dx \quad \text{and} \quad \int_0^t \left[\int_\Omega (\mathbf{f}^2 + \mathbf{f}_t^2)\, dx\right]^{1/2} dt$$

are bounded, then the estimates

$$\psi(t) \leqslant \exp\left[\frac{1}{\nu^2} A(t)\right]\left[\psi(0) + \int_0^t \|\mathbf{f}_t\|\, dt\right], \tag{30}$$

$$\nu \int_0^t F^2(\tau)\, d\tau \leqslant \psi^2(0)$$
$$+ 2\left[\int_0^t \|\mathbf{f}_t\|\, dt\right] \exp\left[\frac{1}{\nu^2} A(t)\right]\left[\psi(0) + \int_0^t \|\mathbf{f}_t\|\, dt\right]$$
$$+ \frac{2}{\nu^2} A(t) \exp\left[\frac{2}{\nu^2} A(t)\right]\left[\psi(0) + \int_0^t \|\mathbf{f}_t\|\, dt\right]^2 \tag{31}$$

hold for $\mathbf{v}$, *where*

$$A(t) = \|\mathbf{a}(x)\|^2 + 2\|\mathbf{a}(x)\| \int_0^t \|\mathbf{f}\|\, dt + 2\left[\left(\int_0^t \|\mathbf{f}\|\, dt\right)\right]^2.$$

Proof: We estimate the nonlinear term

$$J(t) = \int_\Omega \sum_{k,l=1}^2 v_{kt}\, v_{lx_k}\, v_{lt}\, dx_1\, dx_2$$

in the equality (8), by using Hölder's inequality and the inequality (1) of Chap. 1, Sec. 1, which is valid for any of the functions v_{kt}:

$$|J(t)| \leqslant \varphi(t)\left[\int_\Omega \sum_{k,l=1}^2 v_{kt}^2\, v_{lt}^2\, dx\right]^{1/2} \leqslant 2\,\varphi(t)\,\psi(t)\,F(t).$$

Because of this, it follows from the equality (8) that

$$\frac{d}{dt}\psi^2(t) + 2\nu F^2(t) \leqslant 2\|\mathbf{f}_t\|\psi(t) + 4\varphi(t)\psi(t)F(t)$$
$$\leqslant 2\|\mathbf{f}_t\|\psi(t) + \frac{4}{\nu}\varphi^2(t)\psi^2(t) + \nu F^2(t),$$

and therefore

$$\frac{d}{dt}\psi^2(t) + \nu F^2(t) \leqslant 2\psi(t)\|\mathbf{f}_t\| + \frac{4}{\nu}\varphi^2(t)\psi^2(t). \tag{32}$$

From this, in the usual way, we deduce the estimates (30) and (31). In fact, dropping the term $\nu F^2(t)$ in the left-hand side of (32) and multiplying both sides of (32) by

$$\exp\left[-\frac{2}{\nu}\int_0^t \varphi^2(\tau)\,d\tau\right],$$

we obtain

$$\begin{aligned}\psi(t)\frac{d}{dt}&\left[\psi(t)\exp\left(-\frac{2}{\nu}\int_0^t \varphi^2(\tau)\,d\tau\right)\right]\\ &\leqslant \psi(t)\|\mathbf{f}_t\|\exp\left(-\frac{2}{\nu}\int_0^t \varphi^2(\tau)\,d\tau\right).\end{aligned} \tag{33}$$

The function $\psi(t)$ depends continuously on t, and hence it follows from (33) that

$$\psi(t)\exp\left[-\frac{2}{\nu}\int_0^t \varphi^2(\tau)\,d\tau\right] - \psi(0)$$
$$\leqslant \int_0^t \|\mathbf{f}_t\|\exp\left[-\frac{2}{\nu}\int_0^t \varphi^2(\tau)\,d\tau\right]dt.$$

This inequality and (10) imply the inequality (30). Integrating (32) with respect to t and dropping $\psi^2(t)$ in the left-hand side, we obtain (31). This proves the lemma.

We now assume that Ω is a domain in the space E_3, and that Ω is obtained by rotation about the x_3-axis of a planar domain D which lies in the half-plane ($x_2 = 0$, $x_1 > 0$), at a positive distance δ from the x_3-axis. For such domains, the following lemma is valid:

LEMMA 6. *If none of the functions under consideration depends on the angle of rotation about the x_3-axis, if $\mathbf{v} = (v_1, (x_1, x_2, x_3, t), v_2, v_3)$ satisfies the inequalities* (9), (10) *and the equality* (8), *and if, finally, the integrals*

$$\int_\Omega [\mathbf{v}^2(x,0) + \mathbf{v}_i^2(x,0)]\,dx_1\,dx_2\,dx_3 \quad \textit{and} \quad \int_0^t \left[\int_\Omega (\mathbf{f}^2 + \mathbf{f}_t^2)\,dx\right]^{1/2} dt$$

are finite, then estimates of the type (30) *and* (31) *hold for* $\mathbf{v}$.

Proof: The proof of this lemma is analogous to the proof of Lemma 5. It is only necessary to convince ourselves that the inequality

$$\int_\Omega u^4(x)\,dx \leqslant C_8 \int_\Omega u^2(x)\,dx \int_\Omega \sum_{k=1}^{3} u_{x_k}^2\,dx \tag{33a}$$

holds for any function $\mathbf{u}(x_1, x_2, x_3)$ which vanishes on the boundary of Ω and has axial symmetry. To prove this, we introduce cylindrical coordinates in the space of points (x_1, x_2, x_3), and we rewrite (33a) in the form

$$\int_D u^4(r,z)\,r\,dr\,dz \leqslant 2\pi\,C_8 \int_D u^2\,r\,dr\,dz \int_D (u_r^2 + u_z^2)\,r\,dr\,dz.$$

If we set $u r^{1/4} = w$, then w satisfies the inequality (1) of Chap. 1, Sec. 1:

$$\int_D w^4\,dr\,dz \equiv \int_D u^4\,r\,dr\,dz$$

$$\leqslant 2 \int_D u^2 r^{1/2}\,dr\,dz \int_D \left[\left(u_r r^{1/4} + \frac{1}{4} r^{-3/4} u\right)^2 + r^{1/2} u_z^2\right] dr\,dz.$$

It is easy to see that this implies the required inequality (33a), since $r \geqslant \delta > 0$ for the points of D.

3. Existence Theorems

We now prove that the problem (1) has a solution. To do so, we use Galerkin's method. Let $\{\mathbf{a}^k(x)\}$ be a complete system of functions in $J_{0,1}(\Omega)$, which is orthonormal in $\mathbf{L}_2(\Omega)$.* Since, by definition, the set $J_{0,1}(\Omega)$ is dense in $\mathring{J}(\Omega)$, the linear combinations of the functions $\mathbf{a}^k(x)$ are also dense in $\mathring{J}(\Omega)$. The orthogonal complement of $\mathring{J}(\Omega)$ in $\mathbf{L}_2(\Omega)$ consists of the gradients of single-valued functions.

Let the first function $\mathbf{a}^1(x)$ of the system coincide with the initial value of the solution we are looking for, i.e., let

$$\mathbf{v}(x, 0) = \mathbf{a}(x) = \mathbf{a}^l(x).$$

We shall look for approximate solutions $\mathbf{v}^n(x,t)$ of the problem (1) which have the form

$$\mathbf{v}^n(x,t) = \sum_{l=1}^{n} c_{ln}(t)\,\mathbf{a}^l(x).$$

---

* We assume that $\{\mathbf{a}^k(x)\}$ is orthonormal in $\mathbf{L}_2(\Omega)$ only to introduce certain unessential simplifications in the subsequent treatment.

The functions $c_{ln}(t)$ will be found from the conditions

$$c_{ln}|_{t=0} = \delta_1^l \quad (l = 1, 2, \ldots, n), \tag{34}$$

and the conditions

$$(\mathbf{v}_t^n + v_k^n \mathbf{v}_{x_k}^n - \mathbf{f}, \mathbf{a}^l) + \nu(\mathbf{v}_{x_k}^n, \mathbf{a}_{x_k}^l) = 0 \quad (l = 1, 2, \ldots, n),$$

or equivalently,

$$(\mathbf{v}_t^n - \mathbf{f}, \mathbf{a}^l) - (v_k^n \mathbf{v}^n, \mathbf{a}_{x_k}^l) + \nu(\mathbf{v}_{x_k}^n, \mathbf{a}_{x_k}^l) = 0 \quad (l = 1, 2, \ldots, n). \tag{35}$$

The relations (35) are obtained formally from the system (1) if we set $\mathbf{v} = \mathbf{v}^n$, multiply by $\mathbf{a}^l$ and integrate over Ω. They can also be obtained from the integral identity (4), if we set $\mathbf{v} = \mathbf{v}^n$ and $\mathbf{\Phi}(x, t) = \mathbf{a}^l(x)\,\psi(t)$, where $\psi(t)$ is an arbitrary continuous function of t. Because $\psi(t)$ is arbitrary in the resulting relation, we can eliminate the integration with respect to t, thereby obtaining (35). Essentially, the relations (35) express the fact that the approximate solution $\mathbf{v}^n$ satisfies the identity (4) not for all $\mathbf{\Phi}$, but only for $\mathbf{\Phi}$ which can be represented in the form

$$\mathbf{\Phi} = \sum_{l=1}^{n} \psi_l(t)\,\mathbf{a}^l(x),$$

where the $\psi_l(t)$ are arbitrary continuous functions of t. All the other conditions imposed on the generalized solution are satisfied by the $\mathbf{v}^n$ exactly.

The relations (35) represent a system of ordinary differential equations of the form

$$\frac{dc_{ln}(t)}{dt} - \nu \sum_{i=1}^{n} a_{li}\, c_{in}(t) + \sum_{i,p=1}^{n} a_{lip}\, c_{in}(t)\, c_{pn}(t) = f_l(t) \tag{36}$$
$$(l = 1, 2, \ldots, n),$$

for the $c_{ln}(t)$, where the a_{li} and a_{lip} are constants, and $f_l = (\mathbf{f}, \mathbf{a}^l)$. We shall assume that $\mathbf{a}(x) = \mathbf{v}(x, 0) \in J_{0,1}(\Omega)$ and that

$$\int_0^t \left(\int_\Omega |\mathbf{f}|^2\, dx\right)^{1/2} dt$$

is finite for any $t \geqslant 0$.

The a priori estimate (9) allows us to conclude that the system (36) has a unique solution for $t \geqslant 0$ under the conditions (34). In fact, since the system (36) depends analytically on the c_{ln}, it is sufficient to verify that the $|c_{ln}(t)|$ are bounded for any finite $t \geqslant 0$. Because of the orthonormality of the $\mathbf{a}^l$ in $\mathbf{L}_2(\Omega)$, we have

$$\| \mathbf{v}^n(x, t) \|^2 = \sum_{l=1}^{n} c_{ln}^2(t).$$

We now multiply each of the equations (35) by the corresponding $c_{ln}(t)$ and sum the resulting expressions over l from 1 to n. Then, after some simple transformations, we obtain

$$\frac{1}{2}\frac{d}{dt}\| \mathbf{v}^n \|^2 + \nu(\mathbf{v}^n_{x_k}, \mathbf{v}^n_{x_k}) - (\mathbf{f}, \mathbf{v}^n) = 0, \tag{37}$$

which implies (see Lemma 1) the boundedness of the $\| \mathbf{v}^n(x, t) \|$, and hence the boundedness of all the $|c_{ln}(t)|$ for any $t \geqslant 0$.

Thus, the approximating solutions $\mathbf{v}^n(x, t)$ are defined uniquely for all $t \geqslant 0$ by the relations (34) and (35). In proving this, the only fact about the $\{\mathbf{a}^k(x)\}$ which was used is that they are an orthonormal basis in $\mathring{J}(\Omega)$. We now show that under certain conditions on $\mathbf{a}$ and $\mathbf{f}$, the functions $\mathbf{v}^n$ converge as $n \to \infty$ to a limit which is the desired solution of the problem (1). We begin by considering the planar case:

THEOREM 2. *In the case of a plane-parallel two-dimensional flow, the approximate solutions* $\mathbf{v}^n(x, t)$ *converge to the generalized solution* $\mathbf{v}(x, t)$ *of the problem* (1) *for all* $t \geqslant 0$, *provided only that**

$$\mathbf{a}(x) = \mathbf{v}(x, 0) \in W_2^2(\Omega) \cap J_{0,1}(\Omega)$$

and

$$\int_0^t \Big[\int_\Omega (\mathbf{f}^2 + \mathbf{f}_t^2)\, dx \Big]^{1/2} dt < \infty.$$

The domain Ω *can be either bounded or unbounded.*

Proof: First of all, we note that $\mathbf{v}_t(x, 0)$ is determined by the vectors $\mathbf{a}(x)$ and $\mathbf{f}(x, 0)$. In fact, from the Navier-Stokes system

$$\mathbf{v}_t + \operatorname{grad} p = \mathbf{f} + \nu \Delta \mathbf{v} - v_k \mathbf{v}_{x_k},$$

we see that the vector appearing in the right-hand side uniquely determines the vectors $\mathbf{v}_t$ and $\operatorname{grad} p$, since they are orthogonal to

* We might weaken the condition of the theorem concerning $\mathbf{v}(x, 0)$ by changing it to the requirement that the integral

$$\int_\Omega [\mathbf{v}^2(x, 0) + \mathbf{v}_t^2(x, 0)]\, dx$$

be finite, since only this integral figures in the a priori estimates (30) and (31) for the solutions $\mathbf{v}$. However, this weaker condition would require somewhat more delicate arguments in proving the theorem, and hence we assume that the conditions given in the statement of the theorem hold.

each other. We now show that the $\mathbf{v}^n$ satisfy the assumptions of Lemma 5 of the preceding section, i.e., that the estimate

$$\| \mathbf{v}_t^n (x, t) \|^2 + \int_0^t \sum_{k=1}^{2} \| \mathbf{v}_{tx_k}^n \|^2 \, dt \leqslant c(t), \tag{38}$$

and hence the estimate

$$\| \mathbf{v}^n (x, t) \|^2 + \sum_{k=1}^{2} \| \mathbf{v}_{x_k}^n (x, t) \|^2 \leqslant c(t), \tag{39}$$

holds for all $n = 1, 2, \ldots$ with the same monotonically increasing continuous function $c(t)$. To see this, it is sufficient to verify that equations (7) and (8) hold for $\mathbf{v}$ and $\mathbf{v}^n$, and that $\|v^n(x, 0)\|$ $\|\mathbf{v}_t^n(x, 0)\|$ are uniformly bounded. The latter follows from our assumptions on $\mathbf{a}(x)$ and from the fact that $\mathbf{v}^n(x, 0) = \mathbf{a}(x)$. The equations (7) and (37) are the same, and (8) is obtained from (35) by differentiating (35) with respect to t, multiplying the result by dc_{ln}/dt and summing over l from 1 to n. Thus, equations (7) and (8) actually hold for $\mathbf{v} = \mathbf{v}^n$ $(n = 1, 2, \ldots)$.

Because of the estimates (38) and (39), which are uniform in n, we can select a sequence $\{\mathbf{v}^{n_k}\}$ from $\{\mathbf{v}^n\}$ such that $\mathbf{v}^{n_k}$, $\mathbf{v}_{x_p}^{n_k}$, $\mathbf{v}_t^{n_k}$, $\mathbf{v}_{tx_p}^{n_k}$ and $v_i^{n_k} v_j^{n_k}$ converge weakly in $\mathbf{L}_2(Q_T)$ (where T is arbitrary) to $\mathbf{v}$, $\mathbf{v}_{x_p}$, $\mathbf{v}_t$, $\mathbf{v}_{t x_p}$ and $v_i v_j$, respectively. Therefore, the limit function $\mathbf{v}$ will satisfy the inequalities (9), (10) and (31). It can be shown that in fact $\mathbf{v}^{n_k}$ converges to $\mathbf{v}$ in a stronger sense and that the inequality (30) remains true for $\mathbf{v}$, where in (30) we can take any $t_1 \geqslant 0$ as the initial instant of time.* The function $\mathbf{v}$ will obviously satisfy the conditions $\operatorname{div} \mathbf{v} = 0$, $\mathbf{v}|_S = 0$ and $\mathbf{v}|_{t=0} = \mathbf{a}$ in the sense prescribed by the imbedding theorems.

* To verify the inequality (30) for $\mathbf{v}(x, t)$, it is sufficient to convince oneself that a subsequence $\left\{\mathbf{v}^{n'_k}\right\}$ can be selected from $\{\mathbf{v}^{n_k}\}$ such that $\mathbf{v}_t^{n'_k}$ converges weakly in $\mathbf{L}_2(\Omega)$ for any $t \geqslant 0$. We shall assume that $\max_{x \in \Omega} |\mathbf{a}^l(x)| < \infty$. Then, the functions

$$\varphi_{n, l}(t) = (\mathbf{v}_t^n(x, t), \mathbf{a}^l(x)) \quad (n \geqslant l)$$

are uniformly bounded for fixed l and are equicontinuous on $[0, T]$. This can easily be seen by inspecting (35) and recalling the uniform estimates (38) and (39). Consequently, we can select a subsequence $\{n'_k\}$ from the sequence $\{n_k\}$ such that $\varphi_{n'_k l}(t)$ converges uniformly on $[0, T]$ for any $l = 1, 2, \ldots$ Since the $\{\mathbf{a}^l\}$ form a basis in $\mathring{J}(\Omega)$, and since the $\|\mathbf{v}_t^n(x, t)\|$ are uniformly bounded, it can easily be shown that $\left(\mathbf{v}_t^{n'_k}(x, t), \mathbf{b}(x)\right)$ will converge uniformly for any function $\mathbf{b}(x) \in \mathring{J}(\Omega)$, i.e., that $\mathbf{v}_t^{n'_k}(x, t)$ will converge weakly in $\mathbf{L}_2(\Omega)$ for any $t \geqslant 0$.

We still have to verify that $\mathbf{v}$ satisfies the identity (4) for any $\mathbf{\Phi}$ obeying the conditions $\mathbf{\Phi}$, $\mathbf{\Phi}_{x_k} \in \mathbf{L}_2(Q_T)$, $\operatorname{div} \mathbf{\Phi} = 0$, $\mathbf{\Phi}|_S = 0$. Let us denote the class of such functions $\mathbf{\Phi}$ by $\mathfrak{M}$. We now show that it is sufficient to verify that the identity (4) is valid for functions $\mathbf{\Phi}$ of the form

$$\mathbf{\Phi}^m(x, t) = \sum_{l=1}^{m} d_l(t)\, \mathbf{a}^l(x), \tag{40}$$

with arbitrary derivatives $d_l(t)$. The functions $\mathbf{v}_t$, $\mathbf{v}_{x_k}$, $v_k\mathbf{v}$ and $\mathbf{f}$ appearing in (4) are square-summable over Q_T. Therefore, if we show that the functions $\mathbf{\Phi}^m$ of the form (40) approximate an arbitrary function $\mathbf{\Phi}$ of the class $\mathfrak{M}$ in such a way that $\mathbf{\Phi}^m$ and $\mathbf{\Phi}^m_{x_k}$ converge to $\mathbf{\Phi}$ and $\mathbf{\Phi}_{x_k}$ in the $\mathbf{L}_2(Q_T)$ norm, then the validity of (4) for any $\mathbf{\Phi}$ of the form (40) will imply the validity of (4) for any $\mathbf{\Phi}$ in $\mathfrak{M}$. First of all, it is clear that any function $\mathbf{\Phi}$ in $\mathfrak{M}$ can be approximated in the way we need by functions $\mathbf{\Phi}_m$ in $\mathfrak{M}$ which are square-summable over Ω for any $t \in [0, T]$ and which depend continuously on t in the $J_{0,1}(\Omega)$ norm. (This latter condition means that $\|\mathbf{\Phi}_m(x, t + \Delta t) - \mathbf{\Phi}_m(x, t)\|_{J_{0,1}(\Omega)} \to 0$ as $\Delta t \to 0$.) To see this, we can (for example) replace $\mathbf{\Phi}$ by its average $\mathbf{\Phi}_\varrho$ with respect to time and then let the "averaging radius" converge to zero.

Thus, it is sufficient to prove that an arbitrary function of the type $\mathbf{\Phi}_m$ can be approximated in $\mathbf{L}_2(Q_T)$, together with $\mathbf{\Phi}_{mx_k}$, by functions of the form (40). Let $\mathbf{\Phi}$ belong to $\mathfrak{M}$, and let $\mathbf{\Phi}$ depend continuously on t as an element of $J_{0,1}(\Omega)$. We introduce another complete system $\{\mathbf{b}^l(x)\}$ in $J_{0,1}(\Omega)$, which is orthonormal in $J_{0,1}(\Omega)$ and which is related to the $\{\mathbf{a}^l\}$ by a "triangular transformation."* Then we introduce the functions

$$\mathbf{\Phi}^m(x, t) = \sum_{l=1}^{m} e_l(t)\, \mathbf{b}^l(x), \text{ with } e_l(t) = \big(\mathbf{\Phi}(x, t), \mathbf{b}^l(x)\big),$$

which converge to $\mathbf{\Phi}$ in the $J_{0,1}(\Omega)$ norm for any fixed $t \in [0, T]$. Given any preassigned small $\varepsilon > 0$, we select a finite number of points $t_1, \ldots, t_N$ in $[0, T]$ such that for t' and t'' belonging to any of the intervals $[t_k, t_{k+1}]$, the quantity $\|\mathbf{\Phi}(x, t') - \mathbf{\Phi}(x, t'')\|_{J_{0,1}(\Omega)}$ does not exceed ε. Then, we choose m so large that for all the points t_k, the partial sums $\mathbf{\Phi}^m$ of the Fourier series of the function $\mathbf{\Phi}$ in the $\{\mathbf{b}^l\}$ basis differ from $\mathbf{\Phi}$ by less than ε in the $J_{0,1}(\Omega)$ norm. Then, for

---

* This proof could be carried out somewhat differently without introducing an orthonormal system by using the Banach-Steinhaus theorem, as is done in the beginning of the proof of Theorem 12.

any t in $[t_k, t_{k+1}]$, the remainder

$$R_m(t) = \| \mathbf{\Phi}(x, t) - \mathbf{\Phi}^m(x, t) \|_{J_{0,1}(\Omega)}$$

will be small, since

$$\begin{aligned} R_m(t) &\leqslant \| \mathbf{\Phi}(x, t_k) - \mathbf{\Phi}^m(x, t_k) \|_{J_{0,1}} \\ &\quad + \| \mathbf{\Phi}(x, t_k) - \mathbf{\Phi}(x, t) \|_{J_{0,1}} + \| \mathbf{\Phi}^m(x, t_k) - \mathbf{\Phi}^m(x, t) \|_{J_{0,1}} \\ &\leqslant 2\,\varepsilon + \| \mathbf{\Phi}^m(x, t_k) - \mathbf{\Phi}^m(x, t) \|_{J_{0,1}}, \end{aligned}$$

where the norm of the last term does not exceed ε, since it is the partial sum of a Fourier series in an orthonormal basis of the function $\mathbf{\Phi}(x, t_k) - \mathbf{\Phi}(x, t)$, whose norm does not exceed ε. This proves that the $\mathbf{\Phi}^m$ approximate $\mathbf{\Phi}$ in the $J_{0,1}(\Omega)$ norm, uniformly for $t \in [0, T]$. But the functions $\mathbf{\Phi}^m = \sum_{l=1}^{m} e_l\, \mathbf{b}^l$ can be represented as finite sums of the form (40), since the $\{\mathbf{b}^l\}$ are related to the $\{\mathbf{a}^l\}$ by a triangular transformation.

Thus, we have shown that any $\mathbf{\Phi}$ in $\mathfrak{M}$ can be approximated by sums of the form (40), in such a way that $\mathbf{\Phi}^m$ and $\mathbf{\Phi}^m_{x_k}$ converge to $\mathbf{\Phi}$ and $\mathbf{\Phi}_{x_k}$ in the $\mathbf{L}_2(Q_T)$ norm. Because of this, it is sufficient to verify just that the limit function $\mathbf{v}$ found above satisfies the identity (4) for $\mathbf{\Phi}$ of the form (40). Take any $\mathbf{\Phi}^m$ of the form (40). The functions $\mathbf{v}^n$, beginning with $n = m$, satisfy the identities (35) for $l = 1, 2, \ldots, m$. Multiplying each of the equations (35) by its own $d_l(t)$, summing the resulting equations over l from 1 to m, and integrating with respect to t from 0 to T, we obtain

$$\int_0^T \int_\Omega \left(\mathbf{v}^n_t \cdot \mathbf{\Phi}^m + \nu\, \mathbf{v}^n_{x_k} \cdot \mathbf{\Phi}^m_{x_k} - v^n_k\, \mathbf{v}^n \cdot \mathbf{\Phi}^m_{x_k} - \mathbf{f} \cdot \mathbf{\Phi}^m\right) dx\, dt = 0. \quad (41)$$

Then, letting n $(n \geqslant m)$ approach ∞ in (41), along the subsequence n_k chosen above, we see that (41) also holds for the limit function $\mathbf{v}$. We have thereby proved that the function $\mathbf{v}$ is actually a generalized solution of the problem (1). Because of the uniqueness theorem for generalized solutions, the whole sequence $\mathbf{v}^n$ converges to the generalized solution $\mathbf{v}$ of the problem (1), and the proof of Theorem 2 is complete.

We now turn to the general three-dimensional problem. In just the same way as in Theorem 2, using the a priori estimates (9), (10), (14), (20) and (25), we can prove the following theorem:

THEOREM 3. *If the external forces can be derived from a potential* ($\mathbf{f} \equiv 0$), *if* $\mathbf{a}(x) \in W_2^2(\Omega) \cap J_{0,1}(\Omega)$, *and if the condition*

$$\| \mathbf{v}(x, 0) \| \| \mathbf{v}_t(x, 0) \| < \frac{\nu^3}{\beta^2}, \quad (42)$$

holds, where

$$\beta = \sqrt{3} \max_{u \in \overset{\circ}{W}{}_2^1(\Omega)} \frac{\left(\int_\Omega u^4(x)\, dx\right)^{1/2}}{\int_\Omega \sum_{k=1}^{3} u_{x_k}^2\, dx},$$

then the problem (1) *has a generalized solution for any* $t \geqslant 0$.

The domain Ω must be such that $\beta < \infty$. For bounded domains Ω, this is certainly the case. In Theorems 4, 5 and 6 below, Ω can be an arbitrary domain, bounded or unbounded

THEOREM 4. *If* $\mathbf{a}(x) \in W_2^2(\Omega) \cap J_{0,1}(\Omega)$ *and*

$$\left(\| \mathbf{v}(x, 0) \| + \int_0^T \| \mathbf{f} \|\, dt\right) \times \left(\max_{0 \leq t \leq T} \| \mathbf{f} \| + \| \mathbf{v}_t(x, 0) \| + \int_0^T \| \mathbf{f}_t \|\, dt\right) < \frac{\nu^3}{\beta^2}, \tag{43}$$

then the problem (1) *has a generalized solution, at least in the interval* $0 \leqslant t \leqslant T$.

THEOREM 5. *If* $\mathbf{a}(x) \in W_2^2(\Omega) \cap J_{0,1}(\Omega)$ *and*

$$\int_0^t \left[\int_\Omega (\mathbf{f}^2 + \mathbf{f}_t^2)\, dx\right]^{1/2} dt < +\infty,$$

then the problem (1) *has a generalized solution, at least in the interval* $0 \leqslant t \leqslant T$, *whose length is determined by the indicated integral,* $\| \mathbf{a}(x) \|_2$ *and the coefficient* ν.

The quantity T can be calculated by using Lemma 4 of Sec. 2 of this chapter.

Finally, we mention a special case of the three-dimensional problem but one which is not without interest: Let Ω be a domain obtained by rotation about the x_3-axis of a planar domain D lying in the half-plane ($x_2 = 0$, $x_1 > 0$), at a positive distance δ from the x_3-axis. Suppose that $\mathbf{f}$ and $\mathbf{a}$ do not depend on the angle of rotation about the x_3-axis. In this case, the problem has a unique solution "in the large," similar to what was proved in Theorem 2.

THEOREM 6. *If all the data of the problem* (1) *have rotational symmetry with respect to the* x_3*-axis, if the domain lies at a positive distance* δ *from the* x_3-axis, *and if* $\mathbf{a}(x) \in W_2^2(\Omega) \cap J_{0,1}(\Omega)$ *and*

$$\int_0^t \left[\int_\Omega (\mathbf{f}^2 + \mathbf{f}_t^2)\, dx\right]^{1/2} dt < +\infty,$$

then the problem (1) *has a unique solution for all* $t \geqslant 0$.

The proof of this theorem is analogous to the proof of Theorem 2; it is only necessary to use the a priori estimates given by Lemma 6.

4. Differential Properties of Generalized Solutions

Relying on the results of Chap. 5, Sec. 5, we can easily show that the generalized solutions of the problem (1) have second-order derivatives with respect to x_k and satisfy the Navier-Stokes system for almost all (x, t). In fact, let $\mathbf{v}$ be a generalized solution of the problem (1). Then $\mathbf{v}$ has first-order derivatives in $\mathbf{L}_2(Q_T)$. Moreover, $\operatorname{div} \mathbf{v} = 0$, $\mathbf{v}|_S = 0$, $\mathbf{v}|_{t=0} = \mathbf{a}(x)$, and $\mathbf{v}$ satisfies the integral identity (4). In this identity, we can take $\mathbf{\Phi}$ in the form $\mathbf{\Phi}(x, t) = \psi(t)\boldsymbol{\varphi}(x)$, where $\psi(t)$ is an arbitrary continuous function of t, and $\boldsymbol{\varphi}(x) \in J_{0,1}(\Omega)$. Because of the fact that $\psi(t)$ is arbitrary, and because of the properties of $\mathbf{v}$ just mentioned, it follows from this identity that the identity

$$(\mathbf{v}_t, \boldsymbol{\varphi}) + \nu(\mathbf{v}_{x_k} \boldsymbol{\varphi}_{x_k}) - (v_k \mathbf{v}, \boldsymbol{\varphi}_{x_k}) = (\mathbf{f}, \boldsymbol{\varphi}) \tag{44}$$

holds for almost all t, with arbitrary $\boldsymbol{\varphi} \in J_{0,1}(\Omega)$. Take one of the values of t for which (44) is valid. Then, this identity is the same as the integral identity (5) of Chap. 5 for the stationary problem if we take the function $\mathbf{f} - \mathbf{v}_t$ for the free term. Since $\mathbf{f} - \mathbf{v}_t \in \mathbf{L}_2(\Omega)$ for the chosen value of t, it follows from Theorem 6 of Chap. 5, Sec. 4 that $\mathbf{v}$ has derivatives of the form $\partial^2\mathbf{v}/\partial x_k\, \partial x_l$, which are square-summable over any interior subdomain Ω' of the domain Ω. Thus, we have proved the following theorem:

THEOREM 7. *The generalized solution of the problem* (1) *guaranteed by Theorems 2—6 of the preceding section has second-order derivatives with respect to x_k, which are square-summable over any $\Omega' \subset \Omega$ for almost all $t \geqslant 0$.*

Strictly speaking, the generalized solution which we have found has better properties. In fact, it follows from a remark made in connection with Theorem 2 that $\mathbf{v}$ not only has the derivative $\mathbf{v}_{tx_k}$ which is square-summable over Q_T, but also the derivative $\mathbf{v}_t$ which is square-summable over Ω for any $t \geqslant 0$, and that $\|\mathbf{v}_t(x, t)\|$ is continuous and satisfies the inequality (30). This implies that the identity (44) holds for all $t \geqslant 0$, and hence for all $t \geqslant 0$ there exist derivatives $\mathbf{v}_{x_i x_j}(t) \in \mathbf{L}_2(\Omega')$ and their norms $\|\mathbf{v}_{x_i x_j}(x, t)\|_{\mathbf{L}_2(\Omega')}$ are uniformly bounded. If the boundary S is smooth, then $\mathbf{v}_{x_i x_j}(x, t) \in \mathbf{L}_2(\Omega)$.

It could be shown that with the restrictions imposed above on $\mathbf{f}$, the generalized solution $\mathbf{v}$ has derivatives $\mathbf{v}_{tt}$ and $\mathbf{v}_{tx_i x_j}$. For integral norms, the study of the further improvement of the differential properties of $\mathbf{v}$ as $\mathbf{f}$ and $\mathbf{a}$ are improved is carried out in the same way as in the linear problem. For Hölder norms, the following results hold:

1. If inside Q_T, $\mathbf{f}(x, t)$ satisfies a Hölder condition in (x, t), then the generalized solution $\mathbf{v}(x, t)$ has derivatives $\mathbf{v}_t$ and $\mathbf{v}_{tx_ix_j}$ inside Q_T which also satisfy Hölder conditions. In the case of two space variables, this result is valid for the "weak solution." (The definition of the "weak solution" and the corresponding existence theorem are given in Sec. 6 of this chapter.) In fact, we have the following theorem:

2. If $\mathbf{f}(x_1, x_2, t) \in \mathbf{L}_2(Q_T)$, $\mathbf{a}(x_1, x_2) \in \mathring{J}(\Omega)$ and if inside Q_T, $\mathbf{f}$ satisfies a Hölder condition in (x, t), then the problem (1) has a unique solution $\mathbf{v}$, which has derivatives $\mathbf{v}_t$ and $\mathbf{v}_{x_ix_j}$ satisfying Hölder conditions inside Q_T.

The proof of these propositions is not very complicated. First, we have to obtain an integral representation $\mathbf{v} = K(\mathbf{v})$ for $\mathbf{v}$ (where $K(\mathbf{v})$ is the result of applying a nonlinear operator to $\mathbf{v}$), by starting from an integral identity defining $\mathbf{v}$ (to get this, we have to use the basic singular solution of the linearized nonstationary problem, constructed in Chap. 4, Sec. 5). Then, we argue in the same way as in Chap. 5, Sec. 5, in studying the differential properties of generalized solutions of the nonlinear stationary problem. In doing so, we have to convince ourselves that $K(\mathbf{v})$ has better differential properties than $\mathbf{v}$. For two space variables, this improvement in the properties of $\mathbf{v}$ holds for the "weak solution," but in the three-dimensional problem, we need a better solution, e.g., the generalized solution studied above.

Both of the results 1 and 2 are true for the whole region Q_T if $\mathbf{a}(x)$ and S are smooth. However, the proofs are then far more complicated (see the Comments).

5. The Continuous Dependence of the Solutions on the Data of the Problem, and Their Behavior as $t \to +\infty$

We now analyze in more detail the case of plane-parallel flows, since more complete results can be obtained for such flows. The case of general three-dimensional flows is studied in a similar way. Thus, suppose we have a plane-parallel flow $\mathbf{v}(x_1, x_2, t)$. Then $\mathbf{v}(x_1, x_2, t)$ obeys the following theorem:

THEOREM 8. *The solution* $\mathbf{v}(x_1, x_2, t)$ *of the problem* (1), *guaranteed by Theorem* 2, *converges to zero as* $t \to +\infty$ *if* $\int_0^\infty (\|\mathbf{f}\| + \|\mathbf{f}_t\|)\, dt < \infty$. *More precisely, the integrals*

$$\int_\Omega \sum_{k=1}^2 \mathbf{v}_{x_k}^2(x, t)\, dx \quad \text{and} \quad \int_{\Omega_1} \mathbf{v}^2(x, t)\, dx$$

converge to zero as $t \to +\infty$ (*where* Ω_1 *is any finite subdomain of* Ω). *For a bounded domain* Ω, *the convergence of the integral* $\int_0^\infty \|\mathbf{f}\|\, dt$ *implies that* $\|\mathbf{v}(x, t)\|$ *converges to zero.*

Proof: To prove the theorem, we note that $\mathbf{v}$ satisfies the inequalities (10) and (31), which imply that the integrals

$$\int_0^\infty \varphi^2(t)\, dt \quad \text{and} \quad \int_0^\infty F^2(t)\, dt$$

are finite, where

$$\varphi^2(t) = \int_\Omega \sum_{k=1}^2 \mathbf{v}_{x_k}^2(x, t)\, dx, \qquad F^2(t) = \int_\Omega \sum_{k=1}^2 \mathbf{v}_{tx_k}^2(x, t)\, dx.$$

On the other hand,

$$\left| \frac{d}{dt} \varphi^2 \right| = 2 \left| \int_\Omega \sum_{k=1}^2 \mathbf{v}_{x_k} \cdot \mathbf{v}_{tx_k}\, dx \right| \leqslant 2\, \varphi\, F$$

and therefore

$$\int_0^\infty \left| \frac{d}{dt} \varphi^2 \right| dt < \infty.$$

Moreover, it follows from the fact the integrals

$$\int_0^\infty \varphi^2(t)\, dt \quad \text{and} \quad \int_0^\infty \left| \frac{d}{dt} \varphi^2 \right| dt$$

are finite that $\varphi^2(t) \to 0$ as $t \to +\infty$. Because of the inequality

$$\int_{\Omega_1} \mathbf{v}^2(x, t)\, dx \leqslant C_{\Omega_1} \varphi^2(t),$$

which holds for any bounded subdomain Ω_1 of the domain Ω (in the case where Ω is bounded, we can take Ω itself to be Ω_1), we see that $\int_{\Omega_1} \mathbf{v}^2(x, t)\, dx$ also converges to zero as $t \to +\infty$. The last assertion of the theorem is proved in just the same way as in the linear case (see Chap. 4, Sec. 2).

We now compare two flows $\mathbf{v}'(x, t)$ and $\mathbf{v}''(x, t)$, and show that under certain conditions, they differ from each other only slightly for all $t \geqslant 0$.

THEOREM 9. *Let* $\mathbf{v}'(x_1, x_2, t)$ *and* $\mathbf{v}''(x_1, x_2, t)$ *be two solutions of the problem* (1), *corresponding to initial velocities* $\mathbf{a}'(x)$, $\mathbf{a}''(x)$ *and forces* $\mathbf{f}'(x, t)$, $\mathbf{f}''(x, t)$. *Then, their difference* $\mathbf{u}(x, t) = \mathbf{v}'(x, t) - \mathbf{v}''(x, t)$, *satisfies the estimate*

$$\begin{aligned} \|\mathbf{u}(x, t)\| \leqslant \|\mathbf{a}' - \mathbf{a}''\| \exp\left\{\frac{2}{\nu}\int_0^t \tilde{\varphi}^2(\tau)\,d\tau\right\} \\ + \int_0^t \|\mathbf{f}'(x, \xi) - \mathbf{f}''(x, \xi)\| \exp\left\{\frac{2}{\nu}\int_\xi^t \tilde{\varphi}^2(\tau)\,d\tau\right\} d\xi, \end{aligned} \tag{45}$$

where

$$\tilde{\varphi}^2(t) = \int_\Omega \sum_{k=1}^{2} [\mathbf{v}''_{x_k}(x, t)]^2\,dx.$$

Proof: To prove the inequality (45), we form an integral identity obeyed by $\mathbf{u}$. This identity is obtained by taking the difference of the integral identities for $\mathbf{v}'$ and $\mathbf{v}''$, and can be written in the form

$$\int_0^t \int_\Omega (\mathbf{u}_t \cdot \mathbf{\Phi} + \nu\,\mathbf{u}_{x_k} \cdot \mathbf{\Phi}_{x_k} + v'_k\,\mathbf{u}_{x_k} \cdot \mathbf{\Phi} + u_k\,\mathbf{v}''_{x_k} \cdot \mathbf{\Phi} - \mathbf{f} \cdot \mathbf{\Phi})\,dx\,dt = 0,$$

where $\mathbf{f} = \mathbf{f}' - \mathbf{f}''$. As shown above, this implies the identity

$$\int_\Omega (\mathbf{u}_t \cdot \mathbf{\Phi} + \nu\,\mathbf{u}_{x_k} \cdot \mathbf{\Phi}_{x_k} + v'_k\,\mathbf{u}_{x_k} \cdot \mathbf{\Phi} + u_k\,\mathbf{v}''_{x_k} \cdot \mathbf{\Phi} - \mathbf{f} \cdot \mathbf{\Phi})\,dx = 0$$

for almost all $t \geqslant 0$. If we set $\mathbf{\Phi} = \mathbf{u}$, then, after some elementary transformations, we obtain

$$\frac{1}{2}\frac{d}{dt}\|\mathbf{u}\|^2 + \nu\,\varphi^2(t) + \int_\Omega u_k\,\mathbf{v}''_{x_k} \cdot \mathbf{u}\,dx = \int_\Omega \mathbf{f} \cdot \mathbf{u}\,dx, \tag{46}$$

where

$$\varphi^2(t) = \int_\Omega \sum_{k=1}^{2} \mathbf{u}^2_{x_k}(x, t)\,dx.$$

We now estimate the third term by using Schwarz' inequality and the inequality (1) of Chap. 1, Sec. 1:

$$\begin{aligned} \left|\int_\Omega u_k\,\mathbf{v}''_{x_k} \cdot \mathbf{u}\,dx\right| \leqslant \left(\int_\Omega \sum_{k,l=1}^{2} (v''_{lx_k})^2\,dx\right)^{1/2} \\ \times \left(\int_\Omega \sum_{k,l=1}^{2} u_k^2\,u_l^2\,dx\right)^{1/2} \leqslant 2\tilde{\varphi}\varphi\|\mathbf{u}\|. \end{aligned}$$

From this and (46), we obtain

$$\begin{aligned}\frac{1}{2}\frac{d}{dt}\|\mathbf{u}\|^2 + \nu\,\varphi^2(t) &\leqslant 2\,\tilde{\varphi}\varphi\,\|\mathbf{u}\| + \|\mathbf{f}\|\,\|\mathbf{u}\| \\ &\leqslant \frac{\nu}{2}\varphi^2(t) + \frac{2}{\nu}\tilde{\varphi}^2\,\|\mathbf{u}\|^2 + \|\mathbf{f}\|\,\|\mathbf{u}\|.\end{aligned} \tag{47}$$

Then from this inequality, we derive the estimate (45) and the estimate

$$\nu\int_0^t \varphi^2(\tau)\,d\tau \leqslant \|\mathbf{u}\,x,\,0)\|^2 + 2\int_0^t \|\mathbf{f}\|\,\|\mathbf{u}\|\,dt + \frac{4}{\nu}\int_0^t \tilde{\varphi}^2\,\|\mathbf{u}\|^2\,dt, \tag{48}$$

just as was done in Lemma 5, thereby completing the proof of Theorem 9.

We now assume that one of the solutions, say $\mathbf{v}''$, does not depend on t. Let the "generalized Reynolds number" corresponding to $\mathbf{v}''$, i.e., the dimensionless quantity $2\,\tilde{\varphi}\,C_\Omega^*/\nu$ be less than 1. Here, the constant C_Ω^* is determined only by the domain Ω. It equals

$$C_\Omega^* = \max_{b(x)\in \mathring{W}_2^1(\Omega)} \left\{\frac{\int_\Omega b^2(x)\,dx}{\int_\Omega \sum_{k=1}^{2} b_{x_k}^2(x)\,dx}\right\}^{1/2}$$

and is related by the formula $C_\Omega^* = 1/\sqrt{\lambda_1}$ to the smallest eigenvalue λ_1 of the problem $-\Delta u = \lambda\,u$, $u|_S = 0$ in the domain Ω (see (7) of Chap. 1). Let $\mathbf{v}'(x, t)$ be a solution of the nonstationary problem, which corresponds to the same force $\mathbf{f}''(x)$ as $\mathbf{v}''(x)$ and to any initial condition $\mathbf{a}'(x) \in W_2^2(\Omega) \cap J_{0,1}(\Omega)$. We now show that in a certain sense the difference $\mathbf{u} = \mathbf{v}' - \mathbf{v}''$ converges to zero as $t \to +\infty$, i.e., we have the following theorem:

THEOREM 10. *If $\mathbf{v}''$ is a solution of the stationary problem corresponding to the force $\mathbf{f}''(x)$ such that the corresponding generalized Reynolds number $2\,\tilde{\varphi}\,C_\Omega^*/\nu$ is less than 1, and if $\mathbf{v}'(x, t)$ is a solution of the nonstationary problem corresponding to the same force $\mathbf{f}''(x)$ and to any initial condition $\mathbf{a}'(x) \in W_2^2(\Omega) \cap J_{0,1}(\Omega)$, then the difference $\mathbf{u}(x, t)$ between these two solutions satisfies the inequality*

$$\|\mathbf{u}(x, t)\| \leqslant \|\mathbf{u}(x, 0)\| \exp\{-\alpha\,t\},$$

where

$$\alpha = \frac{\nu}{C_\Omega^{*2}}\left(1 - \frac{2\,\tilde{\varphi}\,C_\Omega^*}{\nu}\right).$$

Proof: The function **u** satisfies the inequality (47), or more exactly, the inequality

$$\frac{1}{2}\frac{d}{dt}\|\mathbf{u}\|^2 + \nu\,\varphi^2(t) \leqslant 2\,\tilde{\varphi}\varphi\,\|\mathbf{u}\|, \tag{49}$$

since $\mathbf{f} \equiv 0$. However, because of our assumption concerning $\mathbf{v}''$, we have

$$2\,\tilde{\varphi}\varphi\,\|\mathbf{u}\| \leqslant 2\,\tilde{\varphi}\varphi^2\,C_\Omega^*,$$

and hence it follows from (49) that

$$\frac{1}{2}\frac{d}{dt}\|\mathbf{u}\|^2 + \nu\left(1 - \frac{2\,\tilde{\varphi}\,C_\Omega^*}{\nu}\right)\varphi^2(t) \leqslant 0.$$

But $\|\mathbf{u}\| \leqslant C_\Omega^*\,\varphi$, and therefore

$$\frac{d}{dt}\|\mathbf{u}\|^2 + \frac{2\,\nu}{C_\Omega^{*2}}\left(1 - \frac{2\,\tilde{\varphi}\,C_\Omega^*}{\nu}\right)\|\mathbf{u}\|^2 \leqslant 0$$

and

$$\frac{d}{dt}\left(e^{2\alpha t}\|\mathbf{u}\|^2\right) \leqslant 0,$$

which establishes Theorem 10.

We have proved a series of theorems concerning the behavior of solutions of the two-dimensional nonstationary problem (1) as $t \to +\infty$, when the boundary data and the external forces are varied. Similar results hold for the general case of the three-dimensional problem. For example, under the conditions of Theorem 8, the solution of the problem (1) converges to zero as $t \to +\infty$. However, we proved the fact that the problem has a unique solution for all $t \geqslant 0$ under the assumption that the Reynolds number is small at the initial instant of time, and hence the entire result (concerning existence and stability of solutions) is also obtained only when this assumption is met. In the next section, we shall discuss the existence for all $t \geqslant 0$ of a "worse" generalized solution, where no restrictions are imposed on the size of the initial perturbation.

6. Other Generalized Solutions of the Problem (1)

We again consider the case of the general three-dimensional nonstationary problem (1), assuming first that the domain Ω is bounded. In Sec. 3, it was proved that the Galerkin approximations $\mathbf{v}^n(x, t)$

are uniquely defined for all times $t \geqslant 0$. To show this, we essentially used only the fact that $\mathbf{a}(x) = \mathbf{v}(x, 0) \in \mathring{J}(\Omega)$ and $\int_0^t \|\mathbf{f}\| \, dt < \infty$. In this section, we shall assume that $\mathbf{a}$ and $\mathbf{f}$ satisfy only these conditions. The approximations $\mathbf{v}^n(x, t)$ will be constructed just as in Sec. 3, but this time the coefficients c_{ln} for $t = 0$ will be defined differently:

$$c_{ln}(0) = (\mathbf{a}, \mathbf{a}^l) \qquad (l = 1, 2, \ldots, n). \tag{50}$$

These approximate solutions $\mathbf{v}^n$ satisfy (37) and the estimates (9) and (10), i.e.,

$$\begin{aligned} &\| \mathbf{v}^n(x, t) \| \leqslant \| \mathbf{v}^n(x, t_1) \| + \int_{t_1}^{t} \| \mathbf{f}(x, \tau) \| \, d\tau , \\ &\| \mathbf{v}^n(x, t) \|^2 + 2\nu \int_{t_1}^{t} \int_{\Omega} \sum_{k=1}^{3} (\mathbf{v}^n_{x_k})^2 \, dx \, dt \\ &\leqslant \| \mathbf{v}^n(x, t_1) \|^2 + \sqrt{2} \, \| \mathbf{v}^n(x, t_1) \| \int_{t_1}^{t} \| \mathbf{f} \| \, dt \\ &+ 2 \left(\int_{t_1}^{t} \| \mathbf{f} \| \, dt \right)^2 \end{aligned} \tag{51}$$

for $t \geqslant t_1 \geqslant 0$. Using only these a priori estimates, from the sequence $\{\mathbf{v}^n\}$, $n = 1, 2, \ldots$ we can select a subsequence $\{\mathbf{v}^{n_k}\}$, $k = 1, 2, \ldots$, such that $\mathbf{v}^{n_k}$ and $\mathbf{v}^{n_k}_{x_i}$, $i = 1, 2, 3$, converge weakly in $\mathbf{L}_2(Q_T)$ where T is an arbitrary positive number. (This follows from the weak compactness of bounded sets in the Hilbert space $\mathbf{L}_2(Q_T)$.) The limit function $\mathbf{v}$ has derivatives $\mathbf{v}_{x_k}$, where $\mathbf{v}$ and $\mathbf{v}_{x_k}$ are square-summable over Q_T. Moreover, $\mathbf{v}$ satisfies the relations $\operatorname{div} \mathbf{v} = 0$ and $\mathbf{v}|_S = 0$. However, the question of the sense in which $\mathbf{v}$ satisfies the Navier-Stokes equations and the initial condition requires further investigation. In his paper [14], Hopf proves that the following results are valid for sufficiently well-behaved basis functions (see below):

1. A subsequence $\{\mathbf{v}^{n_k}\}$ can be chosen which converges strongly to $\mathbf{v}$ in $\mathbf{L}_2(Q_T)$;
2. $\mathbf{v}(x, t)$ will belong to $\mathbf{L}_2(\Omega)$ for all $t \geqslant 0$;
3. $\| \mathbf{v}(x, t) - \mathbf{a}(x) \| \to 0$ as $t \to +0$;
4. $\mathbf{v}$ satisfies the integral identity

$$\int_0^T \int_{\Omega} (\mathbf{v} \cdot \mathbf{\Phi}_t + \nu \mathbf{v} \cdot \Delta \mathbf{\Phi} + v_k \mathbf{v} \cdot \mathbf{\Phi}_{x_k} + \mathbf{f} \cdot \mathbf{\Phi}) \, dx \, dt = 0 \tag{52}$$

for all sufficiently smooth solenoidal $\mathbf{\Phi}$, which vanish on S and for $t = 0$, $t = T$.

The $\mathbf{v}$ obtained in this way can also be called a generalized solution of the problem (1). However, it is not clear to what degree this extension of the concept of a solution of the problem (1) is legitimate. It would be justified if we could succed in showing that a uniqueness theorem holds in this class of solutions. However, for the present problem in the general case, no one has yet succeeded in proving or disproving such a uniqueness theorem. Moreover, examples from nonlinear gas dynamics show that a similar replacement of an equation (or system) by an integral identity may not constitute an equivalence; in fact, the integral identity may have an infinite set of solutions, whereas the original equation may allow no more than one solution (for given initial and boundary conditions).

We now prove Hopf's results, modifying somewhat his definition of a generalized solution. By a *weak solution of the problem* (1), we mean a solenoidal vector function $\mathbf{v}(x, t)$ which is square-summable over Ω for all $t \geqslant 0$, with $\mathbf{v}_{x_k} \in \mathbf{L}_2(Q_T)$, which vanishes on the lateral surface of S, and which satisfies the identity

$$\begin{aligned} &\int_0^t \int_\Omega (\mathbf{v} \cdot \mathbf{\Phi}_t - \nu\, \mathbf{v}_{x_k} \cdot \mathbf{\Phi}_{x_k} - v_k\, \mathbf{v}_{x_k} \cdot \mathbf{\Phi} + \mathbf{f} \cdot \mathbf{\Phi})\, dx\, dt \\ &- \int_\Omega \mathbf{v}(x, t) \cdot \mathbf{\Phi}(x, t)\, dx + \int_\Omega \mathbf{a}(x) \cdot \mathbf{\Phi}(x, 0)\, dx = 0, \quad t \in [0, T] \end{aligned} \tag{53}$$

for all smooth solenoidal $\mathbf{\Phi}(x, t)$ satisfying the condition

$$\mathbf{\Phi}|_S = 0.$$

Moreover, as an element of $\mathbf{L}_2(\Omega)$, $\mathbf{v}(x, t)$ must depend continuously on t in the weak topology of $\mathbf{L}_2(\Omega)$, and it must satisfy the inequalities (51) for all t and almost all t_1, including $t_1 = 0$.

THEOREM 11. *If* $\mathbf{a}(x) \in \mathring{J}(\Omega)$ *and* $\int_0^T \|\mathbf{f}\|\, dt < \infty$, *then there exists at least one weak solution of the problem* (1).

Proof: Let $\{\mathbf{v}^n\}$, $n = 1, 2, \ldots$, be the approximate solutions calculated by Galerkin's method. We shall assume that the functions $\{\mathbf{a}^l(x)\}$ form an orthonormal basis in $\mathring{J}(\Omega)$, where $\mathbf{a}^l(x) \in \mathring{W}_2^1(\Omega)$ and $\max_{x \in \Omega} |\mathbf{a}^l(x)| < \infty$. The functions $\mathbf{v}^n$ are defined by the relations (35), which can be rewritten in the form.

$$\frac{d}{dt}(\mathbf{v}^n, \mathbf{a}^l) = -\nu(\mathbf{v}^n_{x_k}, \mathbf{a}^l_{x_k}) - (v^n_k \mathbf{v}^n_{x_k}, \mathbf{a}^l) + (\mathbf{f}, \mathbf{a}^l) \quad (l = 1, 2, \ldots, n). \tag{54}$$

It is not hard to show that $\psi_{n,l}(t) = (\mathbf{v}^n(x, t), \mathbf{a}^l(x))$ for fixed l and $n \geqslant l$ form a uniformly bounded and equicontinuous family of functions on $[0, T]$. The uniform boundedness of the $\psi_{n,l}(t)$ follows from (51), while the equicontinuity is obtained from (54). In fact, integrating (54) with respect to t from t to $t + \Delta t$, and estimating the right-hand side by using Schwarz' inequality, we obtain

$$|\psi_{n,l}(t + \Delta t) - \psi_{n,l}(t)| \leqslant \nu \int_t^{t+\Delta t} \|\mathbf{v}^n\|_1 \|\mathbf{a}^l\|_1 \, dt$$

$$+ C(l) \int_t^{t+\Delta t} \|\mathbf{v}^n\| \|\mathbf{v}^n\|_1 \, dt + \int_t^{t+\Delta t} \|\mathbf{f}\| \|\mathbf{a}^l\| \, dt$$

$$\leqslant C(l) \sqrt{\Delta t} \left(\int_t^{t+\Delta t} \|\mathbf{v}^n\|_1^2 \, dt \right)^{1/2}$$

$$+ C(l) \sqrt{\Delta t} \max_t \|\mathbf{v}^n(x, t)\| \left(\int_t^{t+\Delta t} \|\mathbf{v}^n\|_1^2 \, dt \right)^{1/2} + C(l) \int_t^{t+\Delta t} \|\mathbf{f}\| \, dt.$$

Because of the inequality (51), valid for all $\mathbf{v}^n$, the right-hand side of this inequality converges to zero uniformly in n as $\Delta t \to 0$. By the usual diagonal process, we select a subsequence n_k for which the functions $\psi_{n_k, l}$ are uniformly convergent as $k \to \infty$, for any fixed l. It follows that the $\mathbf{v}^{n_k}(x, t)$ converge weakly in $\mathbf{L}_2(\Omega)$, uniformly for $t \in [0, T]$. In fact, the functions $\mathbf{a}^l$ form a basis in $\mathring{J}(\Omega)$, and the norms $\|\mathbf{v}^n(x, t)\|$ do not exceed a certain constant, which is the same for all n and $t \in [0, T]$. Therefore, for any $\boldsymbol{\psi}(x) \in \mathbf{L}_2(\Omega)$, we have

$$\boldsymbol{\psi} = \sum_{k=1}^{\infty} \psi_k \mathbf{a}^k, \quad \psi_k = (\boldsymbol{\psi}, \mathbf{a}^k), \quad \sum_{k=1}^{\infty} \psi_k^2 < \infty$$

and the quantity

$$|(\mathbf{v}^{n_k}(x, t) - \mathbf{v}^{n_m}(x, t), \boldsymbol{\psi}(x))| \leqslant \sum_{l=1}^{N} |\psi_l| \, |(\mathbf{v}^{n_k} - \mathbf{v}^{n_m}, \mathbf{a}^l)|$$

$$+ \left(\sum_{l=N+1}^{\infty} \psi_l^2 \right)^{1/2} \|\mathbf{v}^{n_k} - \mathbf{v}^{n_m}\|$$

$$\leqslant \sum_{l=1}^{N} |\psi_l| \, |(\mathbf{v}^{n_k} - \mathbf{v}^{n_m}, \mathbf{a}^l)| + C \left(\sum_{l=N+1}^{\infty} \psi_l^2 \right)^{1/2}$$

can be made arbitrarily small for sufficiently large indices n_k and n_m. The limit function $\mathbf{v}$ of the $\mathbf{v}^{n_k}$ belongs to $\mathbf{L}_2(\Omega)$ for all $t \in [0, T]$, and $\|\mathbf{v}(x, t)\| \leqslant C(T)$ (see (51)).

We now show that the $\mathbf{v}^{n_k}$ converge strongly in $\mathbf{L}_2(Q_T)$. To prove this, we use two facts:

1. The uniform boundedness of the integrals

$$\int_0^T \int_\Omega \operatorname{grad}^2 \mathbf{v}^{n_k}\, dx\, dt;$$

2. Friedrich's lemma (see [3]), which asserts that for a fixed domain Ω, given any $\varepsilon > 0$, we can construct N_ε basis functions $\omega_l(x)$ ($l = 1, 2, \ldots, N_\varepsilon$) such that the inequality

$$\int_\Omega u^2(x)\, dx \leqslant \sum_{l=1}^{N_\varepsilon} \Big(\int_\Omega u\omega_l\, dx\Big)^2 + \varepsilon \int_\Omega \operatorname{grad}^2 u\, dx$$

holds for any function $\mathbf{u}(x)$ in $\mathring{W}_2^1(\Omega)$.

We write the last inequality for $\mathbf{u} = v_i^{n_k} - v_i^{n_m}$ and integrate it with respect to t from 0 to T, obtaining

$$\int_0^T \int_\Omega (v_i^{n_k} - v_i^{n_m})^2\, dx\, dt \leqslant \sum_{l=1}^{N_\varepsilon} \int_0^T \Big[\int_\Omega (v_i^{n_k} - v_i^{n_m})\, \omega_l\, dx\Big]^2 dt$$
$$+ \varepsilon \int_0^T \int_\Omega \operatorname{grad}^2 (v_i^{n_k} - v_i^{n_m})\, dx\, dt.$$

The last integral in the right-hand side of this inequality does not exceed a certain constant for any n_k and n_m. Moreover, the first integral can be made arbitrarily small for sufficiently large n_k and n_m, because of the uniform convergence in t of $(v_i^{n_k}, \omega_l)$ as $k \to \infty$. Therefore, the right-hand side of the inequality can be made arbitrarily small for sufficiently large n_k and n_m, and hence the functions $\mathbf{v}^{n_k}$ converge strongly to $\mathbf{v}$ in $\mathbf{L}_2(Q_T)$.

Thus, we have proved that it is possible to select a subsequence $\mathbf{v}^{n_k}(x, t)$ which converges to $\mathbf{v}$ strongly in $\mathbf{L}_2(Q_T)$ and weakly in $\mathbf{L}_2(\Omega)$, uniformly in t, and such that $\partial \mathbf{v}^{n_k}/\partial x_m$ converges weakly in $\mathbf{L}_2(Q_T)$. This guarantees that the limit function $\mathbf{v}$ is an element of $\mathbf{L}_2(\Omega)$ for all $t \in [0, T]$, and that $\mathbf{v}$ depends continuously on t in the weak topology of $\mathbf{L}_2(\Omega)$. Moreover, $\mathbf{v}$ is square-summable over Q_T and has generalized derivatives $\mathbf{v}_{x_k}$ which are square-summable over Q_T, and for all

t and almost all t_1 in $[0, T]$ (including $t_1 = 0$), $\mathbf{v}$ satisfies the inequality (51). In addition, in his paper [14], Hopf proves that

$$\| \mathbf{v}(x, t) - \mathbf{a}(x) \| \to 0 \text{ as } t \to 0.$$

The function $\mathbf{v}(x, t)$ is a weak solution of the problem. In fact, it obviously satisfies the conditions div $\mathbf{v} = 0$ and $\mathbf{v}|_S = 0$. Moreover, the proof that $\mathbf{v}$ satisfies the identity (53) is carried out in just the same way as in Sec. 3. The term

$$\int_0^T \int_\Omega v_i^{n_k} \mathbf{v}_{x_i}^{n_k} \cdot \mathbf{\Phi}^m \, dx \, dt$$

might cause some misgivings, but, because of the strong convergence of $\mathbf{v}^{n_k}$ to $\mathbf{v}$ and the weak convergence of $\mathbf{v}_{x_i}^{n_k}$ to $\mathbf{v}_{x_i}$, this term also has a limit, which equals

$$\int_0^T \int_\Omega v_i \mathbf{v}_{x_i} \cdot \mathbf{\Phi}^m \, dx \, dt.$$

This completes the proof of Theorem 11.

Thus, we have established the existence of at least one weak solution of the problem (1) for all $t \in [0, T]$. It can be shown that this solution has derivatives $\mathbf{v}_t$ and $\mathbf{v}_{x_i x_j}$ which are summable over Q_T with exponent 5/4 (for two space variables, this exponent is 3/2). We shall prove this fact for weak solutions of the Cauchy problem (see Sec. 8), from which in turn, it can easily be deduced that for the weak solutions $\mathbf{v}$ of the boundary-value problem, $\mathbf{v}_t$ and $\mathbf{v}_{x_i x_j}$ are summable with exponent 5/4 over any interior subdomain of the cylinder Q_T.

However, even when these properties of weak solutions are known, no one has succeded in proving the uniqueness of the weak solution. The relation (56) given below may turn out to be useful. Let $\mathbf{v}'(x, t)$ and $\mathbf{v}''(x, t)$, $x = (x_1, x_2)$, be two weak solutions corresponding to $\mathbf{f}(x, t)$ and $\mathbf{a}(x)$. Since $\mathbf{v}'$ and $\mathbf{v}''$ satisfy (54), we find that

$$\int_0^t \int_\Omega (-\mathbf{u} \cdot \mathbf{\Phi}_t + \nu \mathbf{u}_{x_i} \cdot \mathbf{\Phi}_{x_i} + u_k \mathbf{v}'_{x_k} \cdot \mathbf{\Phi} + v''_k \mathbf{u}_{x_k} \cdot \mathbf{\Phi}) \, dx \, dt + \int_\Omega \mathbf{u}(x, t) \cdot \mathbf{\Phi}(x, t) \, dx = 0 \tag{55}$$

for $\mathbf{u} = \mathbf{v}' - \mathbf{v}''$. If we could set $\mathbf{\Phi} = \mathbf{u}$, then (55) would imply

$$\frac{1}{2} \int_\Omega \mathbf{u}^2(x, t) \, dx + \nu \int_0^t \varphi^2(\tau) \, d\tau = - \int_0^t \int_\Omega u_k \mathbf{v}'_{x_k} \cdot \mathbf{u} \, dx \, dt, \tag{56}$$

where

$$\varphi^2(t) = \int_\Omega \sum_{i,j=1}^2 u_{i x_j}^2 \, dx.$$

To give a rigorous proof of the relation (56), we have to take $\mathbf{\Phi}(x, t)$ in (55) to be

$$\mathbf{\Phi}(x, t) = \mathbf{u}_\varrho(x, t) = \frac{1}{2\varrho} \int\limits_{t-\varrho}^{t+\varrho} \mathbf{u}(x, \tau)\, d\tau$$

$$= \int\limits_0^t \frac{\mathbf{u}(x, \tau + \varrho) - \mathbf{u}(x, \tau - \varrho)}{2\varrho}\, d\tau$$

(assuming that $\mathbf{u}(x, t) = 0$ for $t < 0$), and then let ϱ approach zero. It can be shown that this leads to (56).

It follows from the relation (56) and the inequality (1) of Chap. 1, Sec. 1, for the case of two space variables, that $\mathbf{u} \equiv 0$. In fact, this inequality and the inequality $2ab \leqslant \varepsilon a^2 + (b^2/\varepsilon)$ imply

$$\left| \int\limits_\Omega u_k \mathbf{v}'_{x_k} \cdot \mathbf{u}\, dx \right| \leqslant \sqrt{2}\, \tilde{\varphi}(t) \Big(\sum_j \int\limits_\Omega u_j^4\, dx \Big)^{1/2}$$

$$\leqslant \sqrt{2}\, \tilde{\varphi}(t) \sum_j \Big(2 \int\limits_\Omega u_j^2\, dx \int\limits_\Omega \operatorname{grad}^2 u_j\, dx \Big)^{1/2} \tag{57}$$

$$\leqslant \frac{\nu}{2} \varphi^2(t) + \frac{2}{\nu} \tilde{\varphi}^2(t) \int\limits_\Omega \mathbf{u}^2\, dx;$$

where

$$\tilde{\varphi}^2(t) = \int\limits_\Omega \sum_{i,k} v'^2_{ix_k}\, dx.$$

Substituting this estimate in (56) gives

$$\frac{1}{2} \| \mathbf{u}(x, t) \|^2 + \nu \int\limits_0^t \varphi^2(t)\, dt$$

$$\leqslant \frac{\nu}{2} \int\limits_0^t \varphi^2(t)\, dt + \frac{2}{\nu} \int\limits_0^t \tilde{\varphi}^2(t) \| \mathbf{u} \|^2\, dt.$$

This implies the inequality

$$\| \mathbf{u}(x, t) \|^2 \leqslant \frac{4}{\nu} \int\limits_0^t \tilde{\varphi}^2(t) \| \mathbf{u} \|^2\, dt,$$

from which it follows that $\mathbf{u} \equiv 0$, since $\int\limits_0^t \tilde{\varphi}^2(t)\, dt < \infty$. For the case of three space variables, the estimate (1) of Chap. 1, Sec. 1, and hence the estimate (57), are no longer true. Instead of these estimates, one can give a whole series of other estimates, e.g.,

$$\left|\int_\Omega u_k \mathbf{v}'_{x_k} \cdot \mathbf{u}\, dx\right| \leqslant \sqrt{3}\, \tilde{\varphi}(t) \sum_j \left(\int_\Omega u_j^4\, dx\right)^{1/4}$$

$$\leqslant \sqrt{3}\, \tilde{\varphi}(t) \sum_j \left[4 \left(\int_\Omega u_j^2\, dx\right)^{1/2} \left(\int_\Omega \operatorname{grad}^2 u_j\, dx\right)^{3/2}\right]^{1/4}$$

$$\leqslant \frac{\nu}{2} \varphi^2 + \frac{243}{2\nu^3} \tilde{\varphi}^4 \| \mathbf{u} \|^2.$$

Then, arguing just as before in the two-dimensional case, we can prove that $\mathbf{u} \equiv 0$ if we assume that $\mathbf{v}'$ is such that $\int_0^t \tilde{\varphi}^4(t)\, dt < \infty$. Instead of this condition, one could require the integral

$$\int_0^t \| \mathbf{v}'(x, t) \|^8_{\mathbf{L}_4(\Omega)}\, dt$$

to be finite.

In proving Theorem 11, we assumed that the domain Ω is bounded. However, it is not hard to see that Theorem 11 remains true for unbounded domains, in particular, for the Cauchy problem. It is only necessary to choose $\mathbf{\Phi}$ in the identity (53) to be a function of compact support in x, which falls off sufficiently rapidly so that all the integrals appearing in (53) converge. It is not hard to verify the proof of our assertion by starting from Theorem 11. In fact, consider a monotonically increasing sequence of cylinders $Q_n = \{|x| \leqslant R_n,\ 0 \leqslant t \leqslant T\}$, and the corresponding weak solutions $\mathbf{v}_n$. The sequence $\{\mathbf{v}_n\}$ has a subsequence whose limit is the solution we are looking for. All passages to the limit are accomplished as before, and it is only necessary to take the function $\mathbf{\Phi}$ to be of compact support when verifying that the identity (53) holds.

Next, we answer the following question concerning weak solutions: Suppose there are many weak solutions of the problem (1), so that from the sequence $\{\mathbf{v}^n(x, t)\}$ one can in general select subsequences converging to different functions. Suppose the problem (1) has one "good" solution $\mathbf{v}(x, t)$, e.g., the generalized solution in the sense of our previous definition. Then, can this solution $\mathbf{v}$ be found among the limit elements of the sequence $\{\mathbf{v}^n\}$? As we now show, this will be the case if the basis functions $\mathbf{a}^k(x)$ are chosen in a special way.

THEOREM 12. *Let* $\mathbf{v}(x, t)$ *be the generalized solution of the problem* (1), *and let the functions* $\{\mathbf{a}^k(x)\}$ *form a basis in* $H(\Omega)$ *and in* $\mathbf{L}_4(\Omega)$, *which is orthonormal in* $\mathbf{L}_2(\Omega)$. *Then, the entire sequence of approximate solutions*

$\mathbf{v}^n(x, t)$, *calculated by Galerkin's method in the basis* $\{\mathbf{a}^k\}$, *converges to* $\mathbf{v}(x, t)$.

Proof: Let P_n denote the projection operator which associates with any function $\boldsymbol{\varphi}(x)$ the partial sum of its Fourier series with respect to the system $\{\mathbf{a}^k(x)\}$:

$$P_n \boldsymbol{\varphi} = \sum_{k=1}^{n} (\varphi, \mathbf{a}^k)\, \mathbf{a}^k(x).$$

It is easy to see that the P_n are bounded operators in the spaces $H(\Omega)$ and $\mathbf{L}_4(\Omega)$. On the other hand, they converge strongly to the unit operator in these spaces. Therefore, by the Banach-Steinhaus theorem, their norms in both spaces are uniformly bounded, i.e.,

$$\| P_n \|_{H(\Omega)} \leqslant C \quad \text{and} \quad \| P_n \|_{\mathbf{L}_4(\Omega)} \leqslant C.$$

For

$$\mathbf{v}^{(n)}(x, t) = \sum_{k=1}^{n} \big(\mathbf{v}(x, t),\, \mathbf{a}^k(x)\big)\, \mathbf{a}^k(x) \equiv \sum_{k=1}^{n} c_k\, \mathbf{a}^k(x),$$

this gives the estimates

$$\| \mathbf{v}^{(n)}(x, t) \|_{H(\Omega)} = \| P_n \mathbf{v} \|_{H(\Omega)} \leqslant C \| \mathbf{v}(x, t) \|_{H(\Omega)}$$

and

$$\| \mathbf{v}^{(n)}(x, t) \|_{\mathbf{L}_4(\Omega)} \leqslant C \| \mathbf{v}(x, t) \|_{\mathbf{L}_4(\Omega)}.$$

Since, for the generalized solution $\mathbf{v}(x, t)$, the integrals

$$\int_\Omega \sum_{k=1}^{3} v_k^4(x, t)\, dx, \quad t \in [0, T] \quad \text{and} \quad \int_0^T \| \mathbf{v}(x, t) \|^2_{H(\Omega)}\, dt$$

are bounded, it follows from what has been said that the integrals

$$\int_\Omega \sum_{k=1}^{3} [v_k^{(n)}(x, t)]^4\, dx, \quad t \in [0, T]$$

are uniformly bounded, and that as $n \to \infty$, $\mathbf{v}^{(n)}(x, t)$ converges to $\mathbf{v}(x, t)$ in the $H(\Omega)$ norm for almost all $t \in [0, T]$, while $\int_0^T \| \mathbf{v}^{(n)} - \mathbf{v} \|^2_H\, dt \to 0$.

The $\mathbf{v}^n$ satisfy the relation (35), which can be written in the form

$$\frac{d}{dt}(\mathbf{v}^n, \mathbf{a}^l) + \nu(\mathbf{v}^n_{x_i}, \mathbf{a}^l_{x_i}) = (v_k^n \mathbf{v}^n, \mathbf{a}^l_{x_k}) + (\mathbf{f}, \mathbf{a}^l) \tag{58}$$

$$(l = 1, 2, \ldots, n),$$

and similar relations are satisfied by $\mathbf{v}$ for all l. Therefore, we have

$$\frac{d}{dt}(\mathbf{v}^{(n)}, \mathbf{a}^l) + \nu(\mathbf{v}^{(n)}_{x_i}, \mathbf{a}^l_{x_i}) = (v^{(n)}_k \mathbf{v}^{(n)}, \mathbf{a}^l_{x_k}) + (\mathbf{f}, \mathbf{a}^l) + I^n_l \quad (l \leqslant n) \tag{59}$$

where

$$I^n_l = -\nu(\mathbf{v}_{x_i} - \mathbf{v}^{(n)}_{x_i}, \mathbf{a}^l_{x_i}) + (v_k \mathbf{v} - v^{(n)}_k \mathbf{v}^{(n)}, \mathbf{a}^l_{x_k}).$$

We now write $\mathbf{v}^n - \mathbf{v}^{(n)} = \mathbf{R}^n(x, t)$. Subtracting (59) from (58), multiplying the result by $c_{ln}(t) - c_l(t)$, and summing over l from 1 to n, we obtain

$$\frac{1}{2}\frac{d}{dt}(\mathbf{R}^n, \mathbf{R}^n) + \nu(\mathbf{R}^n_{x_i}, \mathbf{R}^n_{x_i}) = (v^n_k \mathbf{v}^n - v^{(n)}_k \mathbf{v}^{(n)}, \mathbf{R}^n_{x_k}) + I^n, \tag{60}$$

where

$$I^n = -\nu(\mathbf{v}_{x_i} - \mathbf{v}^{(n)}_{x_i}, \mathbf{R}^n_{x_i}) + (v_k \mathbf{v} - v^{(n)}_k \mathbf{v}^{(n)}, \mathbf{R}^n_{x_k}).$$

Next, we estimate the terms appearing in the right-hand side of (60) by using Hölder's inequality, Minkowski's inequality and the inequality (3) from Chap. 1, Sec. 1. We estimate the first term as

$$\begin{aligned} |(v^n_k \mathbf{v}^n - v^{(n)}_k \mathbf{v}^{(n)}, \mathbf{R}^n_{x_k})| &= |(v^n_k \mathbf{R}^n, \mathbf{R}^n_{x_k}) + (R^n_k \mathbf{v}^{(n)}, \mathbf{R}^n_{x_k})| \\ &= |(R^n_k \mathbf{v}^{(n)}, \mathbf{R}^n_{x_k})| \leqslant \|\mathbf{R}^n\|_H \left(\int_\Omega \sum_{i,k=1}^{3} (R^n_k v^{(n)}_i)^2\, dx\right)^{1/2} \\ &\leqslant \sqrt{3}\,\|\mathbf{R}^n\|_H \left(\sum_{i=1}^{3}\int_\Omega |v^n_i|^4\, dx\right)^{1/4} \left(\sum_{k=1}^{3}\int_\Omega |R^n_k|^4\, dx\right)^{1/4} \\ &\leqslant C\,\|\mathbf{R}^n\|_H \,\|\mathbf{R}^n\|^{1/4}\,\|\mathbf{R}^n\|_H^{3/4} \\ &\leqslant C\,\|\mathbf{R}^n\|_H \left(\frac{\|\mathbf{R}^n\|}{4\varepsilon^4} + \frac{3}{4}\varepsilon^{4/3}\,\|\mathbf{R}^n\|_H\right), \end{aligned}$$

where ε is any positive number. Choosing ε so that $\frac{3}{4}\varepsilon^{4/3} C = \frac{\nu}{2}$, we have

$$|(v^n_k \mathbf{v}^n - \mathbf{v}^{(n)}_k \mathbf{v}^{(n)}, \mathbf{R}^n_{x_k})| \leqslant \frac{\nu}{2}\|\mathbf{R}^n\|^2_H + C_1\|\mathbf{R}^n\|_H\|\mathbf{R}^n\|.$$

For the second term in the right-hand side of (60), we have the estimate

$$|I^n| \leqslant \nu \|\mathbf{R}^n\|_H \|\mathbf{v} - \mathbf{v}^{(n)}\|_H$$

$$+ \|\mathbf{R}^n\|_H \left(\sum_{i,k=1}^{3} \int_\Omega (v_k v_i - v_k^{(n)} v_i^{(n)})^2 \, dx \right)^{1/2}$$

$$\leqslant \nu \|\mathbf{R}^n\|_H \|\mathbf{v} - \mathbf{v}^{(n)}\|_H + \|\mathbf{R}^n\|_H \left\{ 6 \left[\sum_{k=1}^{3} \int_\Omega v_k^4 \, dx \right]^{1/2} \left[\sum_{i=1}^{3} \int_\Omega (v_i - v_i^{(n)}) \, dx \right]^{1/2} \right.$$

$$\left. + 6 \left[\sum_{i=1}^{3} \int_\Omega (v_i^{(n)})^4 \, dx \right]^{1/2} \left[\sum_{k=1}^{3} \int_\Omega (v_k - v_k^{(n)})^4 \, dx \right]^{1/2} \right\}^{1/2}$$

$$\leqslant C_2 \|\mathbf{R}^n\|_H \|\mathbf{v} - \mathbf{v}^{(n)}\|_H .$$

Substituting these estimates in (60), we obtain

$$\frac{1}{2} \frac{d}{dt} \|\mathbf{R}^n\|^2 + \nu \|\mathbf{R}^n\|_H^2 \leqslant \frac{\nu}{2} \|\mathbf{R}^n\|_H^2 + C_1 \|\mathbf{R}^n\|_H \|\mathbf{R}^n\|$$

$$+ C_2 \|\mathbf{R}^n\|_H \|\mathbf{v} - \mathbf{v}^{(n)}\|_H \leqslant \frac{\nu}{2} \|\mathbf{R}^n\|_H^2 + \frac{\nu}{4} \|\mathbf{R}^n\|_H^2$$

$$+ \frac{C_1^2}{\nu} \|\mathbf{R}^n\|^2 + \frac{\nu}{4} \|\mathbf{R}^n\|_H^2 + \frac{C_2^2}{\nu} \|\mathbf{v} - \mathbf{v}^{(n)}\|_H^2 ,$$

so that

$$\frac{1}{2} \frac{d}{dt} \|\mathbf{R}^n\|^2 \leqslant \frac{C_1^2}{\nu} \|\mathbf{R}^n\|^2 + \frac{C_2^2}{\nu} \|\mathbf{v} - \mathbf{v}^{(n)}\|_H^2 .$$

From this, we find in a familiar way, that $\|\mathbf{R}^n\| \to 0$ as $n \to \infty$, since $\int_0^T \|\mathbf{v} - \mathbf{v}^{(n)}\|_H^2 \, dt \to 0$ as $n \to \infty$. This proves Theorem 12.

In the paper [40], still another attempt is made to prove that the problem (1) has a unique solution "in the large" without any restrictions on the size of the data of the problem. The idea is the following: An additional viscosity $\varepsilon > 0$ is introduced in the Navier-Stokes system (or else averaging is introduced in the nonlinear terms $(v_k)_\varrho \mathbf{v}_{x_k}$). Then, it is proved that the modified system has a unique solution "in the large," and finally, it is shown that the whole set of solutions $\mathbf{v}^\varepsilon(x, t)$ which are found has a unique limit as $\varepsilon \to 0$ (or as $\varrho \to 0$). It is then natural to call this limit the solution of the original problem (1).

In this way, we obtain the following provisional result:

THEOREM 13. *The problem*

$$\left.\begin{aligned} \mathbf{v}_t^\varepsilon + \varepsilon \Delta^2 \mathbf{v}^\varepsilon - \nu \Delta \mathbf{v}^\varepsilon + v_k^\varepsilon \mathbf{v}_{x_k}^\varepsilon + \operatorname{grad} p^\varepsilon = \mathbf{f}, \\ \operatorname{div} \mathbf{v}^\varepsilon = 0, \quad \mathbf{v}^\varepsilon|_S = \Delta \mathbf{v}^\varepsilon|_S = 0, \quad \mathbf{v}^\varepsilon|_{t=0} = \mathbf{a}(x) \end{aligned}\right\} \tag{61}$$

has a unique solution $\mathbf{v}^\varepsilon(x, t)$, p^ε *in* Q_T (*where* T *is any positive number*), *if*

$$\varepsilon > 0, \nu \geqslant 0, \ \mathbf{f} \in \mathbf{L}_2(Q_T), \ \mathbf{a}(x) \in W_2^2(\Omega) \cap J_{0,1}(\Omega).$$

If $\{\mathbf{v}^\varepsilon\}$ *satisfies the inequality*

$$\int_\Omega \sum_{k=1}^{3} |v_k^\varepsilon(x, t)|^{3+\delta} dx \leqslant C(\delta) \tag{62}$$

for some $\delta > 0$, *with the same constant* $C(\delta)$ *for all* $\varepsilon > 0$, *then as* $\varepsilon \to 0$, *the whole sequence of solutions* $\{\mathbf{v}_\varepsilon\}$ *has a unique limit* $\mathbf{v}$, *which must be the weak solution of the problem* (1).

7. Unbounded Domains

Most of the theorems of this chapter are equally valid for both bounded and unbounded domains Ω. However, the requirement that $\mathbf{a}(x)$ be square-summable over Ω has excluded from consideration cases where a nonzero velocity $\mathbf{v}_\infty$ is specified at infinity ($|x| = \infty$). In the preceding chapters, we showed that these more general cases can often be reduced to cases already considered, or to cases close to those considered, by introducing instead of $\mathbf{v}$ a new unknown function $\mathbf{u}(x, t) = \mathbf{v}(x, t) - \mathbf{b}(x)$. Thus, for example, if $\mathbf{a}(x) = \mathbf{v}(x, 0)$ is such that

$$\mathbf{a}_{x_k} \text{ and } \mathbf{a}_{x_k x_j} \in \mathbf{L}_2(\Omega), \quad \max_{|x| \gg 1} |\mathbf{a}, \mathbf{a}_{x_k}| \leqslant \text{const}, \quad \operatorname{div} \mathbf{a} = 0,$$

then we use $\mathbf{a}$ to construct a solenoidal vector field $\mathbf{b}(x)$, which is twice continuously differentiable and has the following properties in Ω:

$$\mathbf{b}|_S = 0, \quad \max_{x \in \Omega} |\mathbf{b}, \mathbf{b}_{x_k}| \leqslant \text{const}, \quad \mathbf{b}_{x_k}, \Delta \mathbf{b} \text{ and } (\mathbf{a} - \mathbf{b}) \in \mathbf{L}_2(\Omega).$$

Then, for the function $\mathbf{u}(x, t) = \mathbf{v}(x, t) - \mathbf{b}(x)$, we have the system

$$\mathbf{u}_t - \nu \Delta \mathbf{u} + (u_k + b_k)(\mathbf{u}_{x_k} + \mathbf{b}_{x_k}) = -\operatorname{grad} p + \mathbf{f} + \nu \Delta \mathbf{b}, \tag{63}$$

$$\operatorname{div} \mathbf{u} = 0, \quad \mathbf{u}|_S = 0, \quad \mathbf{u}(x, 0) = \mathbf{a}(x) - \mathbf{b}(x) \in \mathbf{L}_2(\Omega). \tag{64}$$

The problem (63), (64) differs from the problem already studied only by unessential terms (i.e., linear terms with bounded coefficients), and can be treated similarly. In fact, all the existence theorems which we have proved for the system (1) are also valid for the system (63), (64). The situation is different, however, in studying the behavior of the solution **u** as $t \to \infty$. The presence of the term $u_k \mathbf{b}_{x_k}$ in the system (63) (in the three-dimensional case, instead of **b** we can take the solution of the stationary problem with the given velocity at infinity, and then the terms $b_k \mathbf{b}_{x_k}$ and $\nu \Delta \mathbf{b}$ cancel each other) makes it impossible to assert that estimates of the type (9) and (10) hold, which played a decisive role in our analysis of the behavior of solutions as $t \to \infty$. In particular, we cannot prove that the solution **u** remains bounded in some norm for all $t \geqslant 0$. Nevertheless, it is our opinion that in the problem considered here (i. e., nonstationary flow past an object when a constant velocity $\mathbf{v}_\infty$ is specified at ∞), the solution **u** is bounded for all $t \leqslant 0$. For sufficiently small Reynolds numbers, the solution converges to the solution of the stationary problem, just as in the case of Theorem 10 (this can be proved rigorously). However, for arbitrary Reynolds numbers, it does not converge to a definite stationary solution, but, while remaining bounded, forms a so-called "stable turbulent flow."

8. The Cauchy Problem for the Generalized Navier-Stokes System

In Chap. 4, Sec. 5, we proved that the solution $\mathbf{v}(x, t)$ of the Cauchy problem for the linearized system of Navier-Stokes equations corresponding to zero initial conditions and to a force $\mathbf{f} \in \mathbf{L}_r(x, t)$ $(r > 1)$ is summable in (x, t) with the same exponent r, together with $\mathbf{v}_t$, $\mathbf{v}_{x_k}$, $\mathbf{v}_{x_k x_j}$ and p_{x_k}. We now use this result to prove the following theorem:

THEOREM 14. *At all times $t \geqslant 0$, there exists at least one solution $\mathbf{v}, p$ of the Cauchy problem for the general nonlinear system of Navier-Stokes equations, where $\mathbf{f} \in \mathbf{L}_{5/4}(x, t) \cap \mathbf{L}_2(x, t)$ and $\mathbf{a} \equiv 0$. This solution is such that $\mathbf{v}_{x_k} \in \mathbf{L}_{5/4}(x, t) \cap \mathbf{L}_2(x, t)$ and $\mathbf{v}, \mathbf{v}_t, \mathbf{v}_{x_i x_j} \in \mathbf{L}_{5/4}(x, t)$, $p_{x_i} \in \mathbf{L}_{5/4}(x, t)$. Moreover, for all $t \geqslant 0$, $\mathbf{v}(x, t) \in \mathbf{L}_2(E^n)$ and is continuous in t, and the Navier-Stokes equations are satisfied almost everywhere.*

Proof: For brevity, let us assume that we have zero initial conditions. We take a strip $0 \leqslant t \leqslant T$ of arbitrary fixed height. Since by hypothesis, $\mathbf{f}(x, t)$ is square-summable over this strip, there exists at least one weak solution $\mathbf{v}(x, t)$, $p(x, t)$ of the the problem corresponding to **f** (as proved in Sec. 6 of this chapter). This solution satisfies the identity

$$\iint_{0 \leqslant t \leqslant T} (-\mathbf{v} \cdot \mathbf{\Phi}_t + \nu \mathbf{v}_{x_i} \cdot \mathbf{\Phi}_{x_i})\, dx\, dt = \iint_{0 \leqslant t \leqslant T} (\mathbf{f} - v_k \mathbf{v}_{x_k}) \cdot \mathbf{\Phi}\, dx\, dt. \quad (65)$$

The initial conditions for $\mathbf{v}$ are taken to be zero, while the function $\mathbf{\Phi}$ must be smooth, solenoidal, and equal to zero for $t = T$ and large $|x|$. We know that for the solution $\mathbf{v}$, the integrals

$$\int\limits_{0 \leqslant t \leqslant T}\int \sum_i \mathbf{v}_{x_i}^2 \, dx \, dt \leqslant C(T) \qquad \text{and} \qquad \int \mathbf{v}^2(x, t) \, dx \leqslant C_1$$

are bounded, which shows that the functions $v_k \, v_{ix_k}$ are summable with exponent 5/4 over the strip $0 \leqslant t \leqslant T$. This implies that the identity (65) holds not only for $\mathbf{\Phi}(x, t)$ of compact support, but also, for example, for $\mathbf{\Phi}$ which, together with their derivatives $\mathbf{\Phi}_t$ and $\mathbf{\Phi}_{x_i}$, fall off uniformly in x like $|x|^{-2}$. This remark will be useful later. To prove that the $v_k \, v_{ix_k}$ are really summable with exponent 5/4 over the strip $0 \leqslant t \leqslant T$, we use Hölder's inequality and the inequality (3) of Chap. 1, Sec. 1, obtaining

$$\int\limits_{0 \leqslant t \leqslant T}\int |v_k \, v_{ix_k}|^{5/4} \, dx \, dt \leqslant \Big(\int\limits_{0 \leqslant t \leqslant T}\int v_{ix_k}^2 \, dx \, dt \Big)^{5/8}$$
$$\times \Big(\int\limits_{0 \leqslant t \leqslant T}\int v_k^{10/3} \, dx \, dt \Big)^{3/8} \leqslant C^{5/8}(T) \Big(\int\limits_{0 \leqslant t \leqslant T}\int v_k^{2/3} \, v_k^{8/3} \, dx \, dt \Big)^{3/8}$$
$$\leqslant C^{5/8}(T) \Big\{ \int_0^T \big[\big(\int v_k^2 \, dx\big)^{1/3} \big(\int v_k^4 \, dx\big)^{2/3} \big] \, dx \Big\}^{3/8}$$
$$\leqslant C^{5/8}(T) \Big\{ \int_0^T \Big[C_1^{1/3} \, 4^{2/3} \big(\int v_k^2 \, dx\big)^{1/3} \int \sum_j v_{kx_j}^2 \, dx \Big] \, dt \Big\}^{3/8}$$
$$\leqslant C^{5/8}(T) \sqrt{2} \, C_1^{1/4} \Big(\int\limits_{0 \leqslant t \leqslant T}\int \sum_j v_{kx_j}^2 \, dx \, dt \Big)^{3/8} \leqslant C(T) \sqrt[4]{4 C_1} \, .$$

Thus, we actually have $v_k \, v_{ix_k} \in L_{5/4}(x, t)$ for all i, k.

We now regard the function $\boldsymbol{\psi} = \mathbf{f} - v_k \, \mathbf{v}_{x_k}$ in the identity (65) as a free term (it is summable with exponent 5/4 over the strip $0 \leqslant t \leqslant T$), and we regard the function $\mathbf{v}$ as the generalized solution of the Cauchy problem for the linearized Navier-Stokes equations, with the free term $\boldsymbol{\psi}(x, t)$ and zero initial conditions. We choose $\mathbf{\Phi}$ in (65) to be an arbitrary solution of the adjoint linearized problem (25) of Chap. 4, Sec. 5, corresponding to any smooth vector $\mathbf{F}(x, t)$ of compact support and zero initial conditions $\mathbf{\Phi}(x, T) = 0$.* For such a $\mathbf{\Phi}$, the identity (65) can be written in the form

$$\int\limits_{0 \leqslant t \leqslant T}\int \mathbf{v} \cdot (-\mathbf{\Phi}_t - \nu \, \Delta \mathbf{\Phi}) \, dx \, dt = \int\limits_{0 \leqslant t \leqslant T}\int \boldsymbol{\psi} \cdot \mathbf{\Phi} \, dx \, dt. \tag{66}$$

The equality

$$\int\limits_{0 \leqslant t \leqslant T}\int \mathbf{v}_{x_i} \cdot \mathbf{\Phi}_{x_i} \, dx \, dt = - \int\limits_{0 \leqslant t \leqslant T}\int \mathbf{v} \cdot \Delta \mathbf{\Phi} \, dx \, dt$$

* As noted above (Chap. 4, Sec. 5), $\mathbf{\Phi}$ falls off sufficiently rapidly.

is a consequence of the fact that $\mathbf{v}$, $\mathbf{v}_{x_i}$, $\mathbf{\Phi}_{x_i}$ and $\Delta\mathbf{\Phi}$ are square-summable over the strip $0 \leqslant t \leqslant T$. In fact, the integrals appearing in both sides of the equality converge, and the integral

$$J = \int_0^T \int_{|x|=R} \mathbf{v} \cdot \frac{\partial \mathbf{\Phi}}{\partial n} \, dS \, dt$$

converges to zero as $R \to \infty$ along any subsequence R_k, since

$$|J| \leqslant \frac{1}{2} \int_0^T \int_{|x|=R} \left[\mathbf{v}^2 + \left(\frac{\partial \mathbf{\Phi}}{\partial n} \right)^2 \right] dS \, dt$$

and the integral

$$\int_0^\infty dR \int_0^T \int_{|x|=R} \left[\mathbf{v}^2 + \sum_{i=1}^3 \mathbf{\Phi}_{x_i}^2 \right] dS \, dt < \infty.$$

Thus, the equality (66) is proved.

We now use the results of Chap. 4, Sec. 5. There it was proved that a unique solution $\mathbf{v}'(x, t)$ of the linearized Cauchy problem with zero initial conditions ($\mathbf{v}'(x, 0) = 0$) corresponds to any function $\boldsymbol{\psi} \in \mathbf{L}_{5/4}(x, t)$. This solution $\mathbf{v}'$ satisfies the identity (66) with the same $\mathbf{\Phi}$ as for $\mathbf{v}$, and $\mathbf{v}'$, $\mathbf{v}'_t$, $\mathbf{v}'_{x_i}$, $\mathbf{v}'_{x_i x_j} \in \mathbf{L}_{5/4}(x, t)$, $p'_{x_i} \in L_{5/4}(x, t)$. Subtracting the identity (66) written for $\mathbf{v}'$ from the identity (66) written for $\mathbf{v}$, we obtain

$$\iint_{0 \leqslant t \leqslant T} (\mathbf{v} - \mathbf{v}') \cdot (-\mathbf{\Phi}_t - \nu \Delta \mathbf{\Phi}) \, dx \, dt = 0. \tag{67}$$

The identity (67) is equivalent to the identity

$$\iint_{0 \leqslant t \leqslant T} (\mathbf{v} - \mathbf{v}') \cdot (\mathbf{F} + \operatorname{grad} Q) \, dx \, dt = 0, \tag{68}$$

since $\mathbf{\Phi}$ is a solution of the Cauchy problem (25) of Chap. 4, Sec. 5. The integrals

$$\iint_{0 \leqslant t \leqslant T} \mathbf{v} \cdot \operatorname{grad} Q \, dx \, dt \quad \text{and} \quad \iint_{0 \leqslant t \leqslant T} \mathbf{v}' \cdot \operatorname{grad} Q \, dx \, dt$$

vanish (see Chap. 4, Sec. 5), and as a result, (68) reduces to

$$\iint_{0 \leqslant t \leqslant T} (\mathbf{v} - \mathbf{v}') \cdot \mathbf{F} \, dx \, dt = 0.$$

This implies that $\mathbf{v}$ and $\mathbf{v}'$ coincide, since $\mathbf{F}(x, t)$ is an arbitrary smooth vector function of compact support. We have thereby proved that the weak solution $\mathbf{v}$ has derivatives $\mathbf{v}_t$, $\mathbf{v}_{x_i x_j}$ which are summable, together with p_{x_i}, with exponent 5/4 over the strip $0 \leqslant t \leqslant T$. Here, we have imposed no restrictions whatsoever on the size of $\mathbf{f}$, and the assumption that $\mathbf{v}(x, 0) = 0$ is not essential. This completes the proof of Theorem 14.

The result just obtained also holds for boundary-value problems, However, we shall not give the proof here, since, on the one hand, the proof is based on the use of the theory of nonstationary hydrodynamical potentials and is quite lengthy, and on the other hand, it does not give a complete solution of the whole problem. This is because the question of a uniqueness theorem for the generalized solution $\mathbf{v}$ just found is still open (the existence of $\mathbf{v}$ "in the large" is guaranteed).

Finally, we note that the solution of the Cauchy problem has the following stability in the infinite time interval: Suppose that for all $t \geqslant 0$, a constant velocity $\mathbf{b} = \mathbf{const}$ is maintained at infinity ($|x| = \infty$), and suppose that the initial conditions $\mathbf{a}(x) = \mathbf{v}(x, 0)$ are such that $\mathbf{a}(x) - \mathbf{b} \in \mathbf{L}_2(E^n)$. Then, the solution $\mathbf{v}(x, t)$ of the nonhomogeneous system (1) converges to $\mathbf{b}$ as $t \to \infty$, provided only that

$$\int_0^\infty \left[\int \mathbf{f}^2(x, t)\, dx\right]^{1/2} dt < \infty .$$

In fact, the difference $\mathbf{u}(x, t) = \mathbf{v}(x, t) - \mathbf{b}$ satisfies the system

$$\mathbf{u}_t - \nu \Delta \mathbf{u} + (u_k + b_k)\, \mathbf{u}_{x_k} = -\operatorname{grad} p + \mathbf{f},$$
$$\operatorname{div} \mathbf{u} = 0 .$$

Therefore, the estimate

$$\int \mathbf{u}^2(x, t)\, dx + 2\nu \int_0^t \int \sum_k \mathbf{u}_{x_k}^2\, dx\, dt \leqslant \text{const}$$

holds for $\mathbf{u}$, which shows that in a definite sense, $\mathbf{u}$ converges to zero as $t \to \infty$.

Comments

Chapter 1

We arrived at inequalities of the type (1), (3), (4) and (5) by studying the Navier-Stokes system. Apparently, the inequalities (13) and (14) were first proved by Leray. At present, far-reaching generalizations of all these inequalities are available in the works of V. P. Ilin, Gagliardo, Nirenberg, and K. K. Golovkin. At our request, a proof of the inequality (6) was given by Golovkin.

S. L. Sobolev proved the important theorem on integrals of the potential type [6], which he used together with an integral representation of an arbitrary function as the basis for proving the so-called *Sobolev imbedding theorems*. Lemma 5 is a slightly strengthened version of Sobolev's theorem on integrals of the potential type, which is due to V. P. Ilin. In this book, we essentially use only Sobolev's theorem, from the proof of which it is easy to see that the second of the inequalities (11) holds for any $\alpha < n - \frac{n}{p} - \lambda$.

The inequalities of Sec. 1.5, involving the $W_2^l(\Omega)$ norms, and their generalizations for derivatives of any order and for second-order operators of the elliptic type were proved by us for the case of the Laplace operator in a paper written in 1950 [41], and for the general case in a paper written in 1951 [42]. Complete proofs of these results are given in [2]. For second-order derivatives, a similar result was obtained simultaneously in 1950—1951 by Caccioppoli [43]. The earliest result in this direction, as it came to light recently (see [44]), dates back to 1910. In fact, in the work of S. N. Bernstein [45], an estimate of $\| D_x^2 u \|_{L_2(\Omega)}$ in terms of $\| L u \|_{L_2(\Omega)}$ is given for the solution $u(x)$ of a second-order elliptic equation $L u = f$ with two independent variables, for the case where Ω is a circle (or any other domain with a sufficiently smooth boundary, which can be mapped conformally into a circle).

The results of Sec. 2 are not new, but our presentation of the material may be of some interest. The beginnings of the study of decompositions of vector fields $\mathbf{L}_2(\Omega)$ into orthogonal subspaces can be found in the work of Weyl [46]. Further investigations of these decompositions were carried out by S. L. Sobolev, S. G. Krein, Friedrichs, by us, and by others. E. B. Bykovski has obtained some interesting results, which are definitive in a certain respect, concerning the character of orthogonal subspaces of the space $\mathbf{L}_2(\Omega)$ and curl operators in them. These results, which partially overlap results of Friedrichs [47] (they were obtained before the appearence of Friedrichs' paper) are collected in a review paper by E. B. Bykhovski and N. V. Smirnov [48].

The spaces $\mathring{D}(\Omega)$ and $H(\Omega)$, which we introduce in Secs. 1.4 and 2.3, have shown themselves to be very useful in studying the solution of boundary-value problems in unbounded domains Ω. In the case of bounded Ω, their metrics are equivalent to the $\mathring{W}_2^1(\Omega)$ metric, in which case $\mathring{D}(\Omega)$ has long been used, beginning with Friedrichs' papers in the 1930's.

Chapters 2 and 3

The linearized stationary problem (Stokes problem) for domains of arbitrary form was first solved by using the methods of potential theory in the works of Lichtenstein and Odqvist (simultaneously and independently). A condensed treatment of this work is given in Odqvist's paper [15]. A note by S. G. Krein [49] gives results on investigations of this problem from the point of view of the theory of semi-bounded operators.

In the beginning of Chap. 2, we give a very simple proof of the solvability of the Stokes problem in the space $H(\Omega)$. (The basic idea of the proof stems from a paper by Friedrichs [4] on elliptic operators.) Then, we show that the solution $\mathbf{v}$ which is found has the derivatives appearing in the system, provided only that the forces $\mathbf{f}$ are square-summable functions. In proving this fact (Theorem 3), we use the averaging operation, which was first used for the same purpose by S. L. Sobolev [5, 6] in proving the smoothness of any generalized solution of Laplace's equation. Subsequently, this idea with different modifications and additions was used by various authors to investigate the differential properties of generalized solutions. A particularly interesting and complete development of this idea was given in the papers of Friedrichs [50]. The reader who is familiar with all this work, will recognize a certain peculiarity in the proof of Theorem 2. A specific feature of our problem is the fact that because of the supplementary requirement that all the arbitrary functions must be solenoidal, we cannot use "cutoff functions", as is done, for example, in the case of elliptic equations.

In Theorem 3 of Chap. 2, we prove the square-summability of the second-order derivatives of $\mathbf{v}$ in any strictly interior subdomain of the domain Ω. However, the proof of the square-summability of $\mathbf{v}_{x_i x_j}$ over all Ω requires other, stronger tools. This was done by V. A. Solonnikov [62], using the theory of potentials, as presented in Chap. 3, Sec. 5. Theorem 2′ of Chap. 3 is also due to Solonnikov.

By using the theory of potentials and methods familiar from the theory of electrostatic potentials, it can be proved that $\mathbf{v} \in C_{2,h}(\bar{\Omega})$ and $p \in C_{1,h}(\bar{\Omega})$, provided only that $\mathbf{f} \in C_{0,h}(\bar{\Omega})$ and $S \in \Lambda_{2,h}$.

Chapter 4

In this chapter, just as in Chap. 2, all our considerations (except those of Sec. 5) are carried out in Hilbert spaces, and besides, it is not our goal to obtain solutions with the weakest hypotheses concerning the data of the problem. This is easily done by using Theorem 1 and additional passages to the limit. As remarked in the text, in proving Theorem 1, we have essentially established the uniqueness theorem for the generalized solution in the class of $\mathbf{L}_2(Q_T)$ functions, i.e., for a solution $\mathbf{v}$ which is square-summable over Q_T and has no derivatives at all.

In Theorem 1, we prove the following result, which is the best in terms of $\mathbf{L}_2(Q_T)$: If $\mathbf{f}(x, t) \in \mathbf{L}_2(Q_T)$, then all the derivatives appearing in the system are square-summable over Q_T. The conditions on $\mathbf{a}(x)$ are also necessary to obtain the solution guaranteed by the theorem.

Much effort has been devoted to the study of the solvability of the linear nonstationary problem. On the whole, all efforts have been devoted towards the construction of a theory of nonstationary hydrodynamical potentials. In the paper [15], Odqvist attempted to construct such a theory, but he did not succed in proving the solvability of the resulting system of singular equations. This problem was first solved by Leray for the case of two independent variables. In fact, in the paper [12], Leray constructed nonstationary hydrodynamical potentials and used them to solve the problem (1), (2) for plane-parallel flows in convex domains Ω. To prove the solvability of the resulting singular integral equations. Leray made essential use of the theory of functions of a complex variable. It is only very recently that success has been achieved in extending these results to the three-dimensional case. This was done by K. K. Golovkin [53] and was perfected by V. A. Solonnikov. Leray's idea turns out to apply to both problems, i.e., to construct a potential theory for a domain of arbitrary form, it is best not to use the fundamental singular solution, but rather the solution of the boundary-value problem for a half-space with a delta-function perturbation on the boundary.

The proof of the results of Sec. 2, concerning the properties of the operator $(\partial/\partial t) - \tilde{\Delta}$ in $L_r(Q_T)$ and in $C_{n,h}(Q_T)$ was begun in the paper [54] and completed by K. K. Golovkin and V. A. Solonnikov. Nonstationary potentials for a half-space were constructed and studied by O. V. Guseva [74], independently of K. K. Golovkin.

The functional method presented in Sec. 1 was the first method to be used successfully to solve the nonstationary problem (1), (2) for arbitrary domains in three-dimensional space. This problem was solved by classical methods only for a series of concrete cases, of which we cite the most interesting, i.e., the papers of B. V. Rusanov [27], in which the problem of flow past a circle and a sphere is studied.

Chapter 5

The nonlinear stationary problem "in the small" was investigated by Lichtenstein and Odqvist. Leray in his article [11] proved a series of very interesting a priori estimates for solutions of this problem. These estimates, together with subsequent results obtained by Leray and Schauder [23] on the solution of nonlinear equations with completely continuous operators, essentially solved the problem of the existence of laminar solutions for any Reynolds number, provided only that the external forces and the boundaries of the objects past which the flow occurs are smooth. Unfortunately, Leray himself did not state this explicitly in his later publications, as a result of which it was thought until very recently [61] (at least in the USSR) that the problem of the existence of laminar flows for any Reynolds number was still open. Moreover, many of the hydrodynamicists and mathematicians concerned with this problem were convinced that laminar flows did not exist for arbitrary Reynolds numbers. This conviction was based on numerous experiments, which always showed that the flow was turbulent for large Reynolds numbers. However, it follows from the results of Chap. 5 that the cause of this effect is not that the solution does not exist, but rather that it is unstable, and possibly non-unique. As shown in this chapter, the stationary problem always has a "good solution," even when the objects past which the flow occurs have corners and edges.

In Chap. 5, we present the material in the paper [61], in which many of Leray's ideas on a priori estimates, stemming from [11], are used.

Theorem 7 of Chap. 5 is a generalization to the case of a nonhomogeneous flow at infinity of a result proved by Leray which states that the solution of the stationary problem converges uniformly to zero as $|x| \to \infty$ in the case of a zero boundary condition at infinity ($\mathbf{v}_\infty = 0$). (As Leray himself noted, his proof is not valid for $\mathbf{v}_\infty \neq 0$.) Theorem 7 was proved in M. D. Faddeyev's thesis (Physics Department, Leningrad University, 1959). Here we have given a somewhat simpler proof of the theorem.

In the work of I. I. Vorovich and V. I. Yudovich [51], the possibility of applying Galerkin's method to solve the stationary problem is investigated, and it is proved that there exists a generalized solution of the problem (1), (15) for the case $(\mathbf{a} \cdot \mathbf{n})|_{S_k} = 0$. They also state a series of results on the dependence of the differential properties of these solutions on the data of the problem.

Chapter 6

In this chapter, we present, for the most part, results obtained in the papers [38, 39], which were preceded by the investigations of Leray [12, 13] and Hopf [14]. Leray proved the unique solvability "in the small" of the boundary-value problem (1) for plane-parallel flows in convex domains. For the same problem, he investigated the behavior of "turbulent solutions" at the possible branch points for all values $t \geqslant 0$ of the time. Moreover, he proved the unique solvability "in the large" of the Cauchy problem for the Navier-Stokes equations for the case of two spatial variables, and for a small time interval in the three-dimensional case. All these results were obtained by using nonstationary hydrodynamical potentials.

In Hopf's paper [14] appearing in 1950–1951, the existence of a weak solution "in the large" for the general boundary-value problem (1) is proved. The novelty of Hopf's approach to the solution of the nonstationary problem should be noted, as expressed in the transition from classical to generalized solutions and in the elaboration of methods of obtaining these generalized solutions directly. In studying hydrodynamical problems, we have started from our papers of 1950—1951 (see [2]), which contain the same approach to the solution of nonstationary boundary-value problems and in which, unlike the paper [14], we justify the legitimacy of this approach, i. e., we prove the corresponding uniqueness theorems for the generalized solutions that are introduced. The theory of "generalized solutions" stems originally from the works of N. M. Gyunter [80], S. L. Sobolev [6—10] and Friedrichs [4]. Concerning the paper [14], we also remark that Hopf's results on the convergence of Galerkin's method can easily be carried over to nonstationary problems for equations of various types (also including differential equations in Hilbert spaces).

In Sec. 4, we present a series of results on investigations of the differential properties of generalized solutions of the problem (1), and we indicate how these results are proved. As shown in the text, investigations inside Q_T are not very difficult. However, to investigate the behavior of $\mathbf{v}$ near the boundary S, it has been necessary to make a detailed study of the operator $(\partial/\partial t) - \tilde{\Delta}$ in various spaces. Such investigations have been carried out by K. K. Golovkin, the author and V. A. Solonnikov in the L_p spaces, and by Golovkin and Solonnikov in the Hölder spaces. The results stated at the beginning of Sec. 1, concerning solvability in various Hölder classes, are also due to Golovkin and Solonnikov. For the case $n = 2$, these results were preceded by the results of the paper [53].

In order to obtain limiting estimates in all the indicated spaces, the nonstationary hydrodynamical potentials discussed in the remarks to Chapter 4 have been used.

In Theorem 12 of Chap. 6, we have required that the set of vectors $\{\mathbf{a}^k(x)\}$ form a basis in $\mathbf{L}_4(\Omega)$. However, up to now there are no general criteria which tell when a set of functions forms a basis in one or another Banach space (including $\mathbf{L}_4(\Omega)$). Because of this, it is useful to note that this requirement on $\{\mathbf{a}^k(x)\}$ can be removed if it is known that the integral

$$\int_0^t \| \mathbf{v}(x, t) \|_H^8 \, dt,$$

involving the generalized solution, is finite.

We now indicate some work done in recent years which is devoted to the solvability of the problem (1). In the notes of M. A. Krasnoselski,

S. G. Krein and P. E. Sobolevski [55, 63, 64], the problem (1) is regarded as a special case of the Cauchy problem for an ordinary equation in Hilbert space of the form

$$\frac{dv}{dt} = A\,v + g(t, v, B_1 v, \ldots, B_n v), \quad v(0) = v_0, \tag{i}$$

where A is a linear, self-adjoint, negative operator, g is a smooth function of its arguments, and the B_i are linear operators subordinate to the operator $(-A)^{1/2}$. From the local (with respect to t) existence theorems proved by these authors for the problem (i), they deduce the local solvability of the hydrodynamical problem in a certain class.

In Lions' note [65], the a priori estimate

$$\int_{-\infty}^{\infty} (1 + |\tau|^{\gamma}) \left\| \int_0^{\infty} \mathbf{v}(x, t)\, e^{i\tau t}\, dt \right\|^2_{\mathbf{L}_2(\Omega)} d\tau \leqslant C(J + J^{3/2}),$$

for the solution $\mathbf{v}(x, t)$ of the problem (1) is obtained, where

$$J = \int_0^{\infty} \| \mathbf{f}(x, t) \|^2_{\mathbf{L}_2(\Omega)}\, dt + \| \mathbf{a}(x, t) \|^2_{\mathbf{L}_2(\Omega)},$$

and γ is any number in the interval $(0, 1/4)$.

After this book was written, three more papers devoted to the investigation of solutions of the nonstationary problem (1) have appeared, in connection with our note [38]. In the joint paper by Lions and Prodi [66], a uniqueness theorem is proved for Hopf's weak solution, for the case of two spatial variables. In Prodi's paper [67], a somewhat different proof of the same theorem is given, and a whole series of uniqueness theorems for weak solutions in a three-dimensional space are also proved, with supplementary conditions involving the boundedness of various integrals. We make a few brief remarks about this at the end of Sec. 8.

In his note [68], P. E. Sobolevski continues his investigations (mentioned above) of the problem (1) from the point of view of the nonlinear differential equation (i) in Hilbert space. He proves a local existence theorem for the case of three space variables and a nonlocal existence theorem for the case of two space variables in function classes which differ from those used in the work presented here and in his own previous work, and with somewhat different assumptions concerning $\mathbf{f}$ and $\mathbf{a}$. Moreover, he gives results on the stability of solutions of the problem (1) in the infinite time interval which are close to the results given in [38] and presented in Chap. 6, Sec. 5.

Additional Comments

Several more papers devoted to the nonstationary boundary-value problem appeared during 1960, while this book was being edited for publication. However, the situation concerning the basic problem, i.e., the problem of the unique solvability in the large of the general nonstationary problem, has not changed. As before, this problem still remains open.

In Ohyama's note [69], it is proved that the generalized solution $\mathbf{v}$ constructed in [39] of the equation (1) has continuous derivatives $\mathbf{v}_t$ and $\mathbf{v}_{x_i x_j}$ inside Q_T, if $\mathbf{f}$ satisfies a Hölder condition in (x, t). The author's arguments are close to those we used to investigate the differential properties of the stationary and nonstationary problems.

In V. I. Yudovich's note [70], it is proved that the general Navier-Stokes equations, with a force $\mathbf{f}$ which is periodic in t, have at least one solution with the same period as $\mathbf{f}$, and an approximate method is given for finding the periodic solutions. Moreover, in the same paper, the properties of the operator $(\partial/\partial t) - \tilde{\Delta}$ in $\mathbf{L}_r(Q_T)$ $(r > 1)$ are enumerated, and it is asserted that Hopf's weak solution $\mathbf{v}$ has derivatives $\mathbf{v}_t$ and $\mathbf{v}_{x_i x_j}$ which are summable with exponent $5/4$ over Q_T. However, the author does not say how this is proved. In connection with these results, see Chap. 4, Secs. 2 and 5, and Chap. 6, Sec. 4.

In P. E. Sobolevski's note [71], further improvements are given of his results on the investigation of differential properties of generalized solutions of the problem (1), regarded as a problem of the type (i). The strongest result in the paper is the following: If the force $\mathbf{f}$ satisfies a Hölder condition in (x, t) with exponent $\gamma > 3/4$, then in a small time interval, there exists a solution $\mathbf{v}$ which is classical for $t > 0$. Here we shall not give the restrictions imposed on $\mathbf{a}$ by the author, and we also omit his other results on the solvability of the problem (1) in various classes, because their formulation is quite lengthy; however we have just given the strongest result implied by them. There seems to be some confusion in the proof of the first two theorems on the linear stationary problem, and the author makes essential use of these two theorems in his investigation of the nonstationary problem. However, the theorems themselves are true, and they and stronger limiting results were proved by V. A. Solonnikov in [62] and are presented in Chap. 3, Sec. 5.

In 1960, two more relevant papers were published, by Prodi [72] and by Lions [73]. First of all, these papers contain an analysis of the properties of Hopf's solutions (in [72] for the case where the dimension n of the space equals 2, and in [73] for the case $n = 3$). More precisely, these authors define the weak solution $\mathbf{v}(x, t)$ of the problem as the function for which the integrals

$$\int_{\Omega} \mathbf{v}^2(x, t)\, dx \qquad \text{and} \qquad \int_0^T \int_{\Omega} \sum_i \mathbf{v}_{x_i}^2\, dx\, dt$$

are bounded for $n = 2$, and for which the integrals

$$\int_{\Omega} \sum_i \mathbf{v}_i^4\,(x, t)\, dx \qquad \text{and} \qquad \int_0^T \int_{\Omega} \sum_i \mathbf{v}_{x_i}^2\, dx\, dt$$

are bounded for $n = 3$, and which satisfies the identity

$$\int_0^T \int_{\Omega} (-\,\mathbf{v}\cdot\mathbf{\Phi}_t + \nu\, \mathbf{v}_{x_i}\cdot\mathbf{\Phi}_{x_i} + v_k\, \mathbf{v}_{x_k}\cdot\mathbf{\Phi} - \mathbf{f}\cdot\mathbf{\Phi})\, dx\, dt$$
$$-\int_{\Omega} \mathbf{a}\cdot\mathbf{\Phi}(x, 0)\, dx = 0$$

for all sufficiently well-behaved solenoidal $\mathbf{\Phi}(x, t)$, equal to zero on S and for $t = T$. Regarding this solution, they prove that $\mathbf{v}$ depends continuously on t in the $\mathbf{L}_2(\Omega)$ norm and satisfies an integral identity of the form (53) of Chap. 6, Sec. 6. We note that from the standpoint of the basic problem, i.e., investigation of the unique solvability of problem (1), it is desirable to construct the smoothest solution of the problem for all $t \geqslant 0$. For this reason, in presenting Hopf's results in Chap. 6, Sec. 6, we give not only what Hopf states as a theorem, but also all that can be deduced from his paper regarding the properties of the solutions which he constructs. Then all these properties (which are close to those established in [72] and [73]) are made a basic part of the definition of Hopf's weak solution.

Moreover, the papers [72, 73] contain a proof for the two-dimensional case of the existence of at least one solution of the Navier-Stokes equations which is periodic in t when the force $\mathbf{f}$ is periodic. The proof is based on the following two facts: (a) The $\mathbf{L}_2(\Omega)$ norms of the possible solutions $\mathbf{v}$ of the problem (1) for a fixed periodic force $\mathbf{f}$ do not exceed a certain number R at any instant of time $t \geqslant 0$, if they do not exceed this number for $t = 0$ and if R is taken to be sufficiently large, i.e., the transformation $\mathfrak{M}_t\{\mathbf{v}(x, 0) \to \mathbf{v}(x, t)\}$ maps the sphere $K_R\{\|\mathbf{v}\|_{\mathbf{L}_2(\Omega)} \leqslant R\}$ into itself (this fact is easily deduced from the basic energy relation (54); (b) The mapping $\mathfrak{M}_t$ is continuous in the weak topology of $\mathbf{L}_2(\Omega)$ (the proof of this fact is not easy).

In the paper [70] cited above, the existence of a periodic solution is proved more simply, starting from the fact that the sphere is mapped into itself by all Galerkin approximations to $\mathbf{v}_n$ $(n = 1, 2, \ldots)$ with the same R. Because of the fact that the spaces to which the $\mathbf{v}_n$ belong are finite-dimensional, this implies that at each stage in Galerkin's method, there exists at least one periodic solution $\mathbf{v}_n^*$. Because of the uniform energy estimate for $\mathbf{v}_n^*$ $(n = 1, 2, \ldots)$, the $\mathbf{v}_n^*$ have a limit function $\mathbf{v}$, which is the periodic solution we are looking for.

Finally, we give Serrin's results concerning a priori estimates of the derivatives $D_t^N \mathbf{v}$ for solutions of the two-dimensional problem with $\mathbf{f} \equiv 0$. He showed that

1. The norms $\|D_t^N \mathbf{v}\|_{C_{n,h}(\Omega')}$ where $\Omega' \subset \Omega$, $N \geqslant 0$, are bounded for $t \geqslant \varepsilon > 0$, if the integrals

$$\int_\Omega (D_t^k \mathbf{v})^2 \, dx \qquad (k = 1, 2, \ldots, N + 2),$$

or the norms $\|\mathbf{v}(x, 0)\|_{C_{2N+4}(\Omega)}$ are bounded.

2. The norms $\|D_t^N \mathbf{v}\|_{C_{1,h}(\Omega)}$ are uniformly bounded for $0 \leqslant t < \infty$, if $\|\mathbf{v}(x, 0)\|_{C_{2N+4}(\Omega)}$ is bounded.

While reading the proof of this book, the author became acquainted with the paper by Finn [75] and the paper by I. I. Vorovich and V. I. Yudovich [76] (the latter had just appeared). The first paper contains a proof of Theorem 8 of Chap. 5, Sec. 5, and also some results concerning the asymptotic behavior of solutions of three-dimensional problems as $|x| \to \infty$. The second paper is a new, corrected version of the paper originally submitted in September of 1960. This paper contains results concerning the existence of generalized solutions in a bounded domain, similar to the results of Sec. 2 of the paper [61], and also results of investigations of the differential properties of generalized solutions, similar to the results of the paper [62]. The methods used to investigate differential properties are different from the methods of [62], which are presented here in Chap. 3, Sec. 5.

The investigations of Vorovich on generalized solutions antedate the work by Vorovich and Yudovich. In fact, it was proved (in 1957) by Vorovich (and independently and simultaneously by the author of this book) that the stationary problem in a bounded domain with homogeneous boundary conditions can be solved in the large, in the way shown in Chap. 5, Sec. 1.

The English edition of this book has a new section (Chap. 5, Sec. 4) in which we give effective a priori estimates of the norm $\|\mathbf{u}\|_{H(\Omega)}$ for solutions of stationary problems. Estimates of this type can be found in the papers of Finn [77] and Fujita [78], where they are proved by using a lemma from Hopf's paper [79], under the assumption that $\mathbf{a}|_S$ and S are sufficiently smooth.

REFERENCES*

1. G. Birkhoff, *Hydrodynamics, A Study in Logic, Fact and Similitude,* revised edition, Princeton University Press, Princeton, N. J. (1960).
2. O. A. Ladyzhenskaya, *The Mixed Problem for a Hyperbolic Equation,* Gos. Izd. Tekh.-Teor. Lit., Moscow (1953).
3. R. Courant and D. Hilbert, *Methods of Mathematical Physics,* vol. 1, Interscience Publishers, Inc., New York (1953).
4. K. O. Friedrichs, *Spektraltheorie halbbeschränkter Operatoren und Anwendung auf die Spektralzerlegung von Differentialoperatoren,* part 1, Math. Ann., **109**, 465—487 (1934); part 2, ibid., 685—713 (1934).
5. S. L. Sobolev, *The basic boundary-value problem for a polyharmonic equation in a domain with a degenerate boundary,* Dokl. Akad. Nauk SSSR, **3**, 311—314 (1936).
6. S. L. Sobolev, *Some Applications of Functional Analysis in Mathematical Physics,* Leningrad University Press (1950).
7. S. L. Sobolev, *Méthode nouvelle à résoudre le problème de Cauchy pour les équations linéaires hyperboliques normales,* Mat. Sb., **1**, 39—72 (1936).

8—10. S. L. Sobolev, *On the almost periodicity of solutions of the wave equation,* part 1, Dokl. Akad. Nauk SSSR, **48**, 570—573 (1945); part 2, ibid., **48**, 646—648 (1945); part 3, ibid., **49**, 12—15 (1945).

11. J. Leray, *Étude de diverses équations intégrales non linéaires et de quelques problèmes que pose l'hydrodynamique,* J. Math. Pures Appl., série 9, **12**, 1—82 (1933).
12. J. Leray, *Essai sur les mouvements plans d'un liquide visqueux que limitent des parois,* J. Math. Pures Appl., série 9, **13**, 331—418 (1934).
13. J. Leray, *Sur le mouvement d'un liquide visqueux emplissant l'espace,* Acta Math., **63**, 193—248 (1934).
14. E. Hopf, *Über die Anfangswertaufgabe für die hydrodynamischen Grundgleichungen,* Mach. Nachrichten, **4**, 213—231 (1950—1951).
15. F. K. G. Odqvist, *Über die Randwertaufgaben der Hydrodynamik zäher Flüssigkeiten,* Math. Z., **32**, 329—375 (1930).
16. V. I. Smirnov, *A Course of Higher Mathematics,* vol. 5, Gos. Izd. Fiz.-Mat. Lit., Moscow (1959).
17. O. A. Ladyzhenskaya, *A simple proof of the solvability of the basic boundary-value problems and of the eigenvalue problem for linear elliptic equations,* Vestnik Leningrad. Univ., no. 11, 23—29 (1955).
18. N. M. Gyunter, *Potential Theory and its Application to the Basic Problems of Mathematical Physics,* Gos. Izd. Tekh.-Teor. Lit., Moscow (1953).
19. C. Miranda, *Equazioni alle Derivate Parziali di Tipo Ellittico,* Springer Verlag, Berlin (1955).

---

* Titles of Russian papers and books have been translated into English.

20. N. Aronszain, *Boundary values of functions with finite Dirichlet integral,* Conference on Partial Differential Equations, University of Kansas, Summer 1954, 77—93 (1955).
21. L. N. Slobodetski and V. M. Babich, *On the boundedness of the Dirichlet integral,* Dokl. Akad. Naùk SSSR, **106**, 604—606 (1956).
22. L. N. Slobodetski, *The generalized spaces of S. L. Sobolev and their application to boundary-value problems for partial differential equations,* Uch. Zap. Leningrad. Gos. Ped. Inst. Im. A. I. Gertsena, **197**, 54—112 (1958).
23. J. Leray and J. Schauder, *Topologie et équations fonctionelles.* Ann. Sci. École Norm. Sup., **13**, 45—78 (1934).
24. S. G. Mikhlin, *Integration of Poisson's equation in an infinite domain,* Dokl. Akad. Nauk SSSR, **91**, 1015—1017 (1953).
25. L. Schwartz, *Théorie des Distributions,* Hermann et Cie., Paris, vol. 1 (1950), vol. 2 (1952).
26. I. M. Gelfand and G. E. Shilov, *Generalized Functions,* vol. 1, *Generalized Functions and Operations on Them,* vol. 2, *Spaces of Basic and Generalized Functions,* Gos. Izd. Fiz.-Mat. Lit., Moscow (1958).
27. B. V. Rusanov, *Slow nonequilibrium flow of a viscous fluid past a circular cylinder,* Dokl. Akad. Nauk SSSR, **89**, 983—986 (1953); Vestnik Leningrad. Univ., no. 2, 81—106 (1955).
28. K. Finn and W. Noll, *On the uniqueness and non-existence of Stokes flows,* Arch. Rat. Mech. Analysis, **1**, 95—106 (1957).
29. S. G. Mikhlin, *The Problem of the Minimum of a Quadratic Functional,* Gos. Izd. Tekh.-Teor. Lit., Moscow (1952).
30. I. M. Glazman, *On the application of the decomposition method to multidimensional singular boundary-value problems,* Mat. Sb., **35**, 231—246 (1954).
31. O. A. Ladyzhenskaya, *On the solvability of the basic boundary-value problems for equations of the parabolic and hyperbolic types,* Dokl. Akad. Nauk SSSR, **97**, 395—398 (1954).
32. O. A. Ladyzhenskaya, *On the solution of nonstationary operator equations of various types,* Dokl. Akad. Nauk. SSSR, **102**, 207—210 (1955); *On the solution of nonstationary operator equations,* Mat. Sb., **39**, 491—524 (1956).
33. A. A. Kiselev, *Solution of the linearized equations of nonstationary flow of a viscous incompressible fluid in a bounded domain,* Dokl. Akad. Nauk SSSR, **101**, 43—46 (1955).
34. J. Marcinkiewicz, *Sur les multiplicateurs des séries de Fourier,* Studia Math., **8**, 78—91 (1939).
35. S. G. Mikhlin, *Fourier integrals and singular multiple integrals,* Vestnik Leningrad. Univ., no. 7, 143—155 (1957).
36. S. M. Nikolski, *Inequalities for entire functions of any order and their application in the theory of differentiable functions of several variables,* Trudy Mat. Inst. Steklov, vol. 38, 244—278 (1951), and subsequent papers.
37. N. E. Kochin, I. A. Kibel and N. V. Roze, *Theoretical Hydromechanics,* part 2, Gos. Izd. Tekh.-Teor. Lit., Moscow (1948).
38. O. A. Ladyzhenskaya, *Solution "in the large" of the boundary-value problem for the Navier-Stokes equations for the case of two space variables,* Dokl. Akad. Nauk SSSR, **123**, 427—429 (1958); *Solution "in the large" of the nonstationary boundary value problem for the Navier-Stokes system with two space variables,* Comm. Pure Appl. Math., **12**, 427—433 (1959).

39. A. A. Kiselev and O. A. Ladyzhenskaya, *On the existence and uniqueness of the solution of the nonstationary problem for a viscous incompressible fluid*, Izv. Akad. Nauk SSSR, Ser. Mat., **21**, 655—680 (1957).

40. O. A. Ladyzhenskaya, *On nonstationary solutions of the Navier-Stokes equations*, Vestnik Leningrad. Univ., no. 19, 9—18 (1958).

41. O. A. Ladyzhenskaya, *On the Fourier method for the wave equation*, Dokl. Akad. Nauk SSSR, **75**, 765—768 (1950).

42. O. A. Ladyzhenskaya, *On the closure of the elliptic operator*, Dokl. Akad. Nauk SSSR, **79**, 723—725 (1951).

43. R. Caccioppoli, *Limitazioni integrali per le soluzioni di un'equazione lineare ellittica a derivate parziali*, Giorn. Mat. Battaglini, **80**, 186—212 (1950—1951).

44. S. N. Bernstein, *On some a priori estimates in the generalized Dirichlet problem*, Dokl. Akad. Nauk. SSSR, **124**, 735—738 (1959).

45. S. N. Bernstein, *Sur la généralization du problème de Dirichlet*, part 2, Math. Ann., **69**, 82—136 (1910).

46. H. Weyl, *The method of orthogonal projection in potential theory*, Duke Math. J., **7**, 411—444 (1940).

47. K. O. Friedrichs, *Differential forms on Riemannian manifolds*, Comm. Pure Appl. Math., **8**, 551—590 (1955).

48. E. B. Bykhovski and N. V. Smirnov, *On orthogonal expansions of the space of vector functions which are square-summable over a given domain*, Trudy Mat. Inst. Steklov, vol. 59, 6—36 (1960).

49. S. G. Krein, *On functional properties of the operators of vector analysis and hydrodynamics*, Dokl. Akad. Nauk SSSR, **93**, 969—972 (1953).

50. K. O. Friedrichs, *On the differentiability of the solutions of linear elliptic differential equations*, Comm. Pure Appl. Math., **6**, 299—326 (1953).

51. I. I. Vorovich and V. I. Yudovich, *Stationary flow of a viscous fluid*, Dokl. Akad. Nauk SSSR, **124**, 542—545 (1959).

52. O. A. Ladyzhenskaya, *Stationary motion of a viscous incompressible fluid in a pipe*, Dokl. Akad. Nauk SSSR, **124**, 551—553 (1959).

53. K. K. Golovkin, *On the planar motion of a viscous incompressible fluid*, Trudy Mat. Inst. Steklov, vol. 59, 37—86 (1960).

54. K. K. Golovkin and O. A. Ladyzhenskaya, *On solutions of the nonstationary boundary-value problem for the Navier-Stokes equations*, Trudy Mat. Inst. Steklov, vol. 59, 100—114 (1960).

55. S. G. Krein, *Differential equations in a Banach space and their applications to hydromechanics*, Uspekhi Mat. Nauk, **12**, 208—211 (1957).

56. K. K. Golovkin, *On potential theory for the nonstationary linear Navier-Stokes equations in the case of three space variables*, Trudy Mat. Inst. Steklov, vol. 59, 87—99 (1960).

57. T. Kato, *Growth properties of solutions of the reduced wave equation with a variable coefficient*, Comm. Pure Appl. Math., **12**, 403—425 (1959).

58. P. Lax, *On Cauchy's problem for hyperbolic equations and the differentiability of solutions of elliptic equations*, Comm. Pure Appl. Math., 8, 615—633 (1955).

59. M. I. Vishik and S. L. Sobolev, *The general statement of some boundary-value problems for elliptic partial differential equations*, Dokl. Akad. Nauk SSSR, **111**, 521—523 (1956).

60. O. A. Ladyzhenskaya, *On integral estimates and convergence of approximation methods and of solutions in functionals for linear elliptic operators*, Vestnik Leningrad. Univ., no. 7, 60—69 (1958).
61. O. A. Ladyzhenskaya, *Investigation of the Navier-Stokes equations in the case of stationary motion of an incompressible fluid*, Uspekhi Mat. Nauk, vol. 3, **14**, 75—97 (1959).
62. V. A. Solonnikov, *On estimates of the tensor Green's function for some boundary-value problems*, Dokl. Akad. Nauk SSSR, **130**, 988—991 (1960).
63. M. A. Krasnoselski, S. G. Krein and P. E. Sobolevski, *On differential equations with unbounded operators in Hilbert space*, Dokl. Akad. Nauk SSSR, **112**, 990—993 (1957).
64. M. A. Krasnoselski and S. G. Krein, *On differential equations in a Banach space*, Proceedings of the Third All-Union Mathematical Conference, Moscow, June-July, 1956, vol. 3, 73—80 (1958).
65. J. L. Lions, *Sur l'existence de solutions des équations de Navier-Stokes*, C. R. Acad. Sci. Paris, **248**, 2847—2849 (1959).
66. J. L. Lions and G. Prodi, *Un théorème d'existence et unicité dans les équations de Navier-Stokes en dimension 2*, C. R. Acad. Sci. Paris, **248**, 3519—3521 (1959).
67. G. Prodi, *Un teorema di unicità per le equazioni di Navier-Stokes*, Ann. Mat. Pura Appl., **48**, 173—182 (1959).
68. P. E. Sobolevski, *On the nonstationary equations of the hydrodynamics of a viscous fluid*, Dokl. Akad. Nauk SSSR, **128**, 45—48 (1959).
69. T. Ohyama, *Interior regularity of weak solutions of the time-dependent Navier-Stokes equation*, Proc. Japan Acad., **36**, 273—277 (1960).
70. V. I. Yudovich, *Periodic motions of a viscous incompressible fluid*, Dokl. Akad. Nauk SSSR, **130**, 1214—1217 (1960).
71. P. E. Sobolevski, *On the smoothness of generalized solutions of the Navier-Stokes equations*, Dokl. Akad. Nauk SSSR, **131**, 758—760 (1960).
72. G. Prodi, *Qualche risultato riguardo alle equazioni di Navier-Stokes nel caso bidimensionale*, Rend. Sem. Mat. Univ. Padova, **30**, 1—15 (1960).
73. J. L. Lions, *Sur la régularité et l'unicité des solutions turbulentes des équations de Navier-Stokes*, Rend. Sem. Mat. Univ. Padova, **30**, 16—23 (1960).
74. O. V. Guseva, *On the nonstationary boundary-value problem of the hydrodynamics of a viscous incompressible fluid*, Vestnik Leningrad. Univ., no. 19, 122—137 (1961).
75. R. Finn, *On steady-state solutions of the Navier-Stokes partial differential equations*, Arch. Rat. Mech. Analysis, **3**, 381—396 (1959).
76. I. I. Vorovich and V. I. Yudovich, *Stationary flow of a viscous incompressible fluid*, Mat. Sb., **53**, 393—428 (1961).
77. R. Finn, *On the steady state solutions of the Navier-Stokes equations*, III, Acta Math., **105**, 197—244 (1961).
78. H. Fujita, *On the existence and regularity of the steady-state solutions of the Navier-Stokes equation*, J. Fac. Sci. Univ. Tokyo, vol. 9, part 1, 59—102 (1961).
79. E. Hopf, *Ein allgemeiner Endlichkeitssatz der Hydrodynamik*, Math. Ann., **117**, 764—775 (1941).
80. N. M. Gyunter, *Sur les intégrales de Stieltjes et leurs applications aux problèmes fondamentaux de la physique mathématique*, Trudy Fiz.-Mat. Inst. Steklov, **1**, 1—494 (1932), reprinted by Chelsea Publishing Co., New York (1949).

Name Index

Subject Index

L

M

N

P

R

S

T

W

Y